Teacher's Edition

# Guided Reading and Study Workbook

Prentice Hall

# Physical Science

## Concepts in Action
## With Earth and Space Science

Needham, Massachusetts
Upper Saddle River, New Jersey

Teacher's Edition

# Guided Reading and Study Workbook

Prentice Hall

# Physical Science

## Concepts in Action

With Earth and Space Science



PEARSON
Prentice Hall

ISBN 0-13-069979-9

1 2 3 4 5 6 7 8 9 10 07 06 05 04 03

# Contents

Name ______________________ Class ______________ Date __________



# Section 1.1 What Is Science?
**(pages 2–6)**

*This section describes the characteristics of science and technology. It also discusses the big ideas of physical science.*

## Reading Strategy (page 2)

**Previewing** Skim the section to find out what the main branches of natural science are. Complete the concept map based on what you have learned. For more information on this Reading Strategy, see the **Reading and Study Skills** in the **Skills and Reference Handbook** at the end of your textbook.

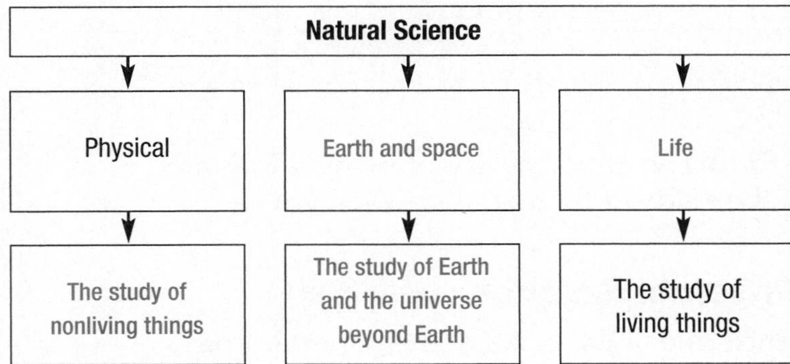


## Science From Curiosity (pages 2–3)

1. Define science. Science is a system of knowledge and methods you use to find knowledge.

2. The questions that lead to scientific discovery are provided by curiosity.

3. Is the following sentence true or false? The results of every scientific experiment are quantitative. false

## Science and Technology (page 3)

4. Is the following sentence true or false? The use of knowledge to solve practical problems is known as curiosity. false

5. How are science and technology related? They are interdependent. Advances in science lead to advances in technology and vice versa.

## Branches of Science (page 4)

6. Name the two general categories that the study of science can be divided into.
   a. Social science  b. Natural science

7. Circle the letters of each branch of natural science.
   (a.) physical science  (b.) Earth and space science
   c. social science  (d.) life science

8. Circle the letter of each sentence that is true about the field of chemistry.
   - (a.) Chemists study reactions involving matter.
   - (b.) Chemists study the composition of matter.
   - (c.) Chemists study the structure of matter.
   - (d.) Chemists study the properties of matter.

9. The study of matter, energy, and the interactions between the two through forces and motion is known as ___physics___.

10. Identify the topics that are included in the science of geology.
    The science of geology includes the origin, history, and structure of the Earth.

11. Is the following sentence true or false? The foundation of space science is astronomy. ___true___

12. Scientists who study the origin and behavior of living things are called biologists, and the study of living things is known as ___biology___.

## The Big Ideas of Physical Science (pages 5–6)

13. Is the following sentence true or false? All of the important rules of nature have already been discovered. ___false___

14. Circle the letter of each sentence that is true about the diameter of the observable universe.
    - a. It is one hundred million meters.
    - b. It is seven hundred billion meters.
    - c. It is seven hundred million billion meters.
    - (d.) It is seven hundred million billion billion meters.

15. Name the two characteristics of matter.
    - a. ___Mass___
    - b. ___Volume___

16. The basic building blocks of matter are called ___atoms___.

17. Is the following sentence true or false? A force causes a change in time. ___false___

18. Describe kinetic energy. Kinetic energy is the energy of motion.

19. Two general types of energy are kinetic energy and ___potential___ energy.

## Science and Your Perspective (page 6)

20. Is the following sentence true or false? The scientific facts of today will not change in the future. ___false___

Name ______________________ Class ______________ Date ___________



# Section 1.2 Using a Scientific Approach

**(pages 7–11)**

*This section describes scientific methods and how they are used to understand the world around you.*

## Reading Strategy (page 7)

**Using Prior Knowledge** Before you read, add to the web diagram what you already know about scientific methods. After you read the section, revise the diagram based on what you have learned. For more information on this Reading Strategy, see the **Reading and Study Skills** in the **Skills and Reference Handbook** at the end of your textbook.

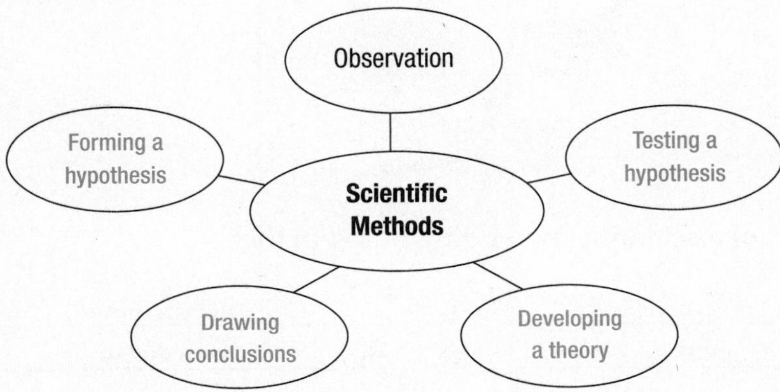


## Scientific Methods (pages 7–9)

1. Identify the goal of any scientific method. The goal of any scientific method is to solve a problem or better understand an observed event.

2. Name three types of variables in an experiment.
   a. Manipulated variable b. Responding variable c. Controlled variable

3. Is the following sentence true or false? If the data from an experiment do not support your hypothesis, you can revise the hypothesis or propose a new one. true

4. How does a scientific theory differ from a hypothesis? A hypothesis is an untested explanation for an observation while a theory is a well-tested explanation for a set of observations.

*Match the following vocabulary terms to the correct definition.*

| | Definition | Vocabulary Terms |
|---|---|---|
| c | 5. Information that you obtain through your senses | a. theory |
| a | 6. A well-tested explanation for a set of observations | b. hypothesis |
| b | 7. A proposed answer to a question | c. observation |

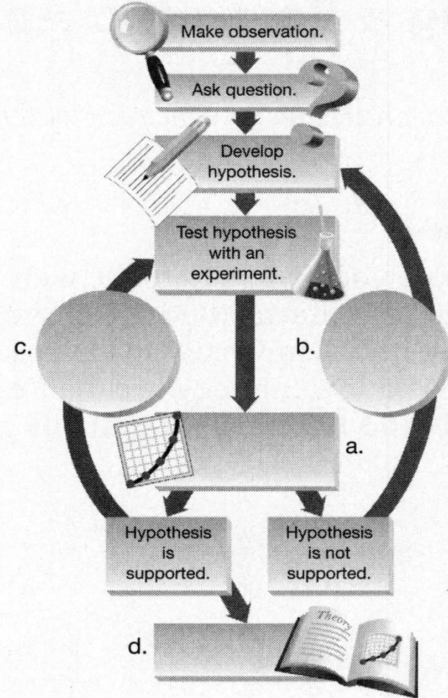


8. Complete the model of a scientific method by filling in the missing steps.

a. Analyze data and draw conclusions

b. Revise hypothesis

c. Test hypothesis with further experiments

d. Develop theory

## Scientific Laws (page 9)

9. Is the following sentence true or false? A scientific law attempts to explain an observed pattern in nature. false

10. All scientists may accept a given scientific law, but different scientists may have different scientific theories to explain it.

## Scientific Models (page 10)

11. Why do scientists use scientific models? Scientists use scientific models to make it easier to understand things that might be too difficult to observe directly.

12. Circle the letters that correctly state what scientists do if data show that a model is wrong.

(a.) Change the model.
(b.) Replace the model.
c. Ignore the data.
d. Revise the data.

## Working Safely in Science (page 11)

13. Circle the letters of safety precautions to follow whenever you work in a science laboratory.

(a.) Study safety rules.
b. Never ask questions.
(c.) Read all procedural steps.
(d.) Understand the procedure.

14. Why should you wash your hands after every experiment? You should wash your hands after experiments to remove chemicals that you may have touched.

Name ______________________ Class ______________________ Date ____________



# Section 1.3 Measurement
**(pages 14–20)**

*This section discusses units of measurement, making and evaluating measurements, and calculations with measurements.*

## Reading Strategy (page 14)

**Previewing** Before you read the section, rewrite the green and blue topic headings in this section as questions in the table below. As you read, write answers to the questions. For more information on this Reading Strategy, see the **Reading and Study Skills** in the **Skills and Reference Handbook** at the end of your textbook.

| Measurement |
| --- |
| Why is scientific notation useful? It makes very large or very small numbers easier to work with. |
| What is SI? SI is a set of metric measuring units used by scientists. |
| What are base units? Base units are the fundamental units of SI. There are seven SI base units, including the meter, the kilogram, the kelvin, and the second. |

## Using Scientific Notation (pages 14–15)

**1.** Scientific notation expresses a value as the product of a number between 1 and 10 and ___a power of ten___.

**2.** Circle the letter of the value that is expressed as $3 \times 10^8$.

a. 300 b. 300,000

c. 30,000,000 (d.) 300,000,000

**3.** Why is scientific notation useful? ___It makes very large or very small numbers easier to work with.___

## SI Units of Measurement (pages 16–18)

**4.** Circle the letters of elements that are required for a measurement to make sense.

a. scientific notation (b.) numbers

c. exponents (d.) units

**5.** Is the following sentence true or false? Units in the SI system include feet, pounds, and degrees Fahrenheit. ___false___

*Match the SI base unit with the quantity that is used to measure.*

| | SI Base Unit | Quantity |
| --- | --- | --- |
| c | **6.** meter | a. Mass |
| a | **7.** kilogram | b. Time |
| d | **8.** kelvin | c. Length |
| b | **9.** second | d. Temperature |

| SI Prefixes | | | |
|---|---|---|---|
| **Prefix** | **Symbol** | **Meaning** | **Multiply Unit By** |
| giga- | G | billion ($10^9$) | 1,000,000,000 |
| mega- | M | million ($10^6$) | 1,000,000 |
| kilo- | k | thousand ($10^3$) | 1000 |
| deci- | d | tenth ($10^{-1}$) | 0.1 |
| centi- | c | hundredth ($10^{-2}$) | 0.01 |
| milli- | m | thousandth ($10^{-3}$) | 0.001 |
| micro- | μ | millionth ($10^{-6}$) | 0.000001 |
| nano- | n | billionth ($10^{-9}$) | 0.000000001 |

10. Complete the table of SI prefixes by filling in the missing information.

11. A ratio of equivalent measurements that is used to convert a quantity expressed in one unit to another unit is called a(n) conversion factor.

## Limits of Measurement (page 19)

12. Circle the letter of each expression that has four significant figures.
    a. $1.25 \times 10^4$
    b. 12.51 (circled)
    c. 0.0125
    d. 0.1255 (circled)

13. Is the following sentence true or false? The precision of a calculated answer is limited by the least precise measurement used in the calculation. true

14. Calculate the density if the mass of a solid material is measured as 15.00 grams and its volume is measured as 5.0 $cm^3$? Round off your answer to the proper number of significant figures.
    Density $= 15.00\ g/5.0\ cm^3 = 3.3\ g/cm^3$

15. Describe the difference between precision and accuracy. Precision refers to how exact a measurement is (the more significant figures, the more precise the measurement is), while accuracy refers to how close the measurement is to the actual value.

## Measuring Temperature (page 20)

16. Circle the letter of the base unit of temperature in SI.
    a. degree Fahrenheit (°F)
    b. degree Celsius (°C)
    c. candela (cd)
    d. kelvin (K) (circled)

17. Write the formula used to convert degrees Celsius to kelvins.
    $K = °C + 273$

# Section 1.4 Presenting Scientific Data
**(pages 22–25)**

*This section describes how scientists organize and communicate data.*

## Reading Strategy (page 22)

**Comparing and Contrasting** After you read this section, compare the types of graphs by completing the table. For more information on this Reading Strategy, see the **Reading and Study Skills** in the **Skills and Reference Handbook** at the end of your textbook.

| Type of Graph | Description | Used For |
|---|---|---|
| Line graph | A graph in which a line is plotted to describe changes that occur in related variables | Showing how a variable responds to changes in another |
| Bar graph | A graph that uses scaled bars to represent various measurements | Comparing sets of measurements or changes |
| Circle graph | A graph consisting of a divided circle, with each "slice" representing a proportional fraction | Showing how a part or share of something relates to the whole |

## Organizing Data (pages 22–24)

1. Circle the letters of tools that scientists use to organize their data.
   a. the Internet
   b. newspapers
   (c.) tables
   (d.) graphs
2. The simplest way to organize data is to present them in a(n) data table.
3. Circle the letter of the place on a line graph where the manipulated variable is generally plotted.
   a. the *y*-axis
   b. the rise
   (c.) the *x*-axis
   d. the run
4. On a line graph, the ratio of the change in the *y*-variable to the corresponding change in the *x*-variable is called the line's slope.
5. Circle the letters of the relationships that are direct proportions.
   (a.) distance traveled versus time at a constant speed
   (b.) the mass of a substance versus its volume
   c. the time to travel a given distance versus average speed
   (d.) the number of fingers in your classroom versus the number of people

Name ______________________ Class ________________ Date ____________



6. Is the following sentence true or false? An inverse proportion is one in which the product of the two variables is constant. true

7. Identify each data organizing tool shown below.

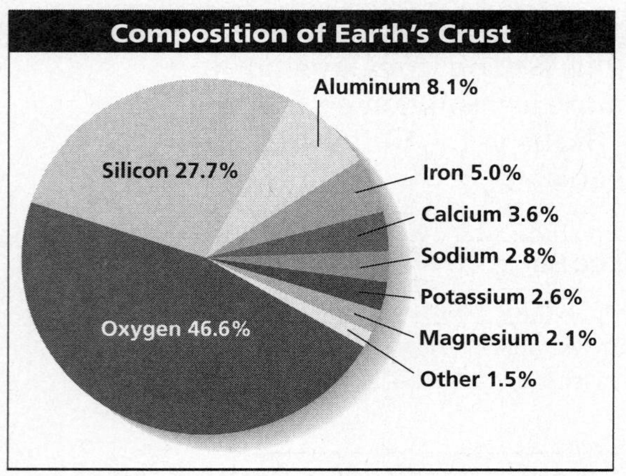


a.

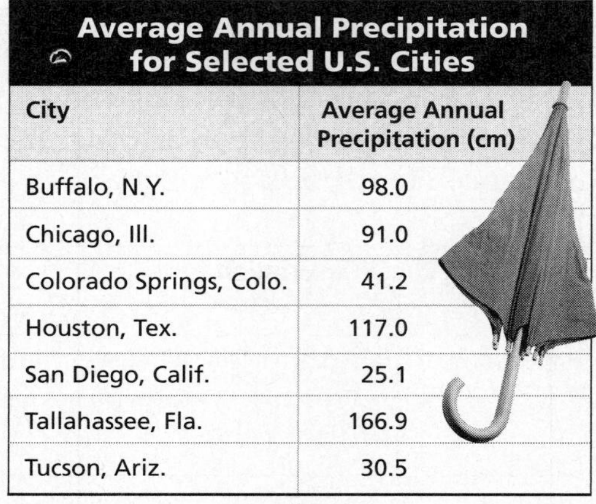

**Average Annual Precipitation for Selected U.S. Cities**

| City | Average Annual Precipitation (cm) |
|---|---|
| Buffalo, N.Y. | 98.0 |
| Chicago, Ill. | 91.0 |
| Colorado Springs, Colo. | 41.2 |
| Houston, Tex. | 117.0 |
| San Diego, Calif. | 25.1 |
| Tallahassee, Fla. | 166.9 |
| Tucson, Ariz. | 30.5 |

b.

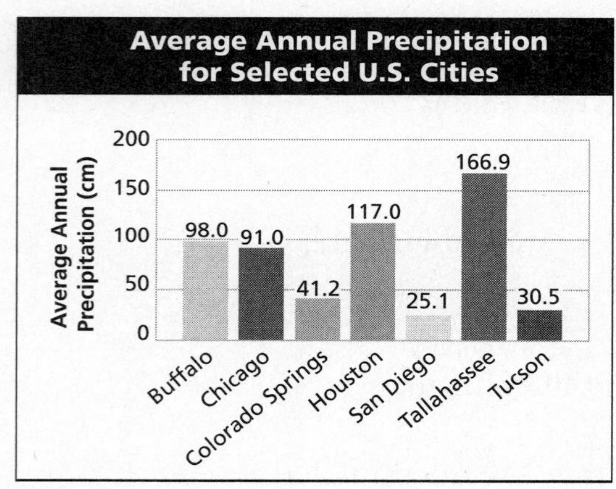


c.

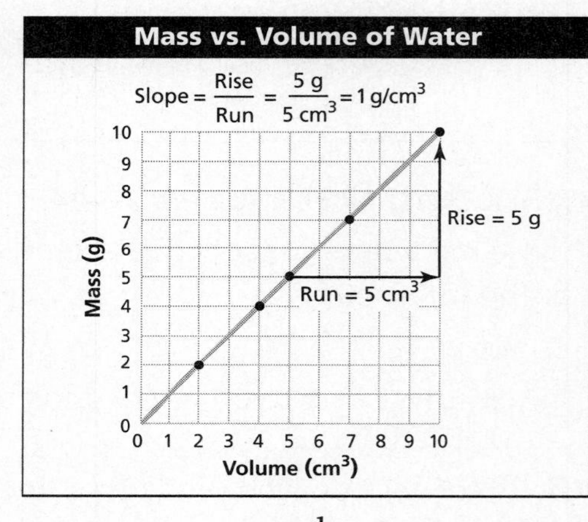


d.

a. Circle graph　　b. Data table

c. Bar graph　　d. Line graph

## Communicating Data (page 25)

8. Name two ways that scientists can report results of their experiments.

a. By writing in scientific journals　　b. By speaking at scientific conferences

9. Is the following statement true or false? Scientists always interpret a given set of data the same way. false

10. Why is peer review an important part of scientific research? It encourages feedback from other scientists and helps researchers to reevaluate their data.

Name ______________________ Class ________________ Date ____________

Chapter 1 **Science Skills**

# WordWise

*Answer the questions by writing the correct vocabulary term in the blanks. Use the circled letter in each term to find the hidden vocabulary word. Then write a definition for the hidden word.*

| Clues | Vocabulary Terms |
|---|---|
| The study of matter, energy, and their interactions | p (h) y s i c s |
| The closeness of a measurement to the actual value of what is being measured | a c c u r a c (y) |
| A gauge of how exact a measurement is | (p) r e c i s i o n |
| The ratio of a vertical change to the corresponding horizontal change in a line | s l (o) p e |
| An instrument used to measure temperature | t h e r m o m e (t) e r |
| The use of knowledge to solve practical problems | t e c (h) n o l o g y |
| A representation of an object or event | m o d (e) l |
| A system of knowledge and the methods used to find that knowledge | (s) c i e n c e |
| A statement that summarizes a pattern found in nature | s c i e n t (i) f i c l a w |
| Information that you obtain through your senses | o b (s) e r v a t i o n |

**Hidden word:** h y p o t h e s i s

**Definition:** A proposed answer to a question

Name ______________________ Class ________________ Date __________



# Using Scientific Notation

Light travels through space at a speed of $3.00 \times 10^8$ meters per second. How long does it take for light to travel from the sun to Earth, which is a distance of $1.50 \times 10^{11}$ meters?

**Math Skill: Scientific Notation**

You may want to read more about this **Math Skill** in the **Skills and Reference Handbook** at the end of your textbook.

**1. Read and Understand**

*What information are you given?*

Speed = $3.00 \times 10^8$ m/s

Total distance = $1.50 \times 10^{11}$ m

**2. Plan and Solve**

*What unknown are you trying to calculate?*

Time = ?

*What formula contains the given quantities and the unknown?*

$$\text{Time} = \frac{\text{Total distance}}{\text{Average speed}}$$

*Replace each variable with its known variable and known value.*

$$\text{Time} = \frac{1.50 \times 10^{11}\text{ m}}{3.00 \times 10^{8}\text{ m/s}}$$

$$= \frac{1.50}{3.00} \times (10^{11-8})(\cancel{\text{m}}/(\cancel{\text{m}}/\text{s}))$$

$$= 0.50 \times 10^{3}\text{ s} = 5.00 \times 10^{2}\text{ s}$$

**3. Look back and check**

*Is your answer reasonable?*

Yes, the number calculated is the quotient of distance and speed, and the units (s) indicate time.

## Math Practice

*On a separate sheet of paper, solve the following problems.*

1. The flow of water in a stream is 210,000 liters per hour. Use scientific notation to calculate the amount of water that flows in a week (168 hours).

   $2.1 \times 10^5$ L/hr $\times$ ($1.68 \times 10^2$ hrs) = $3.5 \times 10^7$ L

2. The density of a liquid is $8.03 \times 10^{-1}$ kilogram per liter. What is the mass (in kg) of liquid in a full 100,000 liter tank?

   $$\frac{8.03 \times 10^{-1}\text{ kg}}{\text{L}} \times (1 \times 10^{5}\text{ L}) = 8.03 \times 10^{4}\text{ kg}$$

3. How many balloons, each containing $6.02 \times 10^{23}$ particles of helium gas, can be filled from a tank that contains $1.204 \times 10^{25}$ helium particles?

   $$\frac{1.204 \times 10^{25}\text{ particles}}{6.02 \times 10^{23}\text{ particles/balloon}} = \left(\frac{1.204}{6.02}\right)(10^{25-23})\text{ balloons} = 0.2 \times 10^{2}\text{ balloons} = 20\text{ balloons}$$

Name ______________________ Class ________________ Date ____________



# Section 2.1 Classifying Matter
**(pages 38–44)**

*This section explains how materials are classified as pure substances or mixtures. It discusses types of pure substances and mixtures.*

## Reading Strategy (page 38)

**Summarizing** As you read, complete the classification of matter in the diagram below. For more information on this Reading Strategy, see the **Reading and Study Skills** in the **Skills and Reference Handbook** at the end of your textbook.

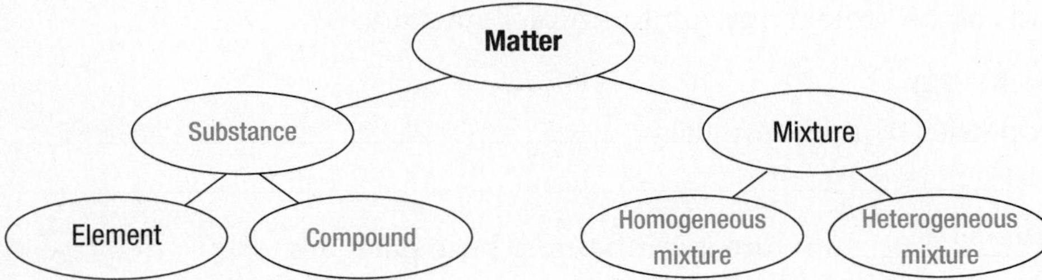


## Pure Substances (page 39)

1. Is the following sentence true or false? Every sample of a pure substance has exactly the same composition and the same properties. true
2. What are the two categories of pure substances?
   a. Elements b. Compounds

## Elements (pages 39–40)

3. What is an element? An element is a substance that cannot be broken down into simpler substances.
4. Is the following sentence true or false? The smallest particle of an element is an atom. true
5. Why does an element have a fixed, uniform composition? An element has a fixed composition because it contains only one type of atom.
6. Circle the letter before each element that is a gas at room temperature.
   a. carbon (b.) oxygen
   c. mercury (d.) nitrogen

*Match each element to its correct symbol.*

| | Element | Symbol |
|---|---|---|
| b | 7. aluminum | a. C |
| c | 8. gold | b. Al |
| a | 9. carbon | c. Au |

Name ______________ Class ______________ Date ______________



## Compounds (page 40)

10. What is a compound? A compound is a substance that is made from two or more simpler substances and can be broken down into those simpler substances.

11. Circle the letter of each sentence that is true about compounds.
    (a.) A compound always contains at least two elements.
    (b.) The substances that make up a compound are always joined in a fixed proportion.
    c. A compound has the same properties as the elements from which it is formed.
    (d.) A compound can be broken down into simpler substances.

## Mixtures (pages 41–42)

12. Why do the properties of a mixture vary? The properties of a mixture can vary because the composition of a mixture is not fixed.

13. A(n) heterogeneous mixture is a mixture whose parts are noticeably different from one another.

14. Is the following sentence true or false? A homogeneous mixture is a mixture in which it is difficult to distinguish the substances from one another. true

## Solutions, Suspensions, and Colloids (pages 42–44)

15. A mixture can be classified as a solution, a suspension, or a colloid based on the size of its largest particles.

16. Circle the letter of the term that identifies the homogeneous mixture that forms when sugar is dissolved in a glass of hot water.
    (a.) solution
    b. suspension
    c. colloid
    d. substance

17. Complete the table about solutions, suspensions, and colloids.

| Solutions, Suspensions, and Colloids | | | |
|---|---|---|---|
| **Type of Mixture** | **Relative Size of Largest Particles** | **Homogeneous or Heterogeneous?** | **Do Particles Scatter Light?** |
| Solution | Small | Homogeneous | No |
| Colloid | Intermediate | Homogeneous | Yes |
| Suspension | Large | Heterogeneous | Yes |

18. Circle the letter before each example of a colloid.
    a. windshield wiper fluid
    (b.) fog
    (c.) homogenized milk
    d. muddy water

19. Is the following sentence true or false? If salt water is poured through a filter, the salt will be trapped on the filter.
    false

Name ______________________ Class ______________ Date __________



# Section 2.2 Physical Properties

**(pages 45–51)**

*This section discusses physical properties and physical changes. It also explains how physical properties can be used to identify materials, select materials, and separate mixtures.*

## Reading Strategy (page 45)

**Building Vocabulary** As you read, write a definition for each term in the table below. For more information on this Reading Strategy, see the **Reading and Study Skills** in the **Skills and Reference Handbook** at the end of your textbook.

| Defining Physical Properties | |
|---|---|
| **Physical Property** | **Definition** |
| Viscosity | The tendency of a liquid to resist flowing |
| Malleability | The ability of a solid to be hammered without shattering |
| Melting Point | The temperature at which a solid changes to a liquid |

## Examples of Physical Properties (pages 45–47)

1. A physical property is any characteristic of a material that can be observed or measured without changing the composition of the substances in the material.
2. Explain why a wooden spoon is a better choice than a metal spoon for stirring a boiling pot of soup. The handle of a wooden spoon will stay cool because wood is not a good conductor of heat.
3. Is the following sentence true or false? A liquid with a high viscosity flows more slowly than a liquid with a low viscosity at the same temperature. true
4. Is the following sentence true or false? Discovering which of two materials can scratch the other is a way to compare the hardness of the materials. true

*Match each term to its definition.*

| | Term | Definition |
|---|---|---|
| c | 5. viscosity | a. The ability of a solid to be hammered without shattering |
| d | 6. conductivity | b. The temperature at which a substance changes from a liquid to a gas |
| a | 7. malleability | c. The resistance of a liquid to flowing |
| f | 8. melting point | d. The ability to allow heat to flow |
| b | 9. boiling point | e. The ratio of the mass of a substance to its volume |
| e | 10. density | f. The temperature at which a substance changes from a solid to a liquid |

Name ______________ Class ______________ Date ______________



11. Which of the substances in the table below are gases at room temperature?

a. Hydrogen b. Nitrogen c. Ammonia

| Melting and Boiling Points of Some Substances | | |
|---|---|---|
| **Substance** | **Melting Point** | **Boiling Point** |
| Hydrogen | −259.3°C | −252.9°C |
| Nitrogen | −210.0°C | −195.8°C |
| Ammonia | −77.7°C | −33.3°C |
| Octane (found in gasoline) | −56.8°C | 125.6°C |
| Water | 0.0°C | 100.0°C |
| Acetic acid (found in vinegar) | 16.6°C | 117.9°C |

## Using Physical Properties (page 48)

12. Describe three steps that can be used to identify a material. First, decide which properties to test. Second, do a test on a sample of the unknown. Third, compare the results with data reported for known materials.

13. Is the following sentence true or false? Usually, people consider only one property when choosing a material. false

## Using Properties to Separate Mixtures (page 50)

14. Two processes that are commonly used to separate mixtures are filtration and distillation.

15. Explain how filtration separates materials based on the size of their particles. Particles that are small enough to pass through the filter are separated from larger particles, which are trapped on the filter.

16. Explain why distillation works for converting seawater into fresh water. Water has a much lower boiling point than the compounds dissolved in seawater. Water can be boiled and collected in a separate container. The dissolved compounds are left behind in the original container.

## Recognizing Physical Changes (page 51)

17. Is the following sentence true or false? In a physical change, some of the substances in a material change, but the properties of the material stay the same. false

18. Explain why the boiling of water is a physical change. When water changes from a liquid to a gas, it remains the same substance.

19. Circle the letter for each process that is a reversible physical change.

(a.) wrinkling a shirt
(b.) freezing water
c. cutting hair
d. peeling an orange

# Section 2.3 Chemical Properties
## (pages 54–58)

*This section discusses chemical properties and describes clues that may show that a chemical change has taken place.*

## Reading Strategy (page 54)

**Relating Text and Visuals** As you read, complete the table by finding examples of the clues for recognizing chemical changes in Figures 19 and 20. For more information on this Reading Strategy, see the **Reading and Study Skills** in the **Skills and Reference Handbook** at the end of your textbook.

| Recognizing Chemical Changes | |
|---|---|
| **Clue** | **Example** |
| Change in color | Copper roof changing color from red to green when exposed to moist air |
| Production of gas | Formation of carbon dioxide gas when vinegar is added to baking soda |
| Formation of precipitate | Formation of cottage cheese curds when acid is added to milk. |

## Observing Chemical Properties (pages 54–55)

1. Is the following sentence true or false? The substances in paraffin do not change when a candle burns. false
2. Circle the letters of the compounds formed when a candle burns.
   a. paraffin
   b. hydrogen
   (c.) water
   (d.) carbon
3. What is a chemical property? A chemical property is any property that produces a change in the composition of matter.
4. Is the following sentence true or false? Flammability is a material's ability to burn in the presence of carbon dioxide. false
5. The property that describes how readily a substance combines chemically with other substances is reactivity.
6. Circle the letter of each property that is a chemical property.
   a. hardness
   b. density
   (c.) flammability
   (d.) reactivity
7. Is the following sentence true or false? Nitrogen is a more reactive element than oxygen. false

8. Why isn't iron used to make coins? Iron is highly reactive in the presence of oxygen and water.

9. What is the benefit of pumping nitrogen gas into seawater that is stored in steel tanks? The nitrogen displaces dissolved oxygen from the seawater, reducing the amount of rust that forms inside the tanks.

## Recognizing Chemical Changes (pages 56–57)

10. A(n) chemical change occurs when a substance reacts and forms one or more new substances.

11. What are three examples of chemical changes?

a. A cake baking  b. Leaves on trees changing color

c. Food being digested

12. Circle the letters of examples of evidence for a chemical change.

(a.) a change in color

b. a filter trapping particles

(c.) the production of a gas

(d.) the formation of a solid precipitate

*Match each example to evidence of a chemical change.*

| Example | Chemical Change |
|---|---|
| b 13. Lemon juice is added to milk. | a. the production of a gas |
| c 14. A silver bracelet darkens when exposed to air. | b. the formation of a precipitate |
| a 15. Vinegar is mixed with baking soda. | c. a change in color |

## Is a Change Chemical or Physical? (page 58)

16. Is the following sentence true or false? When iron is heated until it turns red, the color change shows that a chemical change has taken place. false

17. When matter undergoes a chemical change, the composition of the matter changes.

18. When matter undergoes a chemical change, the composition of the matter stays the same.

19. Complete the following table about chemical changes.

| Chemical Changes | | |
|---|---|---|
| **Type of Change** | **Are New Substances Formed?** | **Example** |
| Chemical | Yes | Iron rusting |
| Physical | No | Sugar dissolving in water |

Name ____________________ Class ______________ Date __________



# WordWise

*Answer the questions by writing the correct vocabulary term in the blanks. Use the circled letter in each term to find the hidden vocabulary word. Then, write a definition for the hidden word.*

| Clues | Vocabulary Terms |
|---|---|
| A mixture that results when substances dissolve to form a homogeneous mixture | (s) o l u t i o n |
| A substance that can be broken down into two or more simpler substances | c o m p o (u) n d |
| A change in which the composition of matter stays the same | p h y (s) i c a l c h a n g e |
| A solid that forms and separates from a liquid mixture | p r e c i (p) i t a t e |
| A substance that cannot be broken down into simpler substances | (e) l e m e n t |
| The ability of a material to allow heat to flow | c o (n) d u c t i v i t y |
| A classification for matter that always has the same composition | p u r e (s) u b s t a n c e |
| The ability of a material to burn | f l a m m a b i l (i) t y |
| A homogeneous mixture containing particles that scatter light | c (o) l l o i d |
| The temperature at which a substance changes from a liquid to gas | b o i l i n g p o i (n) t |

**Hidden Term:** s u s p e n s i o n

**Definition:** A heterogeneous mixture that separates into layers over time

# Melting and Boiling Points

**Math Skill: Data Tables**

You may want to read more about this **Math Skill** in the **Skills and Reference Handbook** at the end of your textbook.

| Melting and Boiling Points of Some Substances | | |
|---|---|---|
| **Substance** | **Melting Point** | **Boiling Point** |
| Hydrogen | −259.3°C | −252.9°C |
| Nitrogen | −210.0°C | −195.8°C |
| Water | 0.0°C | 100.0°C |
| Acetic acid (found in vinegar) | 16.6°C | 117.9°C |
| Table salt | 800.7°C | 1465°C |

Which of the substances in the table above are solids at a temperature of −40°C?

**1. Read and Understand**

*What information are you given?*

Temperature = −40°C

The melting and boiling points of five substances are listed in the table.

**2. Plan and Solve**

*What unknown are you trying to find?*

Which of the five substances are solids at −40°C?

*What guideline can you use?*

Any substance that is a solid at −40°C must have a melting point greater than −40°C.

*Check the melting point of each substance in the table to find out whether it satisfies the guideline.*

Water, acetic acid, and table salt are solids at −40°C.

**3. Look Back and Check**

*Is your answer reasonable?*

Because water, acetic acid, and table salt have melting points equal to or greater than 0°C, they will all be solids at a temperature well below 0°C.

## Math Practice

*On a separate sheet of paper, solve the following problems.*

1. Which substance in the table is a liquid at 105°C? acetic acid
2. Which substance in the table has a melting point closest to room temperature (20°C)? acetic acid
3. Which substance in the table boils at the lowest temperature? hydrogen
4. Which substance has the smallest temperature range as a liquid, hydrogen or nitrogen? hydrogen

Name ______________________ Class ________________ Date ____________



# Section 3.1 Solids, Liquids, and Gases
**(pages 68–73)**

*This section explains how materials are classified as solids, liquids, or gases. It also describes the behavior of these three states of matter.*

## Reading Strategy (page 68)

**Comparing and Contrasting** As you read about the states of matter, replace each letter in the diagram below with one of these phrases: *definite volume, definite shape, variable volume,* or *variable shape.* For more information on this Reading Strategy, see the **Reading and Study Skills** in the **Skills and Reference Handbook** at the end of your textbook.

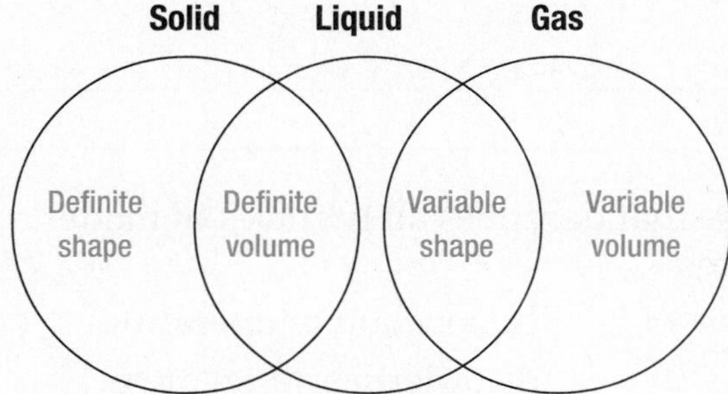


## Describing the States of Matter (pages 68–70)

1. What are three common states of matter?
   a. Solids b. Liquids c. Gases
2. Is the following sentence true or false? The fact that a copper wire can be bent shows that some solids do not have a definite shape. false
3. Circle the letter of each phrase that describes how particles at the atomic level are arranged within most solids.
   a. randomly arranged
   (b.) packed close together
   (c.) arranged in a regular pattern
   d. spaced far apart
4. Is the following sentence true or false? A liquid takes the shape of its container. true
5. What is the state of matter in which a material has neither a definite shape nor a definite volume? gas
6. Compare and contrast the arrangement of particles at the atomic level for a liquid and a solid. Particles in a solid are packed close together in an orderly arrangement. The arrangement of particles in a liquid is more random.
7. What determines the shape and volume of a gas? A gas takes the shape and volume of its container.
8. On the sun, where temperatures are extremely high, matter exists in a state known as plasma.

Name ______________________ Class ________________ Date ____________



9. The state of matter that can exist at extremely low temperatures is called a Bose-Einstein condensate.

10. Complete the table about states of matter.

| States of Matter | | |
|---|---|---|
| **State** | **Shape** | **Volume** |
| Solid | Definite | Definite |
| Liquid | Not definite | Definite |
| Gas | Not definite | Not definite |

## Kinetic Theory (page 71)

11. Describe kinetic energy. Kinetic energy is the energy an object has due to its motion.

12. Circle the letter of the phrase that describes all particles of matter in the kinetic theory of matter.
   a. randomly arranged
   b. constant temperature
   (c.) in constant motion
   d. orderly arrangement

## Explaining the Behavior of Gases (pages 72–73)

13. Is the following sentence true or false? There are forces of attraction among the particles in all matter. true

14. Why can scientists ignore the forces of attraction among particles in a gas under ordinary conditions? The particles in a gas are apart and moving fast, so the forces of attraction are too weak to have a noticeable effect.

15. Is the following sentence true or false? Because of the constant motion of the particles in a gas, the gas has a definite shape and volume. false

## Explaining the Behavior of Liquids (page 73)

16. Do forces of attraction have a stronger effect on the behavior of the particles in a gas or in a liquid? a liquid

17. Circle the letter of each factor that affects the behavior of liquids.
   a. fixed location of particles
   (b.) constant motion of particles
   c. orderly arrangement of particles
   (d.) forces of attraction among particles

## Explaining the Behavior of Solids (page 74)

18. Solids have a(n) definite volume and shape because particles in a solid vibrate in fixed locations.

# Section 3.2 The Gas Laws

**(pages 75–81)**

*This section discusses gas pressure and the factors that affect it. It also explains the relationships between the temperature, volume, and pressure of a gas.*

## Reading Strategy (page 75)

**Identifying Cause and Effect** As you read, identify the variables that affect gas pressure, and write them in the diagram below. For more information on this Reading Strategy, see the **Reading and Study Skills** in the **Skills and Reference Handbook** at the end of your textbook.

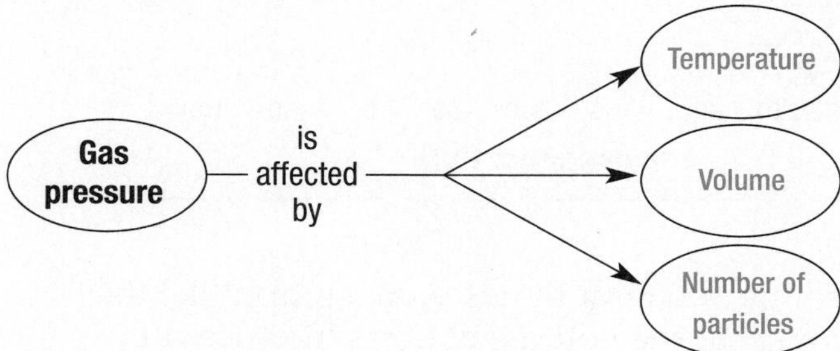


## Pressure (pages 75–76)

1. What is pressure? Pressure is a result of a force distributed over an area.

2. Circle the letter of each unit used to express amounts of pressure.
   a. newton
   b. joule
   (c.) pascal
   (d.) kilopascal

3. What causes the pressure in a closed container of gas? Collisions between particles of gas and the walls of the container cause the pressure.

## Factors that Affect Gas Pressure (pages 76–77)

4. Name the factors that affect the pressure of an enclosed gas.
   a. Its temperature b. Its volume c. The number of its particles

5. Is the following sentence true or false? In a closed container, increasing the temperature of a gas will decrease the force with which particles hit the walls of the container. false

6. What effect does raising the temperature of a gas have on its pressure, if the volume of the gas and the number of its particles are kept constant? The pressure of the gas will increase.

7. How does reducing the volume of a gas affect its pressure if the temperature of the gas and the number of particles are constant?
   Reducing the volume of a gas increases its pressure if the temperature and volume are constant.

8. Increasing the number of particles of a gas will increase its pressure if the temperature and the volume are constant.

## Charles's Law (page 78)

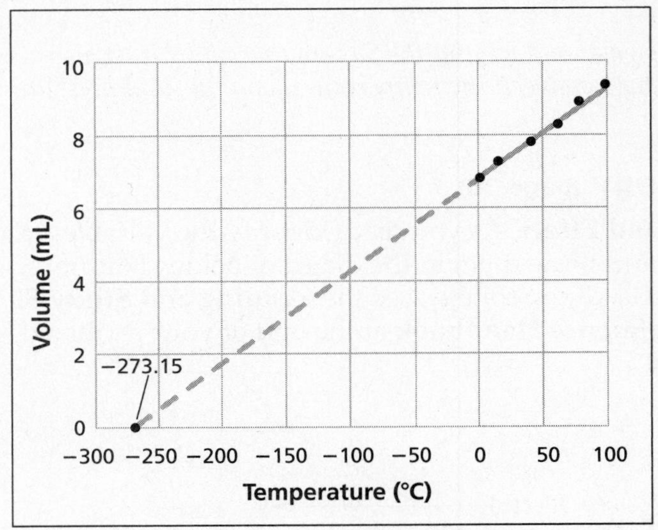


**9.** Jacques Charles recorded the behavior of gases on a graph like the one above. The data shows that the volume of a gas increases at the same rate as the ___temperature___ of the gas.

**10.** A temperature equal to 0 K on the Kelvin temperature scale is known as ___absolute zero___.

**11.** What does Charles's law state? ___The volume of a gas is directly proportional to its temperature in kelvins if the pressure and the number of particles of the gas are constant.___

## Boyle's Law (page 79)

**12.** If the temperature and number of particles of gas in a cylinder do not change, and the volume of the cylinder is reduced by half, the pressure of the gas will be ___twice as much___ as the original pressure.

**13.** Boyle's law states that there is an inverse relationship between the pressure and volume of a gas. Circle the letter of the correct expression of this relationship.

(a.) $P_1V_1 = P_2V_2$

b. $P_1V_2 = P_2V_1$

c. $\frac{P_1}{V_1} = \frac{P_2}{V_2}$

d. $P_1P_2 = V_1V_2$

## The Combined Gas Law (pages 80–81)

**14.** Circle the letters of the factors that are included in the expression of the combined gas law.

(a.) temperature

b. number of particles

(c.) volume

(d.) pressure

Name ______________________ Class ________________ Date ____________



# Section 3.3 Phase Changes
**(pages 84–91)**

*This section explains what happens when a substance changes from one state of matter to another and describes six phase changes.*

## Reading Strategy (page 84)

**Summarizing** As you read, complete the description of energy flow during phase changes in the diagram below. For more information on this Reading Strategy, see the **Reading and Study Skills** in the **Skills and Reference Handbook** at the end of your textbook.

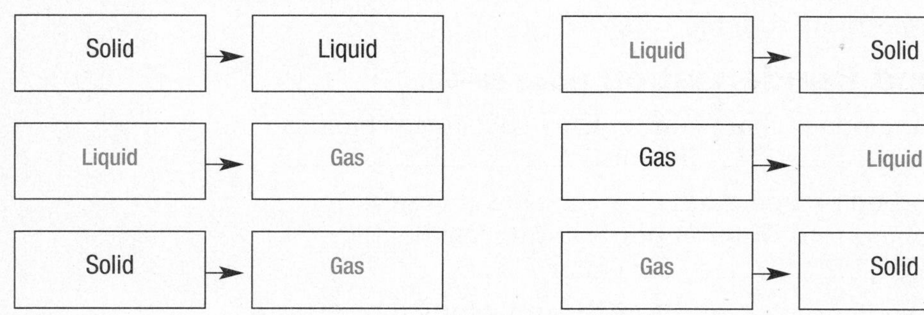


## Characteristics of Phase Changes (pages 84–86)

1. What is a phase change? A phase change is the reversible physical change that takes place when a substance changes from one state of matter to another.

*Match each term with the letter of the phase-change description that best describes it.*

| | Term | Phase-Change |
|---|---|---|
| d | 2. freezing | a. Solid to gas |
| a | 3. sublimation | b. Liquid to gas |
| e | 4. condensation | c. Gas to solid |
| f | 5. melting | d. Liquid to solid |
| c | 6. deposition | e. Gas to liquid |
| b | 7. vaporization | f. Solid to liquid |

8. What happens to the temperature of a substance during a phase change? The temperature of a substance remains constant during a phase change.

9. Is the following sentence true or false? The temperature at which a substance freezes is lower than the temperature at which it melts. false

10. Circle the letter that describes the behavior of a substance during a phase change.
    a. neither absorbs nor releases energy
    b. always absorbs energy
    c. always releases energy
    (d.) either absorbs or releases energy

11. A substance absorbs energy from its surroundings during a(n) endothermic change.

12. The energy absorbed by one gram of ice as it melts is known as the heat of fusion for water.

13. As water freezes, it releases heat to its surroundings. Freezing is an example of a(n) exothermic change.

## Melting and Freezing (page 88)

14. Is the following sentence true or false? Water molecules have a more orderly arrangement in ice than in liquid water. true

15. When liquid water freezes, the average kinetic energy of its molecules decreases, and the arrangement of the molecules becomes more orderly.

## Vaporization and Condensation (page 88–90)

16. Vaporization is the phase change in which a substance changes from a(n) liquid into a(n) gas.

17. The energy absorbed by one gram of water as it changes from its liquid phase into water vapor is known as the heat of vaporization for water.

18. Is the following sentence true or false? When water vapor collects above the liquid in a closed container, the pressure caused by the collisions of this vapor and the walls of the container is called vapor pressure. true

19. The phase change in which a substance changes from a gas into a liquid is called condensation.

20. Compare and contrast the processes of evaporation and boiling by completing the table below.

| Evaporation and Boiling | | | |
|---|---|---|---|
| **Process** | **Phase Change** | **Where It Occurs** | **Temperature** |
| Evaporation | Vaporization | At the surface of a liquid | Below the boiling point of the liquid |
| Boiling | Vaporization | Throughout a liquid | At the boiling point of the liquid |

21. Is the following sentence true or false? A gas absorbs energy as it changes into a liquid. false

## Sublimation and Deposition (page 91)

22. Dry ice can change directly from a solid to a gas without forming a liquid first. This process is an example of sublimation.

23. What is deposition? Deposition is the phase change in which a substance changes directly from a gas to a solid without changing to a liquid first.

Name ______________________ Class __________________ Date ____________

Chapter 3 States of Matter

# WordWise

*Answer the questions by writing the correct vocabulary term in the blanks. Use the circled letter in each term to find the hidden vocabulary word. Then, write a definition for the hidden word.*

| Clues | Vocabulary Terms |
|---|---|
| What is the process that changes a substance from a liquid to a gas below the substance's boiling point? | e v a (p) o r a t i o n |
| Which gas law states that the volume of a gas is directly proportional to its temperature? | C h a (r) l e s ' s L a w |
| What is the phase change in which a substance changes directly from a gas to a solid? | d (e) p o s i t i o n |
| In what state does matter have both a definite shape and a definite volume? | (s) o l i d |
| What is the phase change in which a substance changes from a gas to a liquid? | c o n d e n (s) a t i o n |
| What is the phase change in which a substance changes directly from a solid to a gas? | s (u) b l i m a t i o n |
| During what type of phase change does a substance release energy to its surroundings? | e x o t h e (r) m i c |
| During what type of phase change does a substance absorb energy from its surroundings? | (e) n d o t h e r m i c |

**Hidden Term:** p r e s s u r e

**Definition:** The property of matter that is the result of a force distributed over an area.

# The Combined Gas Law

**Math Skill: Calculating with Significant Figures**

You may want to read more about this **Math Skill** in the **Skills and Reference Handbook** at the end of your textbook.

A gas in a cylinder has a pressure of 235 kPa at a volume of 5.00 L. The volume is reduced to 1.25 L. The temperature does not change. Find the new pressure of the gas.

**1. Read and Understand**

*What information are you given?*

$V_1 = 5.00\text{ L}$ $\quad V_2 = 1.25\text{ L}$ $\quad P_1 = 235\text{ kPa}$

**2. Plan and Solve**

*What unknown are you trying to calculate?* $P_2$

*What expression can you use?*

$$\frac{P_1V_1}{T_1} = \frac{P_2V_2}{T_2}$$

*Cancel out the variable that does not change and rearrange the expression to solve for $P_2$.*

$$P_1V_1 = P_2V_2 \qquad P_2 = \frac{P_1V_1}{V_2}$$

*Replace each variable with its known value.*

$$P_2 = 235\text{ kPa} \times \frac{5.00\text{ L}}{1.25\text{ L}} = 940\text{ kPa}$$

**3. Look Back and Check**

*Is your answer reasonable?*

The volume of a gas is inversely proportional to its pressure if the temperature and number of particles are constant. The volume decreased by a factor of four, from 5.00 L to 1.25 L. The answer, 940 kPa, is four times the original pressure, 235 kPa.

## Math Practice

*On a separate sheet of paper, solve the following problems. The number of particles remains constant for all problems.*

1. A gas has a pressure of 340 kPa at a volume of 3.20 L. What happens to the pressure when the volume is increased to 5.44 L? The temperature does not change.

   $P_2 = 340\text{ kPa} \times \frac{3.20\text{ L}}{5.44\text{ L}} = 200\text{ kPa}$

2. A gas has a pressure of 180 kPa at a temperature of 300 K. At what temperature will the gas have a pressure of 276 kPa? The volume does not change.

   $T_2 = 276\text{ kPa} \times \frac{300\text{ K}}{180\text{ kPa}} = 460\text{ K}$

3. At 47°C, a gas has a pressure of 140 kPa. The gas is cooled until the pressure decreases to 105 kPa. If the volume remains constant, what will the final temperature be in Kelvins? In degrees Celsius?

   $K = 273\text{ K} + 47°\text{C} = 320\text{ K}$

   $T_2 = \frac{105\text{ kPa}}{140\text{ kPa}} \times 320\text{ K} = 240\text{ K}$

   $240\text{ K} - 273 = -33°\text{C}$

Name ______________________ Class ______________ Date __________



# Section 4.1 Studying Atoms
**(pages 100-105)**

*This section discusses the development of atomic models.*

## Reading Strategy (page 100)

**Summarizing** As you read, complete the table about atomic models. For more information on this Reading Strategy, see the **Reading and Study Skills** in the **Skills and Reference Handbook** at the end of your textbook.

| Atomic Models | | |
|---|---|---|
| **Scientist** | **Evidence** | **Model** |
| Dalton | Ratio of masses in compounds | Indivisible, solid spheres |
| Thomson | Deflected beam | Negative charges evenly scattered through positively charged mass of matter (plum pudding model) |
| Rutherford | Deflection of alpha particles passing through gold foil | Positive, dense nucleus |

## Ancient Greek Models of Atoms (page 100)

1. Democritus named the smallest particles of matter ___atoms___ because they could not be divided.
2. List the four elements that Aristotle included in his model of matter.

   a. ___Earth___ b. ___Air___

   c. ___Fire___ d. ___Water___

## Dalton's Atomic Theory (page 101)

3. Is the following sentence true or false? John Dalton gathered evidence for the existence of atoms by measuring the masses of elements that reacted to form compounds. ___true___
4. What theory did Dalton propose to explain why the elements in a compound always join in the same way? He proposed that all matter is made up of individual particles called atoms, which cannot be divided.
5. Circle the letters of the sentences that represent the main points of Dalton's theory of atoms.

   (a.) All elements are composed of atoms.

   (b.) In a particular compound, atoms of different elements always combine the same way.

   c. All atoms have the same mass.

   (d.) Compounds contain atoms of more than one element.

Name ____________________ Class ____________________ Date ____________



## Thomson's Model of the Atom (pages 102–103)

6. Objects with like electric charges repel, and objects with opposite electric charges attract.
7. What happened to the beam when Thomson placed a pair of charged metal plates on either side of the glass tube? The beam was attracted by the positively charged plate and repelled by the negatively charged plate.
8. Thomson concluded that the particles in the glowing beam had a(n) negative charge because they were attracted to a positive plate.
9. Is the following sentence true or false? Thomson's experiments provided the first evidence for the existence of subatomic particles. true
10. Describe Thomson's model. Negative charges are evenly scattered throughout an atom filled with positively charged mass of matter.

## Rutherford's Atomic Theory (pages 104–105)

11. What is an alpha particle? An alpha particle is a fast-moving particle that carries a positive charge.
12. Fill in the table to show what Rutherford hypothesized would happen to the paths of alpha particles as they passed through a thin sheet of gold.

| Rutherford's Hypothesis | |
|---|---|
| Most particles would travel in a straight path from their source to a screen that lit up when struck. | Particles that did not pass straight through would be deflected only slightly. |

13. Circle the letters of the sentences that describe what happened when Marsden directed a beam of particles at a piece of gold foil.
    a. Fewer alpha particles were deflected than expected.
    (b.) More alpha particles were deflected than expected.
    c. None of the alpha particles were deflected.
    (d.) Some alpha particles bounced back toward the source.
14. Circle the letter of the sentence that states what Rutherford concluded from the gold foil experiment.
    a. An atom's negative charge is concentrated in its nucleus.
    b. Thomson's model of the atom was correct.
    (c.) An atom's positive charge is concentrated in its nucleus.
    d. An atom's positive charge is spread evenly throughout the atom.

Name ______________________ Class ________________ Date ____________



# Section 4.2 The Structure of an Atom
**(pages 108–112)**

*This section compares the properties of three subatomic particles. It also discusses atomic numbers, mass numbers, and isotopes.*

## Reading Strategy (page 108)

**Monitoring Your Understanding** Before you read, list in the table shown what you know about atoms and what you would like to learn. After you read, list what you have learned. For more information on this Reading Strategy, see the **Reading and Study Skills** in the **Skills and Reference Handbook** at the end of your textbook.

| What I Know About Atoms | What I Would Like to Learn | What I Have Learned |
|---|---|---|
| Most students will know that atoms are the "building blocks" of matter, and some may know that atoms contain subatomic particles. | Based on the title of the section, students may say that they want to learn more about the structure of atoms. | |

## Properties of Subatomic Particles (pages 108–109)

1. What are three subatomic particles?
   a. Protons b. Electrons c. Neutrons

2. Circle the letter that identifies a subatomic particle with a positive charge.
   a. nucleus
   (b.) proton
   c. neutron
   d. electron

3. Why did Chadwick conclude that the particles produced by his experiment were neutral in charge? A charged object did not deflect the paths of the particles.

## Comparing Subatomic Particles (pages 109–110)

4. Circle the letters of properties that vary among subatomic particles.
   a. color
   (b.) mass
   (c.) charge
   (d.) location in the atom

5. Circle the letter of the expression that accurately compares the masses of neutrons and protons.
   (a.) mass of 1 neutron = mass of 1 proton
   b. mass of 2000 neutrons = mass of 1 proton
   c. mass of 1 electron = mass of 1 proton
   d. mass of 1 neutron = mass of 1 electron

## Atomic Number and Mass Number (page 110)

6. Is the following sentence true or false? Two atoms of the same element can have different numbers of protons. false

7. What is an atomic number? The atomic number of an element equals the number of protons in an atom of that element.

8. Circle the letters that identify quantities that are always equal to an element's atomic number.
   a. number of nuclei
   (b.) number of protons
   c. number of neutrons
   (d.) number of electrons

9. Is the following sentence true or false? Two different elements can have the same atomic number. false

10. What is the mass number of an atom? The mass number of an atom is the sum of the protons and neutrons in the nucleus of that atom.

11. Complete the equation in the table below.

| Number of neutrons = Mass number − Atomic number |
|---|

## Isotopes (page 112)

12. Every atom of a given element has the same number of protons and electrons.

13. Every atom of a given element does not have the same number of neutrons.

14. What are isotopes? Isotopes are atoms of the same element that have different numbers of neutrons and different mass numbers.

15. All oxygen atoms have 8 protons. Circle the letter of the number of neutrons in an atom of oxygen-18.
   a. 8
   b. 9
   (c.) 10
   d. 18

16. Is the following sentence true or false? Isotopes of oxygen have different chemical properties. false

17. Water that contains hydrogen-2 atoms instead of hydrogen-1 atoms is called heavy water.

Name ______________________ Class ________________ Date ____________



# Section 4.3 Modern Atomic Theory
**(pages 113–118)**

*This section focuses on the arrangement and behavior of electrons in atoms.*

## Reading Strategy (page 113)

**Sequencing** After you read, complete the description in the flow chart below of how the gain or loss of energy affects electrons in atoms. For more information on this Reading Strategy, see the **Reading and Study Skills** in the **Skills and Reference Handbook** at the end of your textbook.

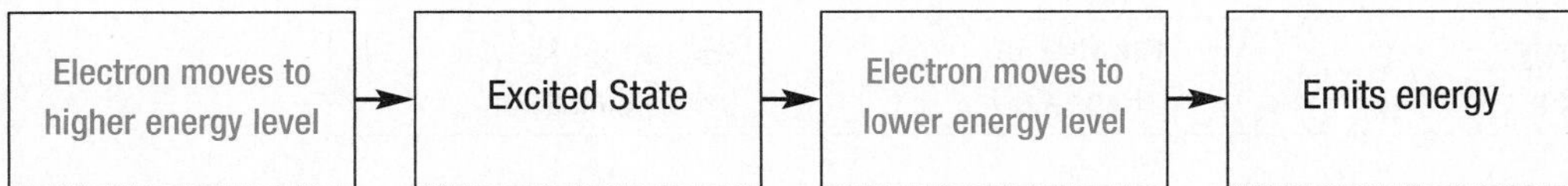


## Bohr's Model of the Atom (pages 113–116)

1. Circle the letter of the sentence that tells how Bohr's model of the atom differed from Rutherford's model.
   a. Bohr's model focused on the nucleus.
   b. Bohr's model focused on the protons.
   c. Bohr's model focused on the neutrons.
   (d.) Bohr's model focused on the electrons.
2. Is the following sentence true or false? In Bohr's model of the atom, electrons have a constant speed and move in fixed orbits around the nucleus. true
3. What can happen to an electron in an atom when the atom gains or loses energy? The electron can move from one energy level to another.
4. What evidence do scientists have that electrons can move from one energy level to another? Scientists can measure the energy gained or lost by electrons.
5. Is the following sentence true or false? When electrons release energy, some of the energy may be released as visible light. true

## Electron Cloud Model (page 116)

6. Is the following sentence true or false? Bohr's model was correct in assigning energy levels to electrons. true
7. When trying to predict the locations and motions of electrons in atoms, scientists must work with probability.
8. What is an electron cloud? An electron cloud is a visual model of the most likely locations for the electrons in an atom.

9. Is the following sentence true or false? Scientists use the electron cloud model to describe the exact location of electrons around the nucleus. false

## Atomic Orbitals (page 117)

10. Is the following sentence true or false? An orbital is a region of space around the nucleus where an electron is likely to be found. true

11. An electron model is a good approximation of how electrons behave in their orbitals.

*Use this table to answer questions 12 and 13.*

| Energy Level | Number of Orbitals | Maximum Number of Electrons |
|---|---|---|
| 1 | 1 | 2 |
| 2 | 4 | 8 |
| 3 | 9 | 18 |
| 4 | 16 | 32 |

12. Higher energy levels have more orbitals than lower energy levels do.

13. What is the relationship between the number of orbitals and the maximum number of electrons in an energy level? The maximum number of electrons in an energy level is twice the number of orbitals.

## Electron Configurations (page 118)

14. What is an electron configuration? An electron configuration is the arrangement of electrons in the orbitals of an atom.

15. Circle the letter of the number of energy levels needed for a lithium atom's three electrons when the atom is in its ground state.
    a. zero
    b. one (circled)
    c. two
    d. three

16. Is the following sentence true or false? An excited state is less stable than a ground state. true

17. Circle the letters of each sentence that is true when all of the electrons in an atom are in orbitals with the lowest possible energies.
    a. The electrons are in the most stable configuration. (circled)
    b. The electrons are in an unstable configuration.
    c. The atom is in an excited state.
    d. The atom is in its ground state. (circled)

Name ______________________ Class ________________ Date ____________



# WordWise

*Solve the clues to determine which vocabulary terms from Chapter 4 are hidden in the puzzle. Then find and circle the terms in the puzzle. The terms may occur vertically, horizontally, or diagonally.*

| e | m | a | s | s | n | u | m | b | e | r | u | n |
|---|---|---|---|---|---|---|---|---|---|---|---|---|
| n | l | o | r | b | i | t | a | l | x | a | p | i |
| r | e | e | n | l | t | p | t | s | p | b | k | s |
| g | n | a | c | a | s | r | d | c | r | h | l | o |
| b | e | l | d | t | g | o | f | l | s | g | a | t |
| l | r | t | s | o | r | t | g | r | n | b | t | o |
| n | g | z | b | m | o | o | p | l | q | d | c | p |
| p | y | q | p | i | u | n | n | m | a | s | s | e |
| s | l | n | m | c | n | n | u | c | l | e | u | s |
| t | e | u | e | n | d | r | i | o | l | k | m | r |
| r | v | c | l | u | s | v | a | b | t | o | p | k |
| z | e | l | x | m | t | w | e | s | r | n | u | e |
| p | l | e | m | b | a | r | l | e | t | a | b | d |
| b | s | a | q | e | t | z | o | c | m | r | n | k |
| r | t | s | i | r | e | h | j | n | s | f | l | t |

| Clues | Hidden Words |
|---|---|
| Dense, positively charged mass in the center of an atom | nucleus |
| Positively charged subatomic particle found in the nucleus | proton |
| Neutral subatomic particle found in the nucleus | neutron |
| Number of protons in an atom of an element | atomic number |
| Sum of the protons and neutrons in the nucleus of an atom | mass number |
| Atoms of the same element having different numbers of neutrons | isotopes |
| Possible energies that electrons in an atom can have | energy levels |
| Visual model of the most likely locations for electrons in an atom | electron cloud |
| Region of space where an electron is likely to be found | orbital |
| Term for an atom whose electrons have the lowest possible energies | ground state |

Name ____________________ Class ______________ Date ____________



# Electrons and Orbitals

Use the table on page 117 of your textbook to find the ratio of the maximum number of electrons to the number of orbitals for each of four energy levels.

**Math Skill: Ratios and Proportions**

You may want to read more about this **Math Skill** in the **Skills and Reference Handbook** at the end of your textbook.

**1. Read and Understand**

*What information are you given?*

The number of orbitals and the maximum number of electrons per energy level

**2. Plan and Solve**

*What unknown are you trying to calculate?*

The ratio of the maximum number of electrons to the number of orbitals in energy levels 1 through 4

*What mathematical expression can you use to calculate the unknown?*

$$\frac{\text{maximum number of electrons}}{\text{number of orbitals}}$$

Level 1: $\frac{2}{1} = \frac{2}{1}$

Level 2: $\frac{4}{2} = \frac{2}{1}$

Level 3: $\frac{18}{9} = \frac{2}{1}$

Level 4: $\frac{32}{16} = \frac{2}{1}$

**3. Look Back and Check**

*Is your answer reasonable?*

The ratio is the same for all four energy levels. Also, each orbital can contain only two electrons.

## Math Practice

*On a separate sheet of paper, solve the following problems.*

1. Calculate the maximum number of electrons for energy levels 5 and 6. Energy level 5 contains 25 orbitals; energy level 6 contains 36 orbitals. Each orbital can contain two electrons at most. For energy level 5, $2 \times 25 = 50$, so the maximum number is 50 electrons. For energy level 6, $2 \times 36 = 72$, so the maximum number is 72 electrons.

2. Energy level 7 can contain a maximum of 98 electrons. How many orbitals are there in energy level 7? Each orbital can contain two electrons at most, so 98 electrons divided by 2 electrons per orbital equals 49 orbitals.

3. A sodium atom has 11 electrons. How many orbitals in a sodium atom contain electrons? Each orbital can contain up to 2 electrons, so 11 electrons divided by 2 is 5 with a remainder of 1. There are 6 occupied orbitals.

Name ______________________ Class ______________ Date ____________



# Section 5.1 Organizing the Elements (pages 126–129)

*This section explains how Mendeleev organized elements into a periodic table. It also discusses the predictions he made about undiscovered elements and how the discovery of those elements supported his version of the table of the table.*

## Reading Strategy (page 126)

**Identifying Main Ideas** As you read, complete the table by identifying the main idea for each topic. For more information on this reading strategy, see the **Reading and Study Skills** in the **Skills and Reference Handbook** at the end of your textbook.

| Topic | Main Idea |
|---|---|
| Mendeleev's proposal | Mendeleev arranged the elements into rows in order of increasing mass so that elements with similar properties were in the same column. |
| Mendeleev's prediction | Mendeleev used the properties of existing elements to predict properties of undiscovered elements. |
| Evidence supporting Mendeleev's table | The close match between Mendeleev's predictions and the actual properties of new elements showed how useful his periodic table could be. |

## The Search for Order (page 126)

1. Is the following sentence true or false? The first elements to be identified were mainly gases. false
2. As the number of known elements grew, so did the need to organize them into groups based on their properties.
3. Circle the letter of each category that the French chemist Antoine Lavoisier used to classify elements.
   (a.) gases
   (b.) metals
   c. liquids
   (d.) nonmetals

## Mendeleev's Periodic Table (pages 127–129)

4. Is the following sentence true or false? Mendeleev needed to organize information about 63 elements. true
5. Mendeleev's strategy for classifying elements was modeled on a(n) card game or solitaire.
6. Circle the letter of each type of information Mendeleev knew about each element.
   (a.) name
   b. number of protons
   (c.) relative mass
   (d.) properties

7. Mendeleev arranged the elements into rows in order of increasing mass so that elements with similar properties were in the same column.

8. Is the following sentence true or false? A periodic table is an arrangement of elements in columns, based on a set of properties that repeat from row to row. true

| Group I | Group II | Group III | Group IV | Group V | Group VI | Group VII | Group VIII |
|---|---|---|---|---|---|---|---|
| H = 1<br>Li = 7 | Be = 9.4 | B = 11 | C = 12 | N = 14 | O = 16 | F = 19 | |
| Na = 23<br>K = 39 | Mg = 24<br>Ca = 40 | Al = 27.3<br>— = 44 | Si = 28<br>Ti = 48 | P = 31<br>V = 51 | S = 32<br>Cr = 52 | Cl = 35.5<br>Mn = 55 | Fe = 56, Co = 59,<br>Ni = 59, Cu = 63. |
| (Cu = 63)<br>Rb = 85 | Zn = 65<br>Sr = 87 | — = 68<br>Yt = 88 | — = 72<br>Zr = 90 | As = 75<br>Nb = 94 | Se = 78<br>Mo = 96 | Br = 80<br>— = 100 | Ru = 104, Rh = 104,<br>Pd = 106, Ag = 108. |
| (Ag = 108)<br>Cs = 133 | Cd = 112<br>Ba = 137 | In = 113<br>Di = 138 | Sn = 118<br>Ce = 140 | Sb = 122<br>— | Te = 125<br>— | I = 127<br>— | — — — — |
| (—)<br>— | —<br>— | —<br>Er = 178 | —<br>La = 180 | —<br>Ta = 182 | —<br>W = 184 | —<br>— | Os = 195, Ir = 197,<br>Pt = 198, Au = 199. |
| (Au = 199)<br>— | Hg = 200<br>— | Tl = 204<br>— | Pb = 207<br>Th = 231 | Bi = 208<br>— | U = 240 | | |

9. Mendeleev published the table above in 1872. Why did Mendeleev leave some locations in his periodic table blank? He left room for undiscovered elements.

10. Circle the letters of two elements that have similar properties.

a. zinc (Zn) (b.) chlorine (Cl)

c. nitrogen (N) (d.) bromine (Br)

11. How did Mendeleev decide where to place arsenic (As) and selenium (Se)? He placed them where they fit best based on their properties.

12. Is the following sentence true or false? Mendeleev was the first scientist to arrange elements in a periodic table. false

13. Describe a test for the correctness of a scientific model. One test is whether the model can be used to make accurate predictions.

14. Mendeleev used the properties of elements located near the spaces in his table to predict properties for undiscovered elements.

15. The close match between Mendeleev's predictions and the actual properties of new elements showed how useful his periodic table could be.

16. Circle the letter of each element that was discovered after Mendeleev published his periodic table that supported Mendeleev's predictions and provided evidence validating the table.

(a.) gallium (b.) scandium

(c.) germanium d. aluminum

Name ______________________ Class ________________ Date ____________



# Section 5.2 The Modern Periodic Table

**(pages 130–138)**

*This section explains the organization of the modern periodic table and discusses the general properties of metals, nonmetals, and metalloids.*

## Reading Strategy (page 130)

**Previewing** Before you read, complete the table by writing two questions about the periodic table on pages 132–133. As you read, write answers to your questions. For more information on this reading strategy, see the **Reading and Study Skills** in the **Skills and Reference Handbook** at the end of your textbook.

| Questions About the Periodic Table | |
|---|---|
| **Question** | **Answer** |
| Students might ask: What does atomic mass mean? | Atomic mass is a value that depends on the distribution of an element's isotopes in nature and the masses of those isotopes. |
| Why are two series of elements placed below the main body of the table? | Two series of elements are placed below the table to make the table more compact. |

Other possible questions: Why are there two numbering systems for the columns? Why is period 7 incomplete?

## The Periodic Law (pages 131–133)

1. Is the following sentence true or false? In the modern periodic table, elements are arranged by increasing number of protons. true

2. Explain why the number of elements per period varies. The number of elements per period varies because the number of available orbitals increases from energy level to energy level.

3. Properties of elements repeat in a predictable way when atomic numbers are used to arrange elements into groups. This pattern of repeating properties is called the periodic law.

## Atomic Mass (page 134)

4. Label the four types of information supplied for chlorine in the diagram.

a. Atomic number  b. Element symbol

c. Element name  d. Atomic mass

5. Define atomic mass. Atomic mass is a value that depends on the distribution of an element's isotopes in nature and the masses of those isotopes

6. Circle the letter of each sentence that is true about a carbon-12 atom.

   (a.) It has 6 protons and 6 neutrons.

   b. Scientists assigned a mass of 6 atomic mass units to the carbon-12 atom.

   (c.) It is used as a standard for comparing the masses of atoms.

   (d.) An atomic mass unit is defined as one twelfth the mass of a carbon-12 atom.

7. Is the following sentence true or false? Most elements exist as a mixture of two or more isotopes. true

8. The mass of an atom of chlorine-37 is greater than the mass of an atom of chlorine-35.

9. Is the following sentence true or false? All values are equally important in a weighted average. false

## Classes of Elements (pages 135–136)

10. Name the three categories into which elements are classified based on their general properties.

    a. Metals

    b. Metalloids

    c. Nonmetals

11. Is the following sentence true or false? All metals react with oxygen in the same way. false

12. An important property of transition elements is their ability to form compounds with distinctive colors.

13. Circle the letter of each sentence that is true about nonmetals.

    (a.) Nonmetals are poor conductors of heat and electric current.

    (b.) Many nonmetals are gases at room temperature.

    (c.) Some nonmetals are extremely reactive and others hardly react at all.

    d. Nonmetals that are solids tend to be malleable.

## Variation Across a Period (page 138)

14. Across a period from left to right, the elements become less metallic and more nonmetallic in their properties.

15. Circle the letter of each Period 3 element that is highly reactive.

    (a.) sodium    b. silicon

    (c.) chlorine    d. argon

# Section 5.3 Representative Groups
**(pages 139–145)**

*This section discusses how the number of valence electrons affects the properties of elements. It also describes properties of elements in Groups 1A through 8A.*

## Reading Strategy (page 139)

**Monitoring Your Understanding** As you read, record an important fact about each element listed in the table. For more information on this reading strategy, see the **Reading and Study Skills** in the **Skills and Reference Handbook** at the end of your textbook.

| Element | Important Fact |
|---|---|
| Magnesium | Possible answers: Magnesium plays a key role in the process that uses sunlight to produce sugar in plants. Mixtures of magnesium and other metals are used in transportation because they can be as strong as steel, but much lighter. |
| Aluminum | Aluminum is the most abundant metal in Earth's crust. It is strong, lightweight, malleable, and a good conductor of electric current. Much less energy is needed to purify recycled aluminum than to extract aluminum from bauxite. |
| Chlorine | Chlorine is a highly reactive, nonmetal gas. Chlorine is used to kill bacteria in drinking water and swimming pools. |

## Valence Electrons (page 139)

1. An electron that is in the highest occupied energy level of an atom is a(n) ____valence____ electron.
2. Elements within a group have the ____same____ number of valence electrons.

## The Alkali Metals (page 140)

3. The reactivity of alkali metals ____increases____ from the top of Group 1A to the bottom.
4. Sodium is stored under oil because it ____reacts with water vapor in air____.

## The Alkaline Earth Metals (page 141)

5. Differences in reactivity among alkaline earth metals are shown by the way they react with ____water____.

*Find and match two properties to each element listed.*

| | Alkaline Earth Metal | Property |
|---|---|---|
| b, c | 6. magnesium | a. Helps build strong teeth and bones |
| a, d | 7. calcium | b. Helps plants produce sugar |
| | | c. Is used to make lightweight bicycle frames |
| | | d. Is the main ingredient in limestone |

## The Boron Family (page 142)

8. List the four metals in Group 3A.

a. Aluminum b. Gallium

c. Indium d. Thallium

9. Circle the letter of each sentence that is true about aluminum.

(a.) It is the most abundant metal in Earth's crust.

(b.) It is often found combined with oxygen in bauxite.

c. It is more reactive than sodium and magnesium.

(d.) It is a good conductor of electric current.

## The Carbon Family (page 142)

10. List the two metalloids in Group 4A.

a. Silicon b. Germanium

11. Except for water, most of the compounds in your body contain carbon.

## The Nitrogen Family (page 143)

12. List the nonmetals in Group 5A.

a. Nitrogen b. Phosphorus

13. Name two elements in the nitrogen family that are contained in fertilizer.

a. Nitrogen b. Phosphorus

## The Oxygen Family (page 143)

14. List the nonmetals in Group 6A.

a. Oxygen b. Sulfur c. Selenium

15. Name the most abundant element in Earth's crust.

Oxygen

## The Halogens (page 144)

16. List the four nonmetals in Group 7A.

a. Fluorine b. Chlorine

c. Bromine d. Iodine

17. Halogens have similar chemical properties but different physical properties.

## The Noble Gases (page 145)

18. Name three characteristics of noble gases.

a. Colorless b. Odorless c. Extremely unreactive

19. How can an element that does not react easily with other elements be useful? It can be used to prevent reactions with such highly reactive elements as oxygen.

Name ______________________ Class ______________________ Date ______________



# WordWise

*Match each definition with the correct term by writing the definition's number in the grid. When you have filled in all the boxes, add up the numbers in each column, row, and the two diagonals. Hint: The sum should be 15 in each case.*

**Definitions**

1. An arrangement of elements in columns based on a set of properties that repeat from row to row
2. A pattern of repeating properties that occurs when atomic numbers are used to arrange elements into groups
3. One twelfth the mass of a carbon-12 atom
4. Elements that are good conductors of heat and electric current
5. Elements that form a bridge between the elements on the left and right sides of the periodic table
6. Elements that are poor conductors of heat and electric current
7. Elements with properties that fall between those of metals and nonmetals
8. An electron that is in the highest occupied energy level of an atom
9. Colorless, odorless, and extremely unreactive gases

| | | | diagonal = 15 |
|---|---|---|---|
| nonmetals 6 | periodic table 1 | valence electron 8 | = 15 |
| metalloids 7 | transition metals 5 | atomic mass unit 3 | = 15 |
| periodic law 2 | noble gas 9 | metals 4 | = 15 |
| = 15 | = 15 | = 15 | diagonal = 15 |

Name ______________________ Class ______________ Date __________



# Calculating Average Atomic Mass

**Math Skill: Percents and Decimals**

You may want to read more about this **Math Skill** in the **Skills and Reference Handbook** at the end of your textbook.

Carbon has two stable isotopes. Carbon-12 has an assigned atomic mass of 12.0000 and a percentage in nature of 98.93%. The atomic mass of carbon-13 is 13.0034 and its percentage in nature is 1.070%. What is the average atomic mass for carbon?

**1. Read and Understand**

*What information are you given?*

carbon-12: atomic mass = 12.0000, % in nature = 98.93
carbon-13: atomic mass = 13.0034, % in nature = 1.070

**2. Plan and Solve**

*What unknown are you trying to calculate?*

Average atomic mass for carbon = ?

*What equation can you use?*

(atomic mass C-12) (% C-12) + (atomic mass C-13) (% C-13)
= average atomic mass of C

*Convert the percentages to decimals and multiply the atomic mass of each isotope by the decimal representing its percentage in nature.*

(12.0000) (0.9893) = 11.8716 rounded to 11.87
(13.0034) (0.01070) = 0.1391364 rounded to 0.1391

*Add the products of the two multiplications to find the average atomic mass for carbon.*

11.87 + 0.1391 = 12.0091 rounded to 12.01

**3. Look Back and Check**

*Is your answer reasonable?*

Because almost all the carbon atoms in nature are carbon-12 atoms, the average atomic mass of carbon (12.01) is close to the atomic mass of carbon-12 (12.0000).

## Math Practice

*On a separate sheet of paper, solve the following problems.*

1. The element boron has two stable isotopes. Boron-10 has an atomic mass of 10.0129 and a percentage in nature of 19.78% The atomic mass of boron-11 is 11.0093 and its percentage in nature is 80.22% What is the average atomic mass for boron?

$$\frac{(1.978 \times 10.0129) + (0.8022 \times 11.0093)}{2} = \frac{1.980 + 8.831}{2} = 10.81$$

2. Nitrogen has two stable isotopes, nitrogen-14 and nitrogen-15. Nitrogen-14 has an atomic mass of 14.0031. Its percentage in nature is 99.63%. What is the percentage in nature of nitrogen-15?

100.00% − 99.63% = 0.37%

Name ______________ Class ______________ Date ______________



# Section 6.1 Ionic Bonding

**(pages 158–164)**

*This section describes the formation of ionic bonds and the properties of ionic compounds.*

## Reading Strategy (page 158)

**Sequencing** As you read, complete the concept map to show what happens to atoms during ionic bonding. For more information on this Reading Strategy, see the **Reading and Study Skills** in the **Skills and Reference Handbook** at the end of your textbook.

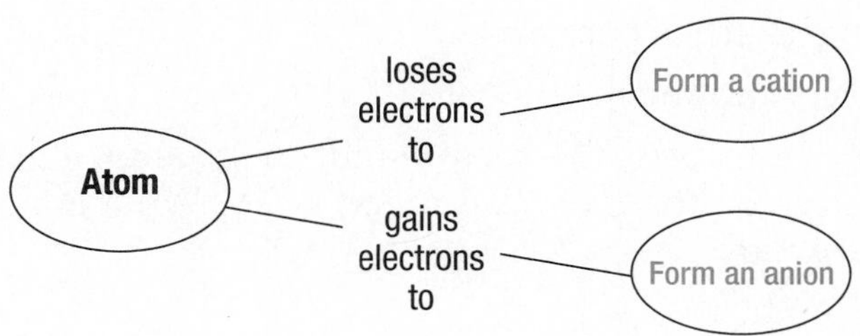


## Stable Electron Configurations (page 158)

1. Describe the type of electron configuration that makes an atom stable and not likely to react. When the highest occupied energy level of an atom is filled with electrons, the atom is stable and not likely to react.

2. Describe an electron dot diagram. An electron dot diagram is a model of an atom in which each dot represents a valence electron.

## Ionic Bonds (pages 159–161)

3. Some elements achieve stable electron configurations through the transfer of ___electrons___ between atoms.

4. By losing one valence electron, a sodium atom achieves the same electron arrangement as an atom of ___neon___.

5. Circle the letter that states the result of a sodium atom transferring an electron to a chlorine atom.
   - (a.) Each atom ends up with a more stable electron arrangement.
   - b. The sodium atom becomes more stable, but the chlorine atom becomes less stable.
   - c. The chlorine atom becomes more stable, but the sodium atom becomes less stable.
   - d. Each atom ends up with a less stable electron arrangement.

6. Is the following sentence true or false? An ion is an atom that has a net positive or negative electric charge. ___true___

7. An ion with a negative charge is called a(n) ___anion___.

8. An ionic bond forms when ___electrons___ are transferred from one atom to another.

9. Is the following sentence true or false? The lower the ionization energy, the easier it is to remove an electron from an atom. ___true___

## Ionic Compounds (pages 161–164)

10. Circle the letter of each piece of information provided by the chemical formula of an ionic compound.
    - (a.) which elements the compound contains
    - b. the charge on each ion in the compound
    - c. how the ions are arranged in the compound
    - (d.) the ratio of ions in the compound

11. Circle the letter of the correct answer. The formula for magnesium chloride is $MgCl_2$. The charge on the magnesium ion is 2+. What is the charge on each chloride ion?
    - a. 2−
    - (b.) 1−
    - c. 0
    - d. 1+

12. Look at the arrangement of ions in a sodium chloride crystal. How many sodium ions surround each chloride ion in this three-dimensional structure?
    - a. 3
    - b. 4
    - (c.) 6
    - d. 8

13. The shape of an ionic crystal depends on ___the arrangement of ions in its lattice___.

14. Identify two factors that determine the arrangement of ions in an ionic crystal.
    a. ___The ratio of ions___ b. ___The relative sizes of the ions___

15. Is the following sentence true or false? The attractions among ions within a crystal lattice are weak. ___false___

Name ______________________ Class ________________ Date ____________



# Section 6.2 Covalent Bonding
**(pages 165–169)**

*This section discusses the formation of covalent bonds and the factors that determine whether a molecule is polar or nonpolar. It also discusses attractions between molecules.*

## Reading Strategy (page 165)

**Relating Text and Visuals** As you read the section, look closely at Figure 9. Complete the table by describing each type of model shown. For more information on this Reading Strategy, see the **Reading and Study Skills** in the **Skills and Reference Handbook** at the end of your textbook.

| Molecular Models | |
|---|---|
| **Model** | **Description** |
| Electron dot | Dots represent valence electrons. |
| Structural formula | A line represents a pair of shared valence electrons. |
| Space-filling | Three-dimensional spheres represent atoms. |
| Electron cloud | Electron clouds represent atoms. |

## Covalent Bonds (pages 165–167)

1. Describe a covalent bond. A covalent bond is a chemical bond in which two atoms share a pair of valence electrons.

2. Circle the letters of molecular models that show orbitals of atoms overlapping when a covalent bond forms.
   a. electron dot
   b. structural formula
   (c.) space-filling
   d. electron cloud

3. Describe a molecule. A molecule is a neutral group of atoms that are joined together by one or more covalent bonds.

4. Is the following sentence true or false? In a covalent bond, the atoms are held together by the attractions between the shared electrons and the protons in each nucleus. true

5. Circle the correct answer. Nitrogen has five valence electrons. How many pairs of electrons must two nitrogen atoms share in order for each atom to have eight valence electrons?
   a. zero
   b. one
   c. two
   (d.) three

Name ______________________ Class ______________________ Date ______________



## Unequal Sharing of Electrons (pages 167–168)

6. In general, elements at the ___top___ of a group have a greater attraction for electrons than elements at the ___bottom___ of a group have.

7. In a hydrogen chloride molecule, the shared electrons spend more time near the ___chlorine___ atom than near the ___hydrogen___ atom.

8. Describe a polar covalent bond. ___A polar covalent bond is a covalent bond in which electrons are not shared equally.___

9. When atoms form a polar covalent bond, the atom with the greater attraction for electrons has a partial ___negative___ charge.

10. Is the following sentence true or false? In a molecule of a compound, electrons are always shared equally by both atoms. ___false___

11. Circle the letter of each factor that determines whether a molecule is polar or nonpolar.
    a. the number of atoms in the molecule
    (b.) the type of atoms in the molecule
    c. the number of bonds in the molecule
    (d.) the shape of the molecule

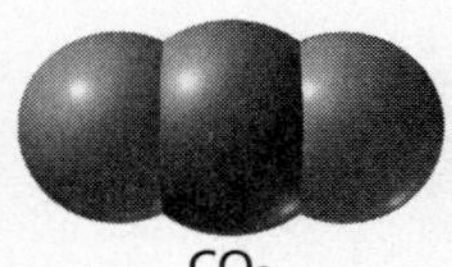
$CO_2$

$H_2O$

12. Compare the shapes of carbon dioxide and water molecules. Circle the letter of the polar molecule.
    a. carbon dioxide    (b.) water

13. Is the following sentence true or false? In a water molecule, the hydrogen side of the molecule has a partial positive charge, and the oxygen side has a partial negative charge. ___true___

## Attraction Between Molecules (page 169)

14. Water has a higher boiling point than carbon dioxide because attractions between polar molecules are ___stronger___ than attractions between nonpolar molecules.

15. Is the following sentence true or false? Attractions among nonpolar molecules explain why nitrogen can be stored as a liquid at low temperatures and high pressures. ___true___

# Section 6.3 Naming Compounds and Writing Formulas

**(pages 170–175)**

*This section explains how to name and write formulas for ionic and molecular compounds.*

## Reading Strategy (page 170)

**Predicting** Before you read, predict the meaning of the term *polyatomic ion,* and write your prediction in the table. After you read, if your prediction was incorrect, revise your definition. For more information on this Reading Strategy, see the **Reading and Study Skills** in the **Skills and Reference Handbook** at the end of your textbook.

| Vocabulary Term | Before You Read | After You Read |
|---|---|---|
| Polyatomic ion | Students should assume that any particle described as an ion has a charge. If they know the meaning of *poly,* they may predict that the ion contains two or more atoms. | A covalently bonded group of atoms that has a positive or negative charge and acts as a unit. |

## Describing Ionic Compounds (pages 171–173)

1. Is the following sentence true or false? The name of an ionic compound must distinguish the compound from other ionic compounds containing the same elements. true

2. What information is provided by the formula for an ionic compound? The formula for an ionic compound describes the ratio of the ions in the compound. The formula indicates which elements the compound contains.

3. Circle the letter of the word that describes a compound made from only two elements.
   a. ionic
   (b.) binary
   c. diatomic
   d. polar

4. Is the following sentence true or false? Names of anions are formed by placing the suffix *-ide* after part of the name of the nonmetal. true

5. When a metal forms more than one ion, the name of the ion contains a Roman numeral to indicate the charge on the ion.

6. What is a polyatomic ion? A polyatomic ion is a covalently bonded group of atoms that has a positive or negative charge and acts as a unit.

7. Is the following sentence true or false? Because all compounds are neutral, the total charges on the cations and anions in the formula of an ionic compound must add up to zero. true

8. Circle the letter of the correct answer. The formula for sodium sulfide is $Na_2S$. The sodium ion has a charge of 1+. What must the charge on the sulfide ion be?

   a. 1+ b. 0

   c. 1− (d.) 2−

**Some Polyatomic Ions**

| Name | Formula | Name | Formula |
|---|---|---|---|
| Ammonium | $NH_4^+$ | Acetate | $C_2H_3O_2^-$ |
| Hydroxide | $OH^-$ | Peroxide | $O_2^{2-}$ |
| Nitrate | $NO_3^-$ | Permanganate | $MnO_4^-$ |
| Sulfate | $SO_4^{2-}$ | Hydrogen sulfate | $HSO_4^-$ |
| Carbonate | $CO_3^{2-}$ | Hydrogen carbonate | $HCO_3^-$ |
| Phosphate | $PO_4^{3-}$ | Hydrogen phosphate | $HPO_4^{2-}$ |

9. Circle the letter that identifies the number of ammonium ions needed to form a compound with one phosphate ion.

   a. one b. two

   (c.) three d. four

## Describing Molecular Compounds (pages 174–175)

10. What information is provided by the name and formula of a molecular compound? The name and formula of a molecular compound describe the type and number of atoms in a molecule of the compound.

11. Describe the general rule for naming molecular compounds. The most metallic element appears first in the name.

12. Is the following sentence true or false? The formula for a molecular compound is written with the symbols for the elements in the same order as the elements appear in the name of the compound. true

13. Circle the letter that identifies the method of naming the number of atoms in molecular compounds.

   (a.) prefix b. suffix

   c. number d. symbol

14. In the formula of a molecular compound, the number of atoms of an element in the molecule is represented by a(n) subscript.

# Section 6.4 The Structure of Metals
**(pages 176–181)**

*This section discusses metallic bonds and the properties of metals. It also explains how the properties of an alloy are controlled.*

## Reading Strategy (page 176)

**Relating Cause and Effect** As you read, complete the concept map to relate the structure of metals to their properties. For more information on this Reading Strategy, see the **Reading and Study Skills** in the **Skills and Reference Handbook** at the end of your textbook.

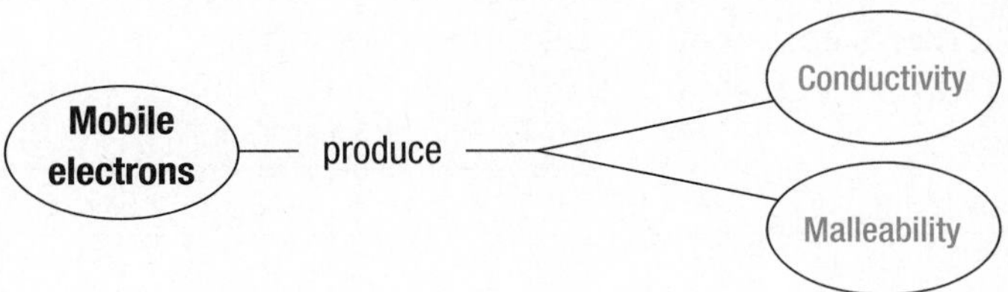


1. Circle the letter of the metal with the highest melting point.
   a. gold
   b. vanadium
   c. titanium
   (d.) tungsten
2. Is the following sentence true or false? The properties of a metal are related to bonds within the metal. true

## Metallic Bonds (pages 176–177)

3. Describe a metallic bond. A metallic bond is the attraction between a metal cation and the cation and the shared electrons that surround it.
4. The cations in a metal form a lattice. What holds the lattice in place? The lattice is held in place by strong metallic bonds between the cations and the surrounding valence electrons.
5. Is the following sentence true or false? The more valence electrons a metal has, the stronger its metallic bonds will be. true

## Explaining Properties of Metals (page 177)

6. Some of the properties of metals can be explained by the mobility of the electrons within a metal lattice.
7. Name two important properties of metals that can be explained by metallic bonding.
   a. Malleability
   b. Ability to conduct an electric current

## Alloys (pages 178–181)

8. Circle the letter of the percentage of gold in jewelry that is labeled 18-karat gold.
   a. 18 percent
   b. 50 percent
   (c.) 75 percent
   d. 100 percent

**9.** Is the following sentence true or false? When a metal such as copper is mixed with gold, the gold becomes softer. false

**10.** Describe an alloy. An alloy is a mixture of two or more elements, at least one of which is a metal.

**11.** How do the hardness and strength of bronze compare to the hardness and strength of copper alone and tin alone? Bronze is harder and stronger than either copper or tin alone.

**12.** Name two factors that scientists can vary to design alloys with specific properties.

a. The types of elements in the alloy

b. The amounts of elements in the alloy

**13.** Complete the following table.

| Comparing Bronze and Brass | | | |
|---|---|---|---|
| **Alloy** | **Component Metals** | **Comparative Hardness of Bronze and Brass** | **Comparative Speed of Weathering** |
| Bronze | Copper, tin | Harder | Weathers more slowly |
| Brass | Copper, zinc | Softer | Weathers more quickly |

**14.** When carbon is added to iron, the lattice becomes harder and stronger than a lattice that contains only iron.

**15.** Circle the letters of the elements that all types of steel contain.

(a.) carbon    b. chromium
(c.) iron    d. manganese

**16.** Circle the letters of each correct description of stainless steel.

a. Stainless steel contains more carbon than chromium.
(b.) Chromium forms an oxide that protects stainless steel from rusting.
(c.) Stainless steel is more brittle than steels that contain more carbon.
d. Stainless steel contains more than 3 percent carbon by mass.

**17.** Explain why pure aluminum is not the best material for the body of a plane. Although aluminum is lighter than most metals, it bends and dents too easily.

**18.** What type of alloy is used to make airplane parts that need to be extremely lightweight? an aluminum-magnesium alloy

Name ______________________ Class ________________ Date ____________



# WordWise

*Unscramble the terms from the following list to fit each of the clues given below.*

| | | |
|---|---|---|
| claimlet | ecumelol | levoctan |
| lorpa | loyal | marfulo |
| mooctyliap | nocii | nonia |
| odbn | starscly | tonica |

| Clues | Vocabulary Terms |
|---|---|
| A type of bond that holds cations and anions together | ionic |
| A type of bond in which two atoms share a pair of valence electrons | covalent |
| A neutral group of atoms that are joined together by one or more covalent bonds | molecule |
| A term describing a covalent bond in which electrons are not shared equally | polar |
| An ion that contains a covalently bonded group of atoms | polyatomic |
| An ion with a negative charge | anion |
| An ion with a positive charge | cation |
| A notation that shows what elements a compound contains and the ratio of the atoms or ions of these elements in the compound | formula |
| Solids whose particles are arranged in a lattice structure | crystals |
| A mixture of two or more elements, at least one of which is a metal | alloy |
| A type of bond that exists between a metal cation and the shared electrons that surround it | metallic |
| The force that holds atoms or ions together | bond |

# Writing Formulas for Ionic Compounds

**Math Skill: Ratios and Proportions**

You may want to read more about this **Math Skill** in the **Skills and Reference Handbook** at the end of your textbook.

What is the ratio of the ions in magnesium iodide? What is the formula for magnesium iodide?

**1. Read and Understand**

*What information are you given?*

The name of the compound is magnesium iodide.

**2. Plan and Solve**

*List the symbols and charges for the cation and anion.*

Mg ion has a charge of 2+ and I ion has a charge of 1−.

*Determine the ratio of ions in the compound.*

Mg with a 2+ charge needs two I ions, each with a charge of 1+. The ratio of the ions in the compound is 1 to 2.

*Write the formula for magnesium iodide.*

$MgI_2$

**3. Look Back and Check**

*Is your answer reasonable?*

Each magnesium atom loses two electrons and each iodine atom gains one electron. So there should be a 1-to-2 ratio of magnesium ions to iodide ions.

## Math Practice

*On a separate sheet of paper, solve the following problems. Refer to Figures 16, 17, and 19 to help you solve the problems.*

1. What is the formula for magnesium fluoride?
   Mg ion has a charge of 2+ and F ion has a charge of 1−. The ratio is 1 to 2, so the formula is $MgF_2$.
2. What is the formula for iron(III) chloride?
   Fe(III) ion has a charge of 3+ and Cl ion has a charge of 1−. The ratio is 1 to 3, so the formula is $FeCl_3$.
3. What is the formula for mercury(II) sulfide?
   Hg ion has a charge of 2+ and S ion has a charge of 2−. The ratio is 1 to 1, so the formula is HgS.
4. What is the formula for potassium dichromate0?
   K ion has a charge of 1+ and $CrO_7$ ion has a charge of 2−. The ratio is 2 to 1, so the formula is $K_2Cr_2O_7$.
5. What is the formula for barium nitrate?
   Ba is in the same group as Mg, so its ion has a charge of 2+. Nitrate ($NO_3$) ion has a charge of 1−, so the ratio is 1 to 2. The formula is $Ba(NO_3)_2$.

# Section 7.1 Describing Reactions
**(pages 192–198)**

*This section discusses the use of chemical equations and how to balance them. It also demonstrates the use of calculations in chemistry.*

## Reading Strategy (page 192)

**Monitoring Your Understanding** Preview the Key Concepts, topic headings, vocabulary, and figures in this section. List two things you expect to learn. After reading, state what you learned about each item you listed. For more information on this Reading Strategy, see the **Reading and Study Skills** in the **Skills and Reference Handbook** at the end of your textbook.

| What I Expect to Learn | What I Learned |
|---|---|
| Answers may vary. Possible answers: How to balance chemical equations | Answers may vary. Possible answers: An unbalanced equation can be balanced by changing the coefficients. |
| How to convert from mass to moles | The mass of a substance can be converted to moles by using the molar mass as a conversion factor. |

## Chemical Equations (pages 192–193)

1. Is the following sentence true or false? The new substances formed as a result of a chemical reaction are called products. true

2. Circle the letter of each sentence that is a correct interpretation of the chemical equation $C + O_2 \longrightarrow CO_2$.
   a. Carbon and oxygen react and form carbon monoxide.
   (b.) Carbon and oxygen react and form carbon dioxide.
   c. Carbon dioxide yields carbon and oxygen.
   (d.) The reaction of carbon and oxygen yields carbon dioxide.

3. Is the following sentence true or false? The law of conservation of mass states that mass is neither created nor destroyed in a chemical reaction. true

4. Circle the letter of the correct answer. According to the equation $C + O_2 \longrightarrow CO_2$, how many carbon atoms react with 14 molecules of oxygen to form 14 molecules of carbon dioxide?
   a. 1 b. 7
   (c.) 14 d. 28

5. In the reaction represented by the equation $C + O_2 \longrightarrow CO_2$, the mass of carbon dioxide produced equals the total mass of carbon and oxygen that reacted.

## Balancing Equations (pages 194–195)

6. Is the following sentence true or false? A chemical equation must be balanced in order to show that mass is conserved during a reaction. ___true___

7. Circle the letter of the name given to the numbers that appear before the formulas in a chemical equation.
   a. subscripts
   b. mass numbers
   c. atomic numbers
   (d.) coefficients

8. Is the following sentence true or false? Because the equation $N_2H_4 + O_2 \longrightarrow N_2 + H_2O$ has two nitrogen atoms on each side, the equation is balanced. ___false___

## Counting With Moles (pages 195–196)

9. Chemists use a counting unit called a(n) ___mole___ to measure amounts of a substance because chemical reactions often involve large numbers of small particles.

10. Circle the letter of the correct answer. If one carbon atom has an atomic mass of 12.0 amu and one oxygen atom has an atomic mass of 16.0 amu, what is the molar mass of carbon dioxide?
    a. 28.0 amu
    b. 44.0 amu
    c. 28.0 g
    (d.) 44.0 g

11. Circle the letter of the correct answer. To convert grams of carbon dioxide to moles of carbon dioxide, you must multiply by which conversion factor?
    a. $\frac{44.0 \text{ g } CO_2}{1 \text{ mol } CO_2}$
    (b.) $\frac{1 \text{ mol } CO_2}{44.0 \text{ g } CO_2}$
    c. $\frac{28.0 \text{ g } CO_2}{1 \text{ mol } CO_2}$
    d. $\frac{1 \text{ mol } CO_2}{28.0 \text{ g } CO_2}$

## Chemical Calculations (pages 197–198)

12. Complete the table.

| Formation of Water | | | |
|---|---|---|---|
| Equation | $2H_2$ + | $O_2$ $\longrightarrow$ | $2H_2O$ |
| Amount | 2 mol | 1 mol | 2 mol |
| Molar Mass | 2.0 g/mol | 32.0 g/mol | 18.0 g/mol |
| Mass (Moles × Molar Mass) | 4.0 g | 32.0 g | 36.0 g |

13. Circle the letter of the correct answer. One mole of oxygen has a mass of 32 grams. What is the mass of four moles of oxygen?
    (a.) 128 g
    b. 144 g
    c. 128 amu
    d. 144 amu

Name ______________________ Class ______________ Date ____________



# Section 7.2 Types of Reactions

**(pages 199–205)**

*This section discusses how chemical reactions are classified into different types.*

## Reading Strategy (page 199)

**Previewing** Skim the section and begin a concept map like the one below that identifies types of reactions with a general form. As you read, add the general form of each type of reaction. For more information on this Reading Strategy, see the **Reading and Study Skills** in the **Skills and Reference Handbook** at the end of your textbook.

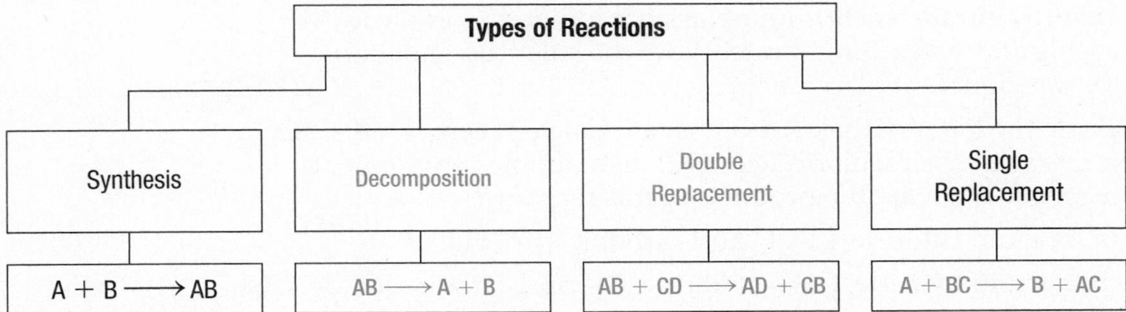


## Classifying Reactions (pages 199–204)

1. Name five general types of chemical reactions. Synthesis, decomposition, single replacement, double replacement, and combustion

2. Circle the letter of each equation that represents a synthesis reaction.
   (a.) $2Na + Cl_2 \longrightarrow 2NaCl$
   b. $2NaCl \longrightarrow 2Na + Cl_2$
   c. $2H_2O \longrightarrow 2H_2 + O_2$
   (d.) $2H_2 + O_2 \longrightarrow 2H_2O$

3. Is the following sentence true or false? A decomposition reaction is the opposite of a synthesis reaction. true

4. Write the equation for the decomposition of calcium carbonate into calcium oxide and carbon dioxide. $CaCO_3 \longrightarrow CaO + CO_2$

5. Circle the letter of the correct answer. Copper reacts with silver nitrate in a single-replacement reaction. What are the products of this reaction?
   a. copper(II) nitride and silver oxide
   (b.) copper(II) nitrate and silver
   c. copper(II) oxide and silver nitrate
   d. copper, nitrogen, and silver oxide

6. What is a double-replacement reaction? A double-replacement reaction is a reaction in which two different compounds exchange positive ions and form two new compounds.

7. Complete the chart by filling in the general forms of the reactions shown.

| General Forms | |
|---|---|
| **Single-Replacement Reaction** | **Double-Replacement Reaction** |
| $A + BC \longrightarrow B + AC$ | $AB + CD \longrightarrow AD + CB$ |

8. Lead(II) nitrate reacts with potassium iodide to form lead(II) iodide and potassium nitrate. Write the balanced equation for this double-replacement reaction. $Pb(NO_3)_2 + 2KI \longrightarrow PbI_2 + 2KNO_3$

9. Circle the letter of the correct answer. Calcium carbonate, $CaCO_3$, reacts with hydrochloric acid, HCl, in a double-replacement reaction. What are the products of this reaction?
   (a.) calcium chloride, $CaCl_2$, and carbonic acid, $H_2CO_3$
   b. calcium hydride, $CaH_2$, chlorine, $Cl_2$, and carbon dioxide, $CO_2$
   c. calcium hydrogen carbonate, $Ca(HCO_3)_2$, and chlorine, $Cl_2$
   d. calcium perchlorate, $Ca(ClO_4)_2$, and methane, $CH_4$

10. Is the following sentence true or false? A combustion reaction is a reaction in which a substance reacts with carbon dioxide, often producing heat and light. false

11. Methane, $CH_4$, burns in oxygen to form carbon dioxide and water. Write the balanced equation for this reaction. $CH_4 + 2O_2 \longrightarrow CO_2 + 2H_2O$

12. Is the following sentence true or false? The reaction that forms water can be classified as either a synthesis reaction or a combustion reaction. true

## Reactions as Electron Transfers (pages 204–205)

13. What is an oxidation-reduction reaction? An oxidation-reduction reaction is a reaction in which electrons are transferred from one reactant to another.

14. Calcium reacts with oxygen to form calcium oxide. Which reactant is oxidized in this reaction? calcium

15. Is the following sentence true or false? When calcium reacts with oxygen, each calcium atom gains two electrons and becomes a calcium ion with a charge of 2–. false

16. Is the following sentence true or false? Oxygen must be present in order for an oxidation-reduction reaction to take place. false

17. The process in which an element gains electrons during a chemical reaction is called reduction.

Name ______________________ Class ______________ Date ____________



# Section 7.3 Energy Changes in Reactions
**(pages 206–209)**

*This section discusses how chemical bonds and energy relate to chemical reactions.*

## Reading Strategy (page 206)

**Comparing and Contrasting** As you read, complete the Venn diagram below to show the differences between exothermic and endothermic reactions. For more information on this Reading Strategy, see the **Reading and Study Skills** in the **Skills and Reference Handbook** at the end of your textbook.

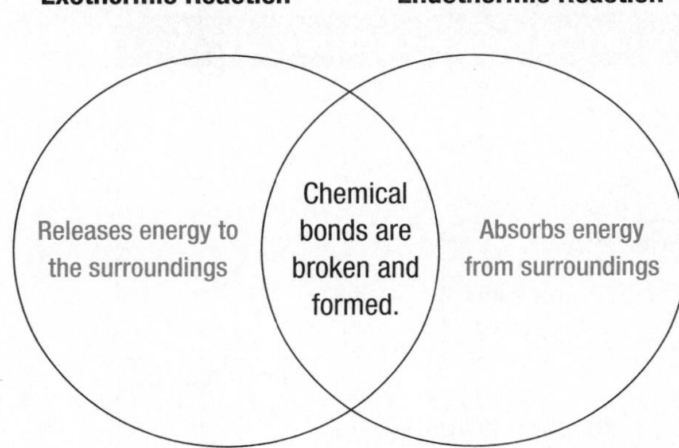


## Chemical Bonds and Energy (pages 206–207)

1. What is chemical energy? Chemical energy is the energy stored in the chemical bonds of a substance.

2. Chemical reactions involve the breaking of chemical bonds in the reactants and the formation of chemical bonds in the products.

3. Is the following sentence true or false? The formation of chemical bonds absorbs energy. false

4. What role does the spark from the igniter play in the reaction that takes place when propane is burned in a gas grill? The spark provides enough energy to break the bonds of reacting molecules and get the reaction started.

5. Is the following sentence true or false? The heat and light given off by a propane stove result from the formation of new chemical bonds. true

6. The combustion of one molecule of propane ($C_3H_8$) results in the formation of 6 C=O double bonds and 8 O–H single bonds.

Name ______________________ Class ______________ Date ____________



## Exothermic and Endothermic Reactions (pages 208–209)

7. During a chemical reaction, energy is either released or ___absorbed___.

8. Is the following sentence true or false? Physical and chemical changes can be either exothermic or endothermic changes. ___true___

9. What is an exothermic reaction? ___An exothermic reaction is a chemical reaction that releases energy to its surroundings.___

10. Is the following sentence true or false? In exothermic reactions, the energy required to break the bonds in the reactants is greater than the energy released as the products form. ___false___

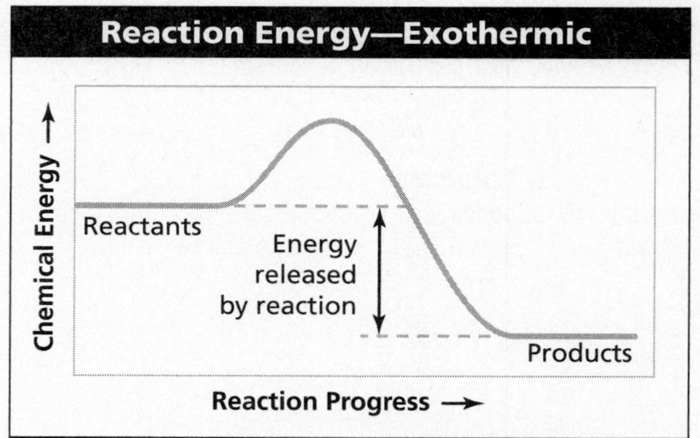


11. Circle the letter of each sentence that is correct for the graph above.
   a. The energy required to break the bonds in the reactants is greater than the energy released as the products form.
   (b.) The energy released as the products form is greater than the energy required to break the bonds in the reactants.
   (c.) The chemical energy of the reactants is greater than the chemical energy of the products.
   d. The chemical energy of the products is greater than the chemical energy of the reactants.

12. In an exothermic reaction, the difference between the chemical energy of the reactants and the chemical energy of the products equals ___the amount of heat released by the reaction___.

13. Where does the energy term appear in the equation for an endothermic reaction? ___The energy term appears on the left side.___

## Conservation of Energy (page 209)

14. In an endothermic reaction, heat from the surroundings plus the chemical energy of the reactants is converted into the ___chemical energy of the products___.

# Section 7.4 Reaction Rates
**(pages 212–215)**

*This section discusses the factors that affect reaction rates.*

## Reading Strategy (page 212)

**Building Vocabulary** As you read, complete the web diagram below with key terms from this section. For more information on this Reading Strategy, see the **Reading and Study Skills** in the **Skills and Reference Handbook** at the end of your textbook.

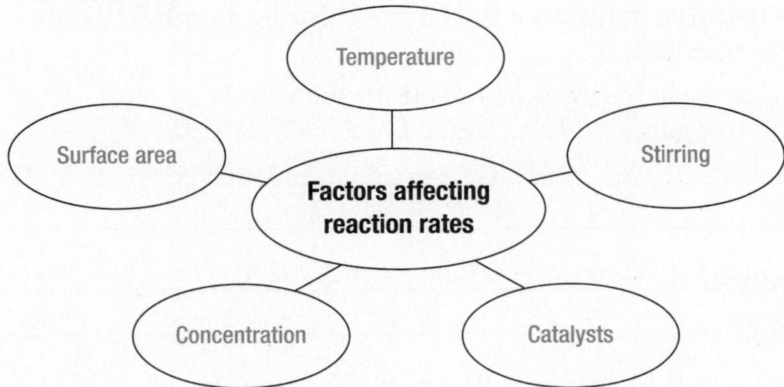


## Reactions Over Time (page 212)

1. Any change that happens over time can be expressed as a(n) ___rate___.

2. What is a reaction rate? A reaction rate is the rate at which reactants change into products over time.

## Factors Affecting Reaction Rates (pages 213–215)

3. Is the following sentence true or false? One way to observe the rate of a reaction is to observe how fast products are being formed. ___true___

4. Is the following sentence true or false? The rate of any reaction is a constant that does not change when the reaction conditions change. ___false___

5. Generally, an increase in temperature will ___increase___ the reaction rate.

6. Is the following sentence true or false? Storing milk in a refrigerator stops the reactions that would cause the milk to spoil. ___false___

7. How does an increase in surface area affect the exposure of reactants to one another? An increase in surface area increases the exposure of reactants to one another.

**8.** Why does increasing the surface area of a reactant tend to increase the reaction rate? The increase in exposure of reactants to one another results in more collisions involving reactant particles. With more collisions, more particles will react.

**9.** Stirring the reactants in a reaction mixture will generally increase the reaction rate.

**10.** Is the following sentence true or false? Increasing the concentration of the reactants will generally slow down a chemical reaction. false

**11.** Is the following sentence true or false? A piece of material dipped in a concentrated dye solution will change color more quickly than in a dilute dye solution. true

**12.** Why does an increase in pressure speed up the rate of a reaction involving gases? Concentration of a gas increases with pressure, and an increase in concentration results in a faster reaction rate due to more frequent collisions between reacting particles.

**13.** What is a catalyst? A catalyst is a substance that affects the rate of a reaction without being used up in the reaction.

**14.** Circle the letters of the sentences that correctly identify why chemists use catalysts.

(a.) to speed up a reaction

b. to enable a reaction to occur at a higher temperature

c. to slow down a reaction

(d.) to enable a reaction to occur at a lower temperature

**15.** Is the following sentence true or false? Because a catalyst is quickly consumed in a reaction, it must be added to the reaction mixture over and over again to keep the reaction going. false

**16.** Identify where the catalyst $V_2O_5$ should go in the formula shown and write it in the correct location.

$$2SO_2 + O_2 \xrightarrow{V_2O_5} 2SO_3$$

**17.** Circle the letter of the correct answer. In the reaction represented by the equation $2H_2O_2 \xrightarrow{Pt} 2H_2O + O_2$, which substance acts as a catalyst?

a. $H_2O_2$ (b.) Pt

c. $H_2O$ d. $O_2$

**18.** One way that a catalyst can lower the energy barrier of a reaction is by providing a surface on which the reacting particles can come together.

# Section 7.5 Equilibrium
**(pages 216–219)**

*This section explains physical and chemical equilibria, and describes the factors that affect chemical equilibrium.*

## Reading Strategy (page 216)

**Outlining** As you read, make an outline of the most important ideas from this section. For more information on this Reading Strategy, see the **Reading and Study Skills** in the **Skills and Reference Handbook** at the end of your textbook.

I. Equilibrium
  A. Types of Equilibria
    1. Physical equilibrium
    2. Chemical equilibrium
  B. Factors affecting chemical equilibrium
    1. Temperature
    2. Pressure
    3. Concentration

## Types of Equilibria (pages 216–217)

1. What is equilibrium? Equilibrium is a state in which the forward and reverse paths of a change take place at the same rate.

2. Circle the letter of the correct answer. In the system described by the equation $H_2O(l) \rightleftharpoons H_2O(g)$, at room temperature, which of the following two physical changes are in equilibrium?
   a. sublimation and condensation
   b. evaporation and melting
   c. sublimation and deposition
   (d.) evaporation and condensation

3. What happens when a physical change does not go to completion?
   A physical equilibrium is established between the forward and reverse changes.

4. What does the single arrow imply about the reaction described in the following equation?

$$CH_4(g) + 2O_2(g) \longrightarrow CO_2(g) + 2H_2O(g)$$

   The single arrow implies that the forward reaction goes to completion.

5. Circle the letter of the correct answer. In the system described by the equation $2SO_2(g) + O_2(g) \rightleftharpoons 2SO_3(g)$, what two reaction types are in equilibrium?
   (a.) synthesis and decomposition
   b. single replacement and decomposition
   c. synthesis and combustion
   d. synthesis and double replacement

6. What happens when a chemical change does not go to completion?
   A chemical equilibrium is established between the forward and reverse reactions.

## Factors Affecting Chemical Equilibrium (pages 218–219)

7. Is the following sentence true or false? A change in reaction conditions does not affect a chemical equilibrium. false

8. Circle the letter of each correct answer. The synthesis of ammonia is described by the equation $N_2(g) + 3H_2(g) \rightleftharpoons 2NH_3(g)$ + heat. Which reaction is favored when the temperature is lowered?
   (a.) the forward reaction
   b. the reverse reaction
   c. the reaction that removes heat from the system
   (d.) the reaction that adds heat to the system

9. Circle the letter of each correct answer. During the synthesis of ammonia, which reaction is favored when hydrogen is added to the system?
   (a.) the forward reaction
   b. the reverse reaction
   (c.) the reaction that removes hydrogen from the system
   d. the reaction that adds hydrogen to the system

10. According to Le Châtelier's principle, how does lowering the concentration of a reaction product affect a chemical equilibrium? Lowering the concentration of a reaction product causes the equilibrium to shift in the direction that forms more of the product.

11. Use the equation $C(s) + H_2O(g)$ + heat $\rightleftharpoons CO(g) + H_2(g)$ to complete the table below.

| An Example of Le Châtelier's Principle | | |
|---|---|---|
| **An increase in** | **Shifts the equilibrium so as to** | **Favoring the** |
| Temperature, concentration of C, or concentration of $H_2O$ | Remove heat | Forward reaction |
| Pressure | Produce fewer gas molecules | Reverse reaction |
| Concentration of $H_2$ | Remove $H_2$, produce fewer gas molecules, or add heat | Reverse reaction |

Name ______________________ Class ______________________ Date ______________



# WordWise

*Answer the questions by writing the correct vocabulary term in the blanks. Use the circled letter in each term to find the hidden vocabulary word. Then, write a definition for the hidden word.*

| Clues | Vocabulary Terms |
|---|---|
| Describes a reaction that releases energy to its surroundings | e x o t h e (r) m i c |
| A state in which the forward and reverse paths of a change take place at the same rate | (e) q u i l i b r i u m |
| A substance that affects the reaction rate without being used up in the reaction | c (a) t a l y s t |
| A reaction in which a compound breaks down into two or more simpler substances | d e (c) o m p o s i t i o n |
| A reaction in which two or more substances react to form a single substance | s y n (t) h e s i s |
| The mass of one mole of a substance | m o l (a) r m a s s |
| A number that appears before a formula in a chemical equation | c o e f f i c i e (n) t |
| A reaction in which a substance reacts rapidly with oxygen, often producing heat and light | c o m b u s (t) i o n |
| The substances formed as the result of a chemical change | p r o d u c t (s) |

**Hidden Term:** r e a c t a n t s

**Definition:** The substances that undergo change in a chemical reaction

# Balancing Chemical Equations

Write a balanced equation for the reaction between potassium and water to produce hydrogen and potassium hydroxide, KOH.

**Math Skill: Formulas and Equations**

You may want to read more about this **Math Skill** in the **Skills and Reference Handbook** at the end of your textbook.

**1. Read and Understand**

*What information are you given?*

Reactants: K, $H_2O$
Products: $H_2$, KOH

**2. Plan and Solve**

*Write a chemical equation with the reactants on the left side and the products on the right.*

$K + H_2O \longrightarrow H_2 + KOH$

*This equation is not balanced. The number of hydrogen atoms on the left does not equal the number of hydrogen atoms on the right. Change the coefficients of $H_2O$ and KOH in order to balance the number of hydrogen atoms.*

$K + 2H_2O \longrightarrow H_2 + 2KOH$

*Change the coefficient of K in order to balance the number of potassium atoms.*

$2K + 2H_2O \longrightarrow H_2 + 2KOH$

**3. Look Back and Check**

*Is your answer reasonable?*

The number of atoms on the left equals the number of atoms on the right.

## Math Practice

*On a separate sheet of paper, solve the following problems.*

1. Magnesium burns in the presence of oxygen to form magnesium oxide, MgO. Write a balanced equation for this reaction.
   $2Mg + O_2 \longrightarrow 2MgO$

2. Hydrogen peroxide, $H_2O_2$, decomposes to form water and oxygen. Write a balanced equation for this reaction.
   $2H_2O_2 \longrightarrow 2H_2O + O_2$

3. Barium hydroxide, $Ba(OH)_2$, reacts with nitric acid, $HNO_3$, to form barium nitrate and water. Write a balanced equation for this reaction.
   $Ba(OH)_2 + 2HNO_3 \longrightarrow Ba(NO_3)_2 + 2H_2O$

# Section 8.1 Formation of Solutions
## (pages 228–234)

*This section explains the parts of a solution, the processes that occur when compounds dissolve, and how the properties of a solution compare with those of its solvent and solute.*

## Reading Strategy (page 228)

**Comparing and Contrasting** Contrast dissociation and ionization by listing the ways they differ in the Venn diagram below. For more information on this reading strategy, see the **Reading and Study Skills** in the **Skills and Reference Handbook** at the end of your textbook.

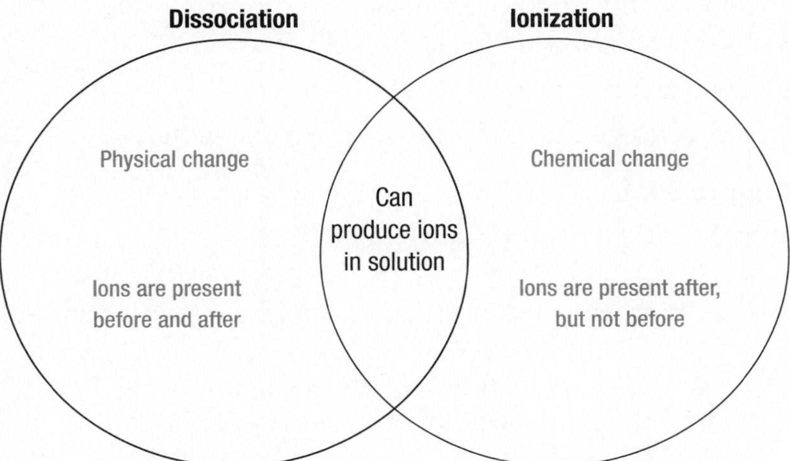


## Dissolving (page 229)

1. Define a solution. A solution is a homogenous mixture of two or more substances.

2. Circle the letter that identifies a substance whose particles are dissolved in a solution.
   a. solvent
   b. solute (circled)
   c. solid
   d. ion

3. Circle the letter that identifies the solvent in air.
   a. oxygen
   b. carbon dioxide
   c. nitrogen (circled)
   d. argon

4. The process in which an ionic compound separates into ions as it dissolves is called dissociation.

5. The process in which particles dissolve by breaking apart and scattering is called dispersion.

6. A(n) proton is transferred from each HCl molecule to a water molecule when hydrogen chloride gas dissolves in water.

7. Is the following sentence true or false? Dissolving by ionization is a physical change. false

Name ______________________ Class ______________ Date ____________



## Properties of Liquid Solutions (page 231)

8. What physical properties of a solution can differ from those of its solute and solvent?

   a. Conductivity

   b. Freezing point

   c. Boiling point

9. Compare the conductivities of solid sodium chloride and saltwater. Solid sodium chloride is a poor conductor of electric current. However, when you dissolve sodium chloride in water, it becomes a good conductor of electric current.

10. Circle the letters that identify what happens to water as it freezes.

    (a.) The water molecules become more organized.

    b. The water molecules become more disorganized.

    c. The water molecules ionize.

    (d.) The water molecules arrange themselves in a hexagonal pattern.

## Heat of Solution (page 232)

11. Dissolving sodium hydroxide in water is a(n) exothermic process, as it releases heat.

12. Dissolving ammonium nitrate in water is a(n) endothermic process, as it absorbs heat.

13. Is the following sentence true or false? Breaking the attractions among solute particles and the attractions among solvent particles releases energy. false

14. Describe heat of solution. The heat of solution is the difference between the energy required to break the attractions among solute particles and the attractions among solvent particles, and the energy released as attractions form between solute and solvent particles.

## Factors Affecting Rates of Dissolving (page 234)

15. How are rates of dissolving similar to rates of chemical reactions? Like reaction rates, dissolving rates vary with the conditions under which the change occurs.

16. Why does powdered sugar dissolve in water faster than granulated sugar? Powdered sugar has more surface area per unit mass than granulated sugar, so collisions between solute and solvent particles can occur at a greater rate.

17. Heating a solvent increases the energy of its particles, making them move faster on average, and increases the rate at which a solid solute can dissolve in the solvent.

18. Explain how stirring or shaking a mixture of powdered detergent and water can affect the rate of dissolving. Stirring or shaking a solution that contains a solid solute moves dissolved particles away from the surface of the solid. It also causes more frequent collisions between the solute and solvent particles.

Name ______________________ Class ______________ Date __________



# Section 8.2 Solubility and Concentration

**(pages 235–239)**

*This section explains solubility, the factors affecting solubility, and different ways of expressing the concentration of a solution.*

## Reading Strategy (page 235)

**Previewing** Before you read the section, rewrite the topic headings as *how, why,* and *what* questions. As you read, write an answer to each question. For more information on this reading strategy, see the **Reading and Study Skills** in the **Skills and Reference Handbook** at the end of your textbook.

| Question | Answer |
|---|---|
| What is solubility? | Solubility is the maximum amount of solute that dissolves in a given amount of solvent at a given temperature. |
| How can the concentration of solutions be expressed? | Solvent, temperature, and pressure |
| What factors affect solubility? | Percent by volume, percent by mass, molarity |

## Solubility (pages 235–237)

1. Define solubility. Solubility is the maximum amount of a solute that dissolves in a given amount of solvent at a constant temperature.

2. List the following solutes in order from most soluble to least soluble in water: table salt, baking soda, table sugar.
   a. Table sugar
   b. Salt
   c. Baking soda

3. Circle the letters that identify how solutions can be classified based on solubility.
   (a.) unsaturated
   b. desaturated
   (c.) saturated
   (d.) supersaturated

4. Describe a saturated solution. A saturated solution is one that contains as much solute as the solvent can hold at a given temperature.

5. A solution that has less than the maximum amount of solute that can be dissolved is called a(n) unsaturated solution.

6. Is the following sentence true or false? It is impossible for a solution to contain more solute than the solvent can hold at a given temperature. false

## Factors Affecting Solubility (page 237)

7. Circle the letters of factors that affect the solubility of a solute.
   - (a.) polarity of the solvent
   - b. amount of solvent
   - (c.) pressure
   - (d.) temperature

8. What is a common guideline for predicting solubility?
   like dissolves like

9. Describe how soap cleans grease off your hands. The polar end of a soap molecule attracts water molecules, and the nonpolar end of the soap molecule attracts grease. The soap molecule breaks up the grease into small droplets that are soluble in water.

10. Is the following statement true or false? In general, the solubility of solids increases as the solvent temperature increases.
    true

11. In general, the solubility of gases decreases as the solvent temperature increases.

12. In general, the solubility of a gas increases as pressure increases.

## Concentration of Solutions (pages 238–239)

13. What does the concentration of a solution refer to? The concentration of a solution is the amount of a solute dissolved in a given amount of solution.

14. Circle the letters that identify ways to express the concentration of a solution.
    - a. density
    - (b.) percent by volume
    - (c.) percent by mass
    - (d.) molarity

15. Complete the equation.
    Percent by volume = $\frac{\text{Volume of solute}}{\text{Volume of solution}} \times 100\%$

16. Write the equation used to calculate percent by mass.
    $\text{Percent by mass} = \frac{\text{Mass of solute}}{\text{Mass of solution}} \times 100\%$

17. Is this sentence true or false? Molarity is the number of moles of a solvent per liter of solution. false

18. How many grams of NaCl are needed to make 1.00 liter of a 3.00 M NaCl solution? 176 g

Name ______________ Class ______________ Date ______________



# Section 8.3 Properties of Acids and Bases
**(pages 240–245)**

*This section describes the general properties of acids and bases.*

## Reading Strategy (page 240)

**Using Prior Knowledge** Before you read, write your definition of each vocabulary term in the table below. After you read, write the scientific definition of each term and compare it with your original definition. For more information on this reading strategy, see the **Reading and Study Skills** in the **Skills and Reference Handbook** at the end of your textbook.

| Term | Your Definition | Scientific Definition |
|---|---|---|
| Acid | Answers will vary. | A compound that produces hydronium ions ($H_3O^+$) when dissolved in water. |
| Base | Answers will vary. | A compound that produces hydroxide ions ($OH^-$) when dissolved in water. |
| Salt | Answers will vary. | A compound produced when the negative ions in an acid combine with the positive ions in a base during neutralization. |

## Identifying Acids (pages 240–241)

1. Define an acid. An acid is a compound that produces hydronium ions ($H_3O^+$) when dissolved in water.

*Match these common acids to their uses.*

| | Acids | Uses |
|---|---|---|
| c | **2.** acetic acid | a. Fertilizer production |
| d | **3.** sulfuric acid | b. Carbonated beverages |
| e | **4.** hydrochloric acid | c. Vinegar |
| b | **5.** carbonic acid | d. Car batteries |
| a | **6.** nitric acid | e. Digestive juices in stomach |

7. Describe some general properties of acids. Acids have sour taste, react with metals, and turn blue litmus paper red.

8. Place the following substances in the correct column in the table: lemons, vinegar, grapefruit, sour milk, tomatoes.

| Foods Containing Acetic Acid | Foods Containing Citric Acid | Foods Containing Butyric Acid |
|---|---|---|
| Vinegar | Lemons, grapefruit, tomatoes | Sour milk |

9. The reaction between an acid and a metal can be classified as a(n) single-replacement reaction.

10. Explain why an indicator is useful. It allows you to classify a solution as an acid or a base.

## Identifying Bases (pages 242–243)

11. Define a base. A base is a compound that produces hydroxide ions ($OH^-$) when dissolved in water.

12. Use the following compounds to complete the chart: aluminum hydroxide, calcium hydroxide, magnesium hydroxide, and sodium hydroxide.

| Common Bases | | |
|---|---|---|
| **Name** | **Formula** | **Uses** |
| Sodium hydroxide | $NaOH$ | Drain cleaner, soap production |
| Magnesium hydroxide | $Mg(OH)_2$ | Antacid, laxative |
| Calcium hydroxide | $Ca(OH)_2$ | Concrete, plaster |
| Aluminum hydroxide | $Al(OH)_3$ | Deodorant, antacid |

13. What can a gardener add to the soil to change the flowers of a hydrangea from pink to blue? acid

14. Circle the letter that describes how basic solutions generally taste.
   - a. sweet
   - b. sour
   - (c.) bitter
   - d. salty

15. Is the following sentence true or false? Bases turn red litmus paper blue. true

## Neutralization and Salts (page 244)

16. The reaction between an acid and a base is called neutralization.

17. Describe how a salt can be produced by a chemical reaction. During neutralization, the negative ions from the acid combine with the positive ions from the base to produce a salt.

18. Write a chemical equation describing the neutralization reaction between calcium hydroxide and hydrochloric acid.

$Ca(OH)_2 + 2HCl \longrightarrow CaCl_2 + 2H_2O$

## Proton Donors and Acceptors (page 245)

19. Acids can be described as proton donors; bases can be described as proton acceptors.

20. When hydrogen chloride ionizes in water, which reactant is the proton donor? Which reactant is the proton acceptor? HCl is the proton donor. $H_2O$ is the proton acceptor.

Name ______________ Class ______________ Date ______________



# Section 8.4 Strength of Acids and Bases

**(pages 246–249)**

*This section explains how to describe acids and bases in terms of both concentration and strength.*

## Reading Strategy (page 246)

**Comparing and Contrasting** As you read, complete the diagram by comparing and contrasting acids and bases. For more information on this reading strategy, see the **Reading and Study Skills** in the **Skills and Reference Handbook** at the end of your textbook.

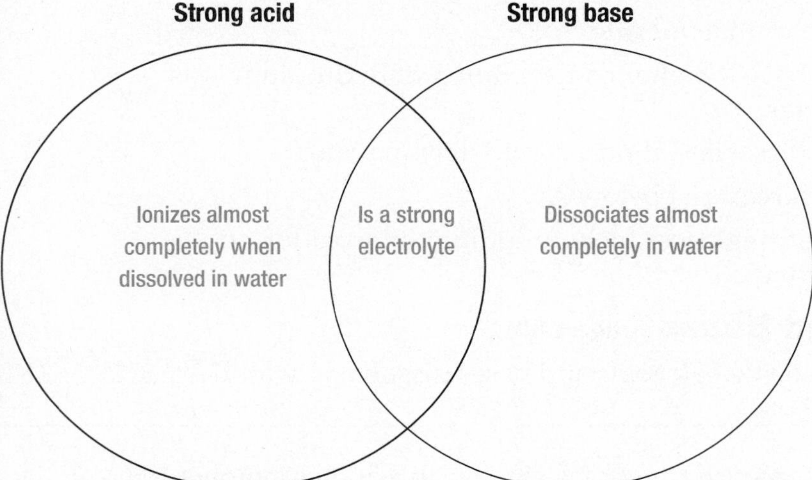


## The pH Scale (page 247)

1. What is the name of the number scale chemists use to describe the concentration of hydronium ions in a solution?
   the pH scale
2. The pH scale ranges from 0 to 14.
3. Circle the letter that indicates the pH of a neutral solution.
   a. 0
   b. 3
   (c.) 7
   d. 12
4. Water is neutral because it contains small but equal concentrations of hydronium ions and hydroxide ions.
5. Is the following sentence true or false? The higher the pH value of a solution, the greater the $H_3O^+$ ion concentration is.
   false
6. If you add acid to pure water, the concentration of $H_3O^+$ increases and the concentration of OH decreases.

## Strong Acids and Bases (pages 247–248)

7. What happens when strong acids and bases dissolve in water? The compounds ionize or dissociate almost completely.

8. Is the following sentence true or false? A strong acid always has a lower pH than a weak acid. false

9. Circle the letters that identify a strong acid.
   (a.) HCl
   b. $Ca(OH)_2$
   c. $H_2O$
   (d.) $HNO_3$

10. When dissolved in water, sodium hydroxide almost completely dissociates into sodium ($Na^+$) and hydroxide ($OH^-$) ions.

11. Circle the sentences that are true.
    a. Strong bases have a higher concentration of hydronium ions than pure water.
    (b.) Strong bases dissociate almost completely in water.
    c. Strong bases have a pH below 7.
    (d.) Examples of strong bases include sodium hydroxide and calcium hydroxide.

## Weak Acids and Bases (page 248)

12. What happens when weak acids and bases dissolve in water? The compounds ionize or dissociate only slightly.

13. Is the following sentence true or false? A weak acid has a higher pH than a strong acid of the same concentration. true

14. Describe the difference between concentration and strength. Concentration is the amount of solute dissolved in a given amount of solution. Strength refers to the solute's tendency to form ions in water.

15. Describe a buffer. A buffer is a solution that is resistant to large changes in pH.

## Electrolytes (page 249)

16. An electrolyte is a substance that ionizes or dissociates into ions when it is dissolved in water.

17. Is the following sentence true or false? Strong acids and bases are weak electrolytes because they dissociate or ionize almost completely in water. false

18. Is acetic acid an example of a weak electrolyte? Explain. Yes. Acetic acid only partially ionizes.

Name ______________________ Class ________________ Date ____________



# WordWise

*Use the clues below to identify some of the vocabulary terms from Chapter 8. Write the words on the line, putting one letter in each blank. When you finish, the words enclosed in the circle will reveal an important term.*

## Clues

1. A(n) ______ solution is one in which you can dissolve more solute.
2. A substance in which other materials dissolve is called a(n) ____________.
3. A(n) ________________ is a substance that forms ions when dissolved in water.
4. A(n) ________________ is a solution containing either a weak acid and its salt or a weak base and its salt.
5. A(n) ________________ is a compound that produces hydroxide ions when dissolved in water.
6. The process in which a substance breaks up into smaller particles as it dissolves is called ________________.
7. The reaction between an acid and a base is called ________________.
8. A(n) ________________ is a compound that produces hydronium ions when dissolved in water.
9. When neutral molecules gain or lose electrons, the process is known as ________________.
10. The number of moles of solute that is dissolved in 1 liter of solution is ________________.

## Vocabulary Terms

1. u n s a t u r a t e d
2. s o l v e n t
3. e l e c t r o l y t e
4. b u f f e r
5. b a s e
6. d i s p e r s i o n
7. n e u t r a l i z a t i o n
8. a c i d
9. i o n i z a t i o n
10. m o l a r i t y

**Hidden Word:** s o l u b i l i t y

**Definition:** The maximum amount of solute that normally dissolves in a given amount of solvent at a certain temperature.

# Calculating the Molarity of a Solution

**Math Skill: Calculating with Significant Figures**

You may want to read more about this **Math Skill** in the **Skills and Reference Handbook** at the end of your textbook.

Suppose you dissolve 58.5 grams of sodium chloride into enough water to make exactly 1.00 liter of solution. What is the molarity of the solution?

**1. Read and Understand**

*What information are you given?*

Mass of solute = 58.5 g NaCl

Volume of solution = 1.00 L

**2. Plan and Solve**

*What unknown are you trying to solve?*

Molarity = ?

*What equation can you use?*

$$\text{Molarity} = \frac{\text{moles of solute}}{\text{liters of solution}}$$

*Convert the mass of the solute into moles.*

$$\text{Moles of solute} = \frac{\text{Mass of NaCl}}{\text{Molar mass of NaCl}}$$

$$= \frac{58.5 \text{ g NaCl}}{58.5 \text{ g NaCl/mol NaCl}} = 1.00 \text{ mol NaCl}$$

*Solve the equation for molarity.*

$$\text{Molarity} = \frac{1.00 \text{ mol NaCl}}{1.00 \text{ L}} = 1.00 \text{ M NaCl}$$

**3. Look Back and Check**

*Is your answer reasonable?*

A 1.00 M NaCl solution contains 1.00 mole of NaCl per liter of solution. The answer is reasonable.

## Math Practice

*On a separate sheet of paper, solve the following problems.*

1. Suppose you had 4.0 moles of solute dissolved into 2.0 liters of solution. What is the molarity?

$$\text{Molarity} = \frac{\text{moles of solute}}{\text{liters of solution}} = \frac{4.0 \text{ moles}}{2.0 \text{ liters}} = 2.0 \text{ M}$$

2. A saltwater solution containing 43.9 grams of NaCl has a total volume of 1.5 liters. What is the molarity?

$$\text{Molarity} = \frac{43.9 \text{ g NaCl} \times (1 \text{ mol NaCl}/58.5 \text{ g NaCl})}{1.5 \text{ L}} = 0.50 \text{ M}$$

3. Table sugar has a molar mass of 342 grams. How many grams of table sugar are needed to make 2.00 liters of a 0.500 M solution?

$2.00 \text{ L} \times 0.500 \text{ mol/L} \times 342 \text{ g/mol} = 342 \text{ g}$

Name ______________________ Class ________________ Date ____________



# Section 9.1 Carbon Compounds
## (pages 262–269)

*This section describes different forms of carbon that exist in nature. It also discusses saturated and unsaturated hydrocarbons. It explains the formation of fossil fuels and describes the products of their combustion.*

## Reading Strategy (page 262)

**Previewing** Before you read, use the models in Figure 2 to describe the arrangement of carbon atoms in each form of carbon. For more information on this Reading Strategy, see the **Reading and Study Skills** in the **Skills and Reference Handbook** at the end of your textbook.

| Forms of Carbon | |
|---|---|
| Diamond | Rigid, three-dimensional network |
| Graphite | Widely spaced layers |
| Buckminsterfullerene | Hollow spheres with a surface of carbon atoms arranged in alternating hexagons and pentagons |

1. The two elements that all organic compounds contain are carbon and hydrogen.

2. Circle the letter of the approximate percentage of all known compounds that are organic compounds.
   a. 10 percent
   b. 30 percent
   c. 60 percent
   (d.) 90 percent

## Forms of Carbon (page 263)

3. Circle the letter of each form of carbon.
   a. soot
   (b.) diamond
   (c.) fullerenes
   (d.) graphite

4. Describe a network solid. A network solid is a solid in which all the atoms are linked by covalent bonds.

5. Circle the letter of each property of graphite.
   (a.) soft
   b. rigid
   c. compact
   (d.) slippery

## Saturated Hydrocarbons (pages 264–265)

6. Is the following sentence true or false? A hydrocarbon is an organic compound that contains carbon, hydrogen, and oxygen. false

7. Is the following sentence true or false? A saturated hydrocarbon contains only single bonds. true

8. Name the factors that determine the properties of a hydrocarbon.
   a. The number of carbon atoms b. How the atoms are arranged
9. Name the three ways that carbon atoms can be arranged in hydrocarbon molecules.
   a. A straight chain b. A branched chain c. A ring

10. Circle the letter of the correct answer. What does a structural formula show that a molecular formula does not?
    a. the type of atoms in the compound
    b. the number of atoms in a molecule of the compound
    (c.) the arrangement of atoms in the compound
    d. the state of the compound at room temperature
11. Describe isomers. Isomers are compounds that have the same molecular formula but different structural formulas.

## Unsaturated Hydrocarbons (page 266)

12. Circle the letter of each type of unsaturated hydrocarbon.
    (a.) alkene
    b. alkane
    (c.) alkyne
    (d.) aromatic hydrocarbon
13. Circle the letter of the most reactive type of hydrocarbon.
    a. alkanes
    b. alkenes
    (c.) alkynes
    d. aromatic hydrocarbons

## Fossil Fuels (page 267–268)

14. Define fossil fuels. Fossil fuels are mixtures of hydrocarbons that formed from the remains of plants or animals.

15. Circle the letter of each fossil fuel.
    (a.) coal
    (b.) natural gas
    c. ferns
    (d.) petroleum
16. Is the following sentence true or false? In a distillation tower, compounds with lower boiling points condense first. false

## Combustion of Fossil Fuels (pages 268–269)

17. Circle the letter of each primary product of the complete combustion of fossil fuels.
    (a.) carbon dioxide
    b. carbon monoxide
    c. sulfur dioxide
    (d.) water
18. When an insufficient amount of oxygen is available for complete combustion of a fossil fuel, one product of the combustion reaction is the deadly gas carbon monoxide.
19. Why is rain always slightly acidic? Carbon dioxide dissolves in water droplets and forms carbonic acid.

# Section 9.2 Substituted Hydrocarbons
**(pages 272–274)**

*This section discusses organic compounds that contain atoms of elements other than carbon and hydrogen. It also explains the relationship between the properties of organic compounds and functional groups.*

## Reading Strategy (page 272)

**Monitoring Your Understanding** As you read, complete the table by connecting each functional group with the type of compound that contains the functional group. For more information on this Reading Strategy, see the **Reading and Study Skills** in the **Skills and Reference Handbook** at the end of your textbook.

| Connecting Functional Groups to Types of Compounds | |
|---|---|
| **Functional Group** | **Type of Compound** |
| –OH | Alcohol |
| –COOH | Organic acid |
| $-NH_2$ | Organic base |

1. Name the two main products when methane and chlorine react.
   a. Hydrogen chloride
   b. Chloromethane
2. To which environmental problem have researchers connected halocarbons containing chlorine and fluorine? Halocarbons containing chlorine and fluorine are connected to the depletion of Earth's protective ozone layer.
3. Describe a substituted hydrocarbon. A substituted hydrocarbon is a hydrocarbon in which one or more hydrogen atoms have been replaced by an atom or group of atoms.
4. Is the following sentence true or false? The functional group in a substituted hydrocarbon determines the properties of the compound. true

## Alcohols (page 273)

5. Methanol and ethanol are two examples of a class of organic compounds called alcohols.
6. The functional group in an alcohol is represented as –OH and is called a(n) hydroxyl group.
7. Identify two ways a halocarbon can be produced.
   a. A halocarbon reacts with a base
   b. An alkene reacts with water

## Organic Acids and Bases (pages 273–274)

8. What two physical properties do organic acids tend to have?
   a. A sharp taste
   b. A strong odor
9. Is the following sentence true or false? Amines are organic bases. true
10. Name three products where amines can be found.
    a. Paints
    b. Dyes
    c. Disinfectants
11. Complete the following table.

| Substituted Hydrocarbons | | |
|---|---|---|
| Type of Compound | Name of Functional Group | Formula of Functional Group |
| Alcohol | Hydroxyl | $-OH$ |
| Organic acid | Carboxyl | $-COOH$ |
| Organic base | Amino | $-NH_2$ |

## Esters (page 274)

12. What type of compound gives many flowers a pleasant odor?
    Esters
13. Which two types of compounds can react and form esters?
    a. Organic acid
    b. Alcohol
14. Circle the letter of the other product of the reaction that forms an ester.
    a. an alcohol
    b. carbon dioxide
    c. a salt
    (d.) water
15. Is the following sentence true or false? Esters are used to make various fruit flavors in processed foods. true

Name ______________________ Class ______________ Date __________



# Section 9.3 Polymers
**(pages 275–280)**

*This section explains how polymers form. It also discusses examples of synthetic and natural polymers.*

## Reading Strategy (page 275)

**Identifying Main Ideas** As you read, complete the concept map to summarize two main ideas about polymers. For more information on this Reading Strategy, see the **Reading and Study Skills** in the **Skills and Reference Handbook** at the end of your textbook.

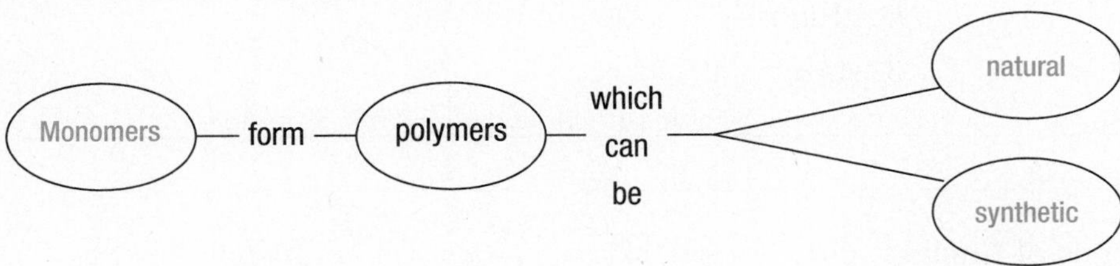


1. Describe a polymer. A polymer is a large molecule that forms when many smaller molecules are linked together by covalent bonds.

2. The smaller molecules that join together to form a polymer are called monomers.

3. Is the following sentence true or false? More than one type of monomer can be present in some polymers. true

4. Name the two general classifications of polymers.
   a. Natural b. Synthetic

## Synthetic Polymers (page 276)

5. Name three polymers that can be synthesized.
   a. Polyethylene b. Nylon c. Rubber

6. Is the following sentence true or false? The more carbon atoms there are in a polyethylene chain, the harder the polymer is.
   true

## Natural Polymers (pages 278–280)

7. Name four types of polymers that are produced in plant and animal cells.
   a. Starches b. Nucleic acids
   c. Cellulose d. Proteins

8. Circle the letter of the molecular formula of a simple sugar.
   a. $CH_2O$ (b.) $C_6H_{12}O_6$
   c. $C_{12}H_{22}O_{11}$ d. $C_{12}H_{24}O_{12}$

9. Circle the letter of the simple sugar glucose and fructose can react to form.

a. glucose b. fructose

c. cellulose (d.) sucrose

10. How are starches used in plants? Plants store starches for food and to build stems, seeds, and roots.

11. Simple sugars, slightly more complex sugars, and polymers built from sugar monomers are classified as carbohydrates.

12. Circle the letter of the main component of cotton and wood.

(a.) cellulose b. glucose

c. protein d. starch

13. Define nucleic acids. Nucleic acids are large nitrogen-containing polymers found mainly in the nuclei of cells.

14. Name the two types of nucleic acid.

a. Deoxyribonucleic acid (DNA) b. Ribonucleic acid (RNA)

15. Name the three parts of a nucleotide in DNA.

a. Phosphate group b. Deoxyribose sugar c. Organic base

16. Circle the letter of the term that best describes the structure of DNA.

a. helix (b.) double helix

c. ring d. chain

17. How does DNA store information? The order of the base pairs in a strand is a code that is used to produce proteins.

18. Is the following sentence true or false? The human body can manufacture all of the essential amino acids. false

19. Amino acids are the monomers that cells use to build the polymers known as proteins.

20. Complete the following concept map about amino acids.

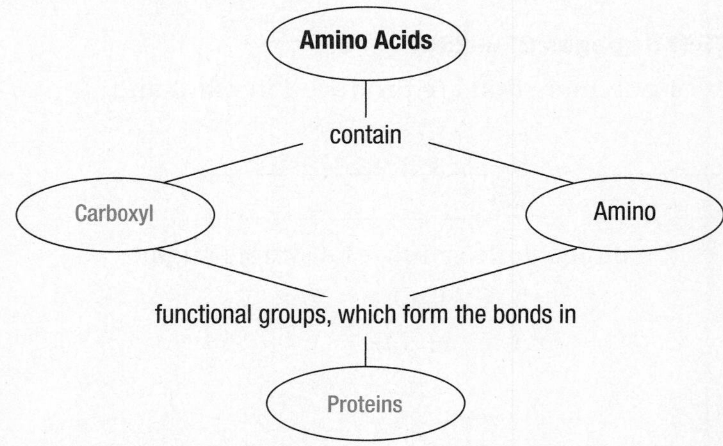

Name ____________________ Class ____________________ Date ____________



# Section 9.4 Reactions in Cells
## (pages 282–284)

*This section describes and compares photosynthesis and cellular respiration. It also discusses the roles of enzymes and vitamins.*

## Reading Strategy (page 282)

**Summarizing** As you read, complete the table by recording a main idea for each heading. For more information on this Reading Strategy, see the **Reading and Study Skills** in the **Skills and Reference Handbook** at the end of your textbook.

| Heading | Main Idea |
|---|---|
| Photosynthesis | During photosynthesis, energy from sunlight is converted into chemical energy. |
| Cellular Respiration | During cellular respiration, the energy stored in the products of photosynthesis is released. |
| Enzymes and Vitamins | Enzymes and vitamins are compounds that help cells function efficiently at normal body temperature. |

1. Two processes that allow organisms to meet their energy needs are photosynthesis and cellular respiration.

## Photosynthesis (page 282)

2. Describe what happens during photosynthesis. During photosynthesis, plants chemically combine carbon dioxide and water into carbohydrates.

3. Circle the letter of each requirement for photosynthesis to occur.
   - (a.) chlorophyll
   - b. oxygen
   - c. carbohydrates
   - (d.) light

4. Identify the energy conversion that takes place during photosynthesis. Energy from sunlight is converted into chemical energy.

5. Circle the letter of each product of photosynthesis.
   - a. carbon dioxide
   - (b.) carbohydrates
   - (c.) oxygen
   - d. water

6. Is the following sentence true or false? When all the reactions in photosynthesis are complete, energy from sunlight has been stored in the covalent bonds of molecules. true

## Cellular Respiration (page 283)

7. During cellular respiration, the energy stored in the products of photosynthesis is released.

**8.** How is cellular respiration related to photosynthesis? Each process produces the reactants for the other process.

**9.** Is the following sentence true or false? Carbohydrates produce more energy per gram than fats do. false

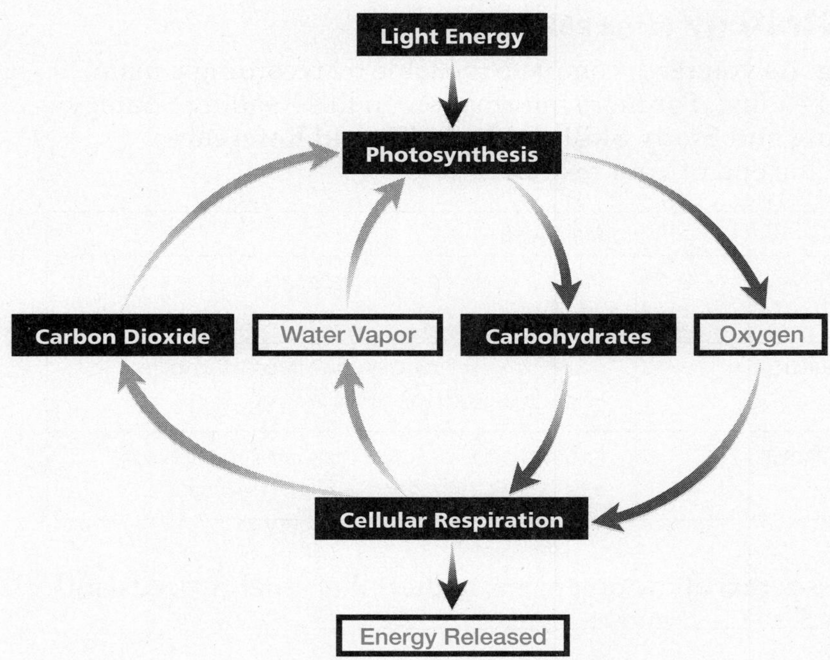


**10.** Complete the diagram relating photosynthesis to cellular respiration.

a. Water vapor b. Oxygen c. Energy released

## Enzymes and Vitamins (page 284)

**11.** Describe what enzymes and vitamins have in common. Enzymes and vitamins help cells function efficiently at normal body temperature.

**12.** Define enzymes. Enzymes are proteins that act as catalysts for reactions in cells.

**13.** Is the following sentence true or false? Enzymes require high temperatures in order to function. false

**14.** Is the following sentence true or false? Some enzymes require a co-enzyme in order to function. true

**15.** Define vitamins. Vitamins are organic compounds that organisms need in small amounts, but cannot produce.

**16.** Is the following sentence true or false? All vitamins dissolve in water and must be replaced daily. false

**17.** Identify the property of vitamin A that allows it to build up in body tissues over time. Vitamin A dissolves in fats.

Name ______________________ Class __________________ Date ____________

Chapter 9 Carbon Chemistry

# WordWise

*Complete the following crossword puzzle, using the clues provided below.*

**Clues across:**

1. A hydrocarbon in which all of the bonds are single bonds
2. A compound containing carbon and hydrogen, often combined with other elements such as oxygen and nitrogen
3. A small molecule that joins with other small molecules to form a polymer
4. _____ acid: a large nitrogen-containing polymer found mainly in the nuclei of cells
5. Organic compounds that contain only carbon and hydrogen

**Clues down:**

6. An organic compound that organisms need in small amounts, but cannot produce
7. Organic compounds that contain both carboxyl and amino functional groups
8. Compounds with the same molecular formula but different structural formulas
9. A polymer in which at least 100 amino acid monomers are linked through bonds between an amino group and a carboxyl group
10. _____ solid: a type of solid in which all of the atoms are linked by covalent bonds

| | | | | | | | | | | | | | | | | | | |
|---|---|---|---|---|---|---|---|---|---|---|---|---|---|---|---|---|---|---|
| | | | | | | | | | | | | | | 6 V | | | | |
| | | | | | | | | | | | | | | I | | | | |
| | | | | | | | | 1 S | 7 A | T | U | R | A | T | E | D | | |
| | | | | | 8 I | | | | M | | | | | A | | | | |
| | | | | | S | | | | I | | | | | M | | | | |
| | | | 9 P | | 2 O | R | G | A | N | I | C | | | I | | | | |
| | | | R | | M | | | | O | | | | | N | | 10 N | | |
| 3 M | O | N | O | M | E | R | | | A | | | | | | | E | | |
| | | | T | | R | | 4 N | U | C | L | E | I | C | | | T | | |
| | | | E | | S | | | | I | | | | | | | W | | |
| | | | I | | | | 5 H | Y | D | R | O | C | A | R | B | O | N | S |
| | | | N | | | | | | S | | | | | | | R | | |
| | | | | | | | | | | | | | | | | K | | |

Name ______________________ Class ______________ Date ____________



# Balancing Equations for Organic Reactions

**Math Skill: Ratios and Proportions**

You may want to read more about this **Math Skill** in the **Skills and Reference Handbook** at the end of your textbook.

When propane, $C_3H_8$, combines with oxygen, the products are carbon dioxide and water. Write a balanced equation for the complete combustion of propane.

**1. Read and Understand**

*What information are you given?*

Reactants = propane ($C_3H_8$) and oxygen ($O_2$)

Products = carbon dioxide ($CO_2$) and water ($H_2O$)

**2. Plan and Solve**

*What unknowns are you trying to determine?*

The coefficients for the equation

*What equation contains the given information?*

$C_3H_8 + O_2 \longrightarrow CO_2 + H_2O$ (unbalanced equation)

*First, balance the equation for carbon. Because there are 3 carbon atoms in $C_3H_8$, you need to place the coefficient 3 in front of $CO_2$.*

$C_3H_8 + O_2 \longrightarrow 3CO_2 + H_2O$

*Next, balance the equation for hydrogen. Because there are 8 hydrogen atoms in $C_3H_8$ and only 2 hydrogen atoms in $H_2O$, you need to place the coefficient 4 in front of $H_2O$.*

$C_3H_8 + O_2 \longrightarrow 3CO_2 + 4H_2O$

*Finally, balance the equation for oxygen. Because there are 6 oxygen atoms in 3 molecules of $CO_2$ and 4 oxygen atoms in 4 molecules of $H_2O$ for a total of 10 oxygen atoms, you need to place the coefficient 5 in front of $O_2$.*

$C_3H_8 + 5O_2 \longrightarrow 3CO_2 + 4H_2O$

**3. Look Back and Check**

*Is your answer reasonable?*

Each side of the equation has 3 carbon atoms, 8 hydrogen atoms, and 10 oxygen atoms. The equation is balanced.

## Math Practice

*On a separate sheet of paper, solve the following problems.*

1. Balance the equation for the reaction of benzene and hydrogen to form cyclohexane.

   $C_6H_6 + \underline{\ 3\ } H_2 \xrightarrow{Pt} C_6H_{12}$

2. Write a balanced equation for the complete combustion of methane, $CH_4$. $CH_4 + 2O_2 \longrightarrow CO_2 + 2H_2O$

3. Write a balanced equation for the combustion of glucose, $C_6H_{12}O_6$.

   $C_6H_{12}O_6 + 6O_2 \longrightarrow 6CO_2 + 6H_2O$

Name ______________________ Class ______________ Date __________



# Section 10.1 Radioactivity
**(pages 292–297)**

*This section discusses the different types of nuclear radiation and how they affect matter.*

## Reading Strategy (page 292)

**Previewing** Before you read the section, rewrite the topic headings in the table as *how, why,* and *what* questions. As you read, write an answer to each question. For more information on this Reading Strategy, see the **Reading and Study Skills** in the **Skills and Reference Handbook** at the end of your textbook.

| Exploring Radioactivity | |
|---|---|
| **Question** | **Answer** Student answers may include: |
| What is nuclear decay? | Nuclear decay is the process in which a radioisotope spontaneously decays into another isotope. |
| What are types of nuclear radiation? | Alpha, beta, gamma |
| What are the effects of nuclear radiation? | Nuclear radiation can ionize atoms, molecules may change, and cellular function may break down. |
| How can nuclear radiation be detected? | Nuclear radiation can be detected with devices such as Geiger counters and film badges. |

## Nuclear Decay (pages 292–293)

**1.** Describe radioactivity. Radioactivity is the process in which an unstable atomic nucleus emits charged particles and energy.

**2.** A radioisotope is any atom that contains an unstable nucleus.

**3.** Describe what happens to radioisotopes during nuclear decay. Over time, radioisotopes spontaneously change into other isotopes, including isotopes of other elements.

## Types of Nuclear Radiation (pages 293–296)

**4.** Nuclear radiation is charged particles and energy that are emitted from the nuclei of radioisotopes.

**5.** Circle the letters that identify each common type of nuclear radiation.

a. X-rays
(b.) alpha particles
(c.) beta particles
(d.) gamma rays

**6.** Circle the letters that identify which groups of particles make up an alpha particle.

a. two electrons
(b.) two protons
(c.) two neutrons
d. four neutrons

7. How is the product isotope different from the reactant isotope in alpha decay? The product isotope has two fewer protons and two fewer neutrons than the reactant isotope.

8. Circle the letters that identify each event that takes place during beta decay.
   a. A proton decomposes into a neutron and an electron.
   (b.) A neutron decomposes into a proton and an electron.
   (c.) An electron is emitted from the nucleus.
   d. A neutron is emitted from the nucleus.

9. Why are beta particles more penetrating than alpha particles?
   Beta particles have a smaller mass and a faster speed.

10. Is the following sentence true or false? All nuclear radiation consists of charged particles. false

11. What is a gamma ray? A gamma ray is a penetrating ray of energy emitted by an unstable nucleus.

12. How fast do gamma rays travel through space?
   Gamma rays travel through space at the speed of light.

13. Complete the following table about nuclear radiation.

| Characteristics of Nuclear Radiation | | | |
|---|---|---|---|
| Radiation Type | Charge | Mass (amu) | Usually Stopped By |
| Alpha particle | 1− | 4 | Paper or clothing |
| Beta particle | 1− | $\frac{1}{1836}$ | Aluminum sheet |
| Gamma ray | 0 | 0 | Several meters of concrete |

## Effects of Nuclear Radiation (pages 296–297)

14. How does nuclear radiation affect atoms? Nuclear radiation can ionize atoms.

15. Is the following sentence true or false? One potential danger of radon gas is that prolonged exposure to it can lead to lung cancer.
   true

## Detecting Nuclear Radiation (page 297)

16. Name two devices that are used to detect nuclear radiation.
   a. Geiger counters  b. Film badges

Name ______________________ Class ________________ Date __________



# Section 10.2 Rates of Nuclear Decay

**(pages 298–301)**

*This section discusses half-lives and explains how nuclear decay can be used to estimate the age of objects.*

## Reading Strategy (page 298)

**Identifying Details** As you read, complete the concept map below to identify details about radiocarbon dating. For more information on this Reading Strategy, see the **Reading and Study Skills** in the **Skills and Reference Handbook** at the end of your textbook.

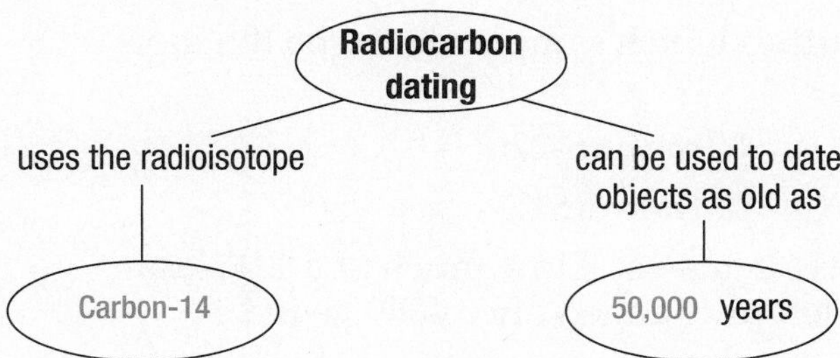


## Half-life (pages 299–300)

1. A nuclear decay rate describes how fast nuclear changes take place in a radioactive substance ______.

2. Is the following sentence true or false? All radioisotopes decay at the same rate. false

3. Describe a half-life. A half-life is the time required for one half of a sample of a radioisotope to decay.

4. Circle the letter that describes a sample of a radioisotope after two half-lives.
   a. One eighth of the original sample is unchanged.
   (b.) One quarter of the original sample is unchanged.
   c. Half of the original sample is unchanged.
   d. Three quarters of the original sample is unchanged.

5. Circle the letter of the correct answer. Iodine-131 has a half-life of 8.07 days. What fraction of a sample of iodine-131 is left unchanged after 16.14 days?
   a. $\frac{1}{2}$ (b.) $\frac{1}{4}$
   c. $\frac{1}{8}$ d. $\frac{1}{16}$

6. Is the following sentence true or false? Like chemical reaction rates, nuclear decay rates vary with the conditions of reaction.
   false

Name ______________ Class ______________ Date ______________



*Use the following table to answer questions 7 and 8.*

| Half-Lives of Selected Radioisotopes | |
|---|---|
| **Isotope** | **Half-life** |
| Radon-222 | 3.82 days |
| Iodine-131 | 8.07 days |
| Thorium-234 | 24.1 days |
| Radium-226 | 1620 years |
| Carbon-14 | 5730 years |

**7.** Circle the letter that identifies which sample would be the most unchanged after 100 years.

a. iodine-131
(b.) radium-226
c. radon-222
d. thorium-234

**8.** Circle the letter of the correct answer. How much of a 1.00 gram sample of radium-226 is left unchanged after 4860 years?

a. 0.500 g
b. 0.250 g
(c.) 0.125 g
d. 0.050 g

## Radioactive Dating (pages 300–301)

**9.** How is carbon-14 formed in the upper atmosphere? Carbon-14 is formed in the upper atmosphere when neutrons produced by cosmic rays collide with nitrogen-14 atoms.

**10.** Circle the letter that identifies the correct equation for the beta decay of carbon–14.

(a.) ${}^{14}_{6}C \longrightarrow {}^{14}_{7}N + {}^{0}_{-1}e$
b. ${}^{14}_{6}C \longrightarrow {}^{13}_{5}B + {}^{1}_{1}p$
c. ${}^{14}_{6}C \longrightarrow {}^{14}_{5}B + {}^{0}_{-1}e$
d. ${}^{14}_{6}C \longrightarrow {}^{10}_{4}Be + {}^{4}_{2}He$

**11.** Is the following sentence true or false? Plants and animals continue to absorb carbon from the atmosphere after they die. false

**12.** How is the age of an object determined in radiocarbon dating? The age of an object is determined by comparing its carbon-14 levels with carbon-14 levels in the atmosphere.

**13.** Circle the letter of each characteristic of radiocarbon dating.

(a.) Carbon-14 levels in the atmosphere can change over time.
b. Carbon-14 levels in the atmosphere stay constant.
(c.) Scientists often use objects of known age in radiocarbon dating.
d. Objects of known age are not useful in radiocarbon dating.

**14.** Is the following sentence true or false? Radiocarbon dating is highly accurate in dating objects that are more than 50,000 years old. false

# Section 10.3 Artificial Transmutation

**(pages 303–305)**

*This section discusses transmutations, transuranium elements, and particle accelerators.*

## Reading Strategy (page 303)

**Monitoring Your Understanding** Preview the Key Concepts, topic headings, vocabulary, and figures in this section. List two things you expect to learn. After reading, state what you learned about each item you listed. For more information on this Reading Strategy, see the **Reading and Study Skills** in the **Skills and Reference Handbook** at the end of your textbook.

| Understanding Artificial Transmutation | |
|---|---|
| **What I Expect to Learn** Student answers may include: | **What I Learned** |
| Examples of artificial transmutation | Rutherford's transmutation of nitrogen-14 into oxygen-17; the synthesis of neptunium-239 |
| Uses of transuranium elements | Smoke detectors (americium-241); space probes (plutonium-238) |

## Nuclear Reactions in the Laboratory (page 303)

1. Define transmutation. Transmutation is the conversion of atoms of one element to atoms of another element.

2. An example of a transmutation that occurs naturally is nuclear decay.

3. How do scientists perform artificial transmutations? Scientists can perform artificial transmutations by bombarding atomic nuclei with high-energy particles such as protons, neutrons, or alpha particles.

4. Circle the letter that identifies the scientist who performed the first artificial transmutation.
   - (a.) Ernest Rutherford
   - b. Niels Bohr
   - c. Enrico Fermi
   - d. Lise Meitner

5. The experiment that produced the first artificial transmutation also provided evidence that the nucleus contains protons.

## Transuranium Elements (page 304)

6. Describe a transuranium element. A transuranium element is an element with an atomic number greater than that of uranium (92).

7. Is the following sentence true or false? All transuranium elements are radioactive. true

Name ______________________ Class ______________ Date ___________



8. Scientists can synthesize a transuranium element by the artificial transmutation of a(n) ___lighter___ element.

9. Circle the letter of the first transuranium element to be synthesized.
   a. plutonium
   b. americium
   c. technetium
   (d.) neptunium

10. Circle the letter of the element that is used as a source of radiation in smoke detectors.
    a. uranium
    (b.) americium
    c. technetium
    d. plutonium

## Particle Accelerators (page 305)

11. Why are particle accelerators needed for some transmutations? Some transmutations will occur only if the bombarding particles are moving at extremely high speeds.

12. Is the following sentence true or false? A particle accelerator can accelerate charged particles to speeds very close to the speed of light. ___true___

13. Describe a quark. A quark is a subatomic particle theorized to be among the basic units of matter.

14. Circle the letter that identifies the number of quarks in each proton or neutron.
    a. zero
    b. two
    (c.) three
    d. six

15. Complete the following concept map about alpha particles.

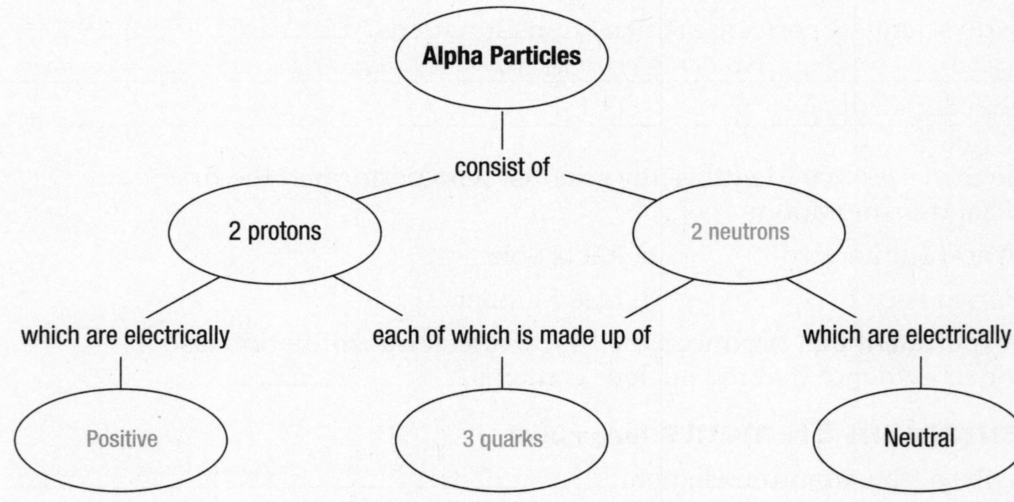

# Section 10.4 Fission and Fusion
**(pages 308–315)**

*This section discusses nuclear forces and the conversion of mass into energy. It also describes the nuclear processes of fission and fusion.*

## Reading Strategy (page 308)

**Comparing and Contrasting** As you read, contrast fission and fusion in the Venn diagram below by listing the ways they differ. For more information on this Reading Strategy, see the **Reading and Study Skills** in the **Skills and Reference Handbook** at the end of your textbook.

**Contrasting Fission and Fusion**

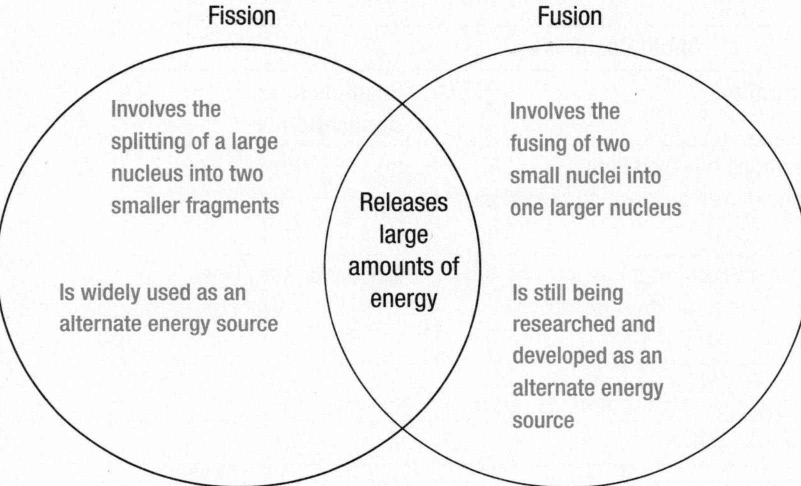


## Nuclear Forces (pages 308–309)

1. Describe the strong nuclear force. The strong nuclear force is the attractive force that binds protons and neutrons together in the nucleus.

2. Is the following sentence true or false? Over very short distances, the strong nuclear force is much greater than the electric forces among protons. true

3. Electric forces in atomic nuclei depend on the number of protons.

4. Is the following sentence true or false? The strong nuclear force on a proton or neutron is much greater in a large nucleus than in a small nucleus. false

5. All nuclei with 83 or more protons are radioactive.

## Fission (pages 309–313)

6. Describe fission. Fission is the splitting of an atomic nucleus into two smaller parts.

7. Fission can produce very large amounts of energy from very small amounts of mass.

**8.** Circle the letter that identifies what *c* represents in Einstein's mass-energy equation, $E = mc^2$.

a. the charge on a proton
(b.) the speed of light
c. the charge on an electron
d. the specific heat of the material

**9.** Is the following sentence true or false? During nuclear reactions mass is not conserved, but energy is conserved. false

**10.** Describe what can happen to a uranium-235 nucleus that absorbs a neutron. The nucleus can undergo fission, splitting into two smaller nuclei and releasing energy and more neutrons.

**11.** Complete the following table.

| Chain Reactions | | |
|---|---|---|
| **Type of Chain Reaction** | **Description** | **Example of An Application** |
| Uncontrolled | All neutrons released during fission are free to cause other fissions. | Nuclear weapons |
| Controlled | Some of the neutrons released during fission are absorbed by nonfissionable materials. | Nuclear power plants |

**12.** Describe a critical mass. A critical mass is the smallest possible mass of a fissionable material that can sustain a chain reaction.

**13.** Is the following sentence true or false? Unlike power plants that burn fossil fuels, nuclear power plants do not emit air pollutants such as oxides of sulfur and nitrogen. true

**14.** Describe what happens during a meltdown. During a meltdown, the core of the reactor melts and radioactive material may be released.

## Fusion (page 315)

**15.** The state of matter in which atoms have been stripped of their electrons is plasma.

**16.** Circle the letter of each main problem that scientists must face in designing a fusion reactor.

(a.) Extremely high temperatures are necessary for a fusion reaction to start.
(b.) The plasma that results from the reaction conditions must be contained.
c. The hydrogen needed as a starting material is extremely scarce.
d. Fusion reactions produce large quantities of radioactive waste.

Name ______________________ Class ______________ Date __________



# WordWise

*Write the answer to each definition using one of the scrambled words below.*

| | | |
|---|---|---|
| abte petalric | dorataivyicit | fonius |
| gnostr rauncel crefo | licticar sams | lunarce tiadorian |
| magma yar | onisifs | pahal claptrie |
| pieatodorsoi | ruqak | samlap |

| Definition | Term |
|---|---|
| A subatomic particle theorized to be among the basic units of matter | quark |
| Charged particles and energy that are emitted from the nuclei of radioisotopes | nuclear radiation |
| A positively charged particle made up of two protons and two neutrons | alpha particle |
| A state of matter in which atoms have been stripped of their electrons | plasma |
| The process in which an unstable atomic nucleus emits charged particles and energy | radioactivity |
| A penetrating ray of energy emitted by an unstable nucleus | gamma ray |
| The attractive force that binds protons and neutrons together in the nucleus | strong nuclear force |
| The splitting of an atomic nucleus into two smaller parts | fission |
| An electron emitted by an unstable nucleus | beta particle |
| The smallest possible mass of a fissionable material that can sustain a chain reaction | critical mass |
| A process in which the nuclei of two atoms combine to form a larger nucleus | fusion |
| Any atom containing an unstable nucleus | radioisotope |

# Nuclear Equations for Alpha Decay

**Math Skill: Formulas and Equations**

You may want to read more about this **Math Skill** in the **Skills and Reference Handbook** at the end of your textbook.

Write a balanced nuclear equation for the alpha decay of polonium-218.

**1. Read and Understand**

*What information are you given?*

Reactant isotope = polonium-218

Radiation emitted = $^{4}_{2}\text{He}$ (alpha particle)

*Use the periodic table to obtain the atomic number of polonium.*

Reactant isotope = $^{218}_{84}\text{Po}$

**2. Plan and Solve**

*What unknowns are you trying to calculate?*

Atomic number of product isotope, $Z$ = ?

Mass number of product isotope, $A$ = ?

Chemical symbol of product isotope, X = ?

*What equation contains the given information?*

$$^{218}_{84}\text{Po} \longrightarrow {}^{A}_{Z}\text{X} + {}^{4}_{2}\text{He}$$

*Write and solve equations for atomic mass and atomic number.*

$218 = A + 4$     $84 = Z + 2$

$218 - 4 = A$     $84 - 2 = Z$

$214 = A$     $82 = Z$

On the periodic table, lead, Pb, has an atomic number of 82. So, X is Pb. The balanced nuclear equation is shown below.

$$^{218}_{84}\text{Po} \longrightarrow {}^{214}_{82}\text{Pb} + {}^{4}_{2}\text{He}$$

**3. Look Back and Check**

*Is your answer reasonable?*

The mass number on the left equals the sum of the mass numbers on the right. The atomic number on the left equals the sum of the atomic numbers on the right. The equation is balanced.

## Math Practice

*On separate sheet of paper, solve the following problems.*

1. Write a balanced nuclear equation for the alpha decay of uranium-238.

$$^{238}_{92}\text{U} \longrightarrow {}^{234}_{90}\text{Th} + {}^{4}_{2}\text{He}$$

2. Write a balanced nuclear equation for the alpha decay of thorium-230.

$$^{230}_{90}\text{Th} \longrightarrow {}^{226}_{88}\text{Ra} + {}^{4}_{2}\text{He}$$

Name ______________________ Class ________________ Date ____________



# Section 11.1 Distance and Displacement
**(pages 328–331)**

*This section defines distance and displacement. Methods of describing motion are presented. Vector addition and subtraction are introduced.*

## Reading Strategy (page 328)

**Predicting** Write a definition for *frame of reference* in your own words in the left column of the table. After you read the section, compare your definition to the scientific definition and explain why a frame of reference is important. For more information on this Reading Strategy, see the **Reading and Study Skills** in the **Skills and Reference Handbook** at the end of your textbook.

| Frame of Reference | |
|---|---|
| **Frame of reference probably means** | **Frame of reference actually means** |
| Sample answer: The range of distances or area that you are considering in a problem | A system of objects that are not moving with respect to one another |

1. What two things must you know to describe the motion of an object?
You must know the direction the object is moving and how fast the object is moving.

## Choosing a Frame of Reference (pages 328–329)

2. Is the following sentence true or false? A frame of reference is not necessary to describe motion accurately and completely. false

3. What is a frame of reference? It is a system of objects that are not moving relative to one another.

4. Movement in relation to a frame of reference is called relative motion.

5. Imagine that you are a passenger in a car. Circle the letter of the best frame of reference you could use to determine how fast the car is moving relative to the ground.
   a. the people sitting next to you in the backseat
   b. the driver of the car
   c. a van traveling in the lane next to your car
   (d.) a sign post on the side of the road

## Measuring Distance (page 329)

6. Distance is the length of a path between two points.

7. Circle the letter of the SI unit best suited for measuring the length of a room in your home.
   a. kilometers
   (b.) meters
   c. centimeters
   d. millimeters

Name ______________ Class ______________ Date ______________



## Measuring Displacements (page 330)

8. Is the following sentence true or false? Five blocks south is an example of a displacement. true

9. Compare and contrast distance and displacement. Distance is the length of a path between two points, whereas displacement is the direction from a starting point and the length of a straight line from the starting point to the ending point.

10. What would your total displacement be if you walked from your front door, around the block, and then stopped when you reached your front door again?
    a. one block
    b. two blocks
    c. the entire distance of your trip
    (d.) zero

## Combining Displacements (pages 330–331)

11. A vector is a quantity that has both magnitude and direction.

12. Circle the letter of each answer that could describe the magnitude of a vector.
    (a.) length
    b. direction
    (c.) amount
    (d.) size

13. To combine two displacements that are in opposite directions, the magnitudes subtract from one another.

*For questions 14 and 15, refer to the figure below.*

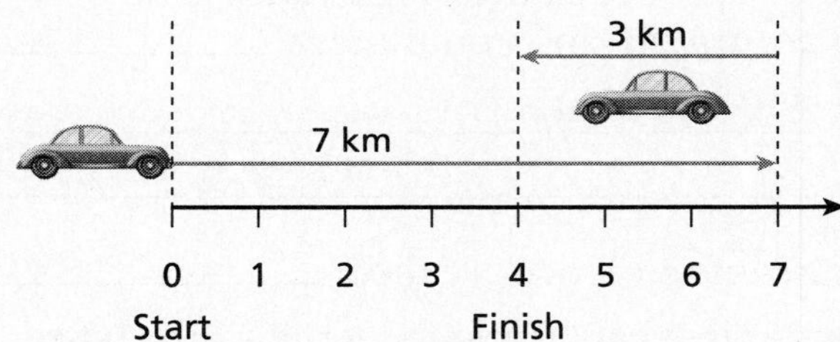


14. The magnitudes of the two displacement vectors are 7 km and 3 km.

15. Because the two displacements are in opposite directions, the magnitude of the total displacement is 4 km.

16. Circle the letter that answers the question. What is the displacement of a cyclist who travels 1 mile north, then 1 mile east, and finally 1 mile south?
    a. 3 miles east
    b. 1 mile north
    c. 3 miles south
    (d.) 1 mile east

17. The vector sum of two or more other vectors is called the resultant vector.

Name ______________________ Class ________________ Date ____________

Chapter 11 Motion

# Section 11.2 Speed and Velocity

**(pages 332–337)**

*This section defines and compares speed and velocity. It also describes how to calculate average speed.*

## Reading Strategy (page 332)

**Monitoring Your Understanding** After you read this section, identify several things you have learned that are relevant to your life. Explain why they are relevant to you. For more information on this Reading Strategy, see the **Reading and Study Skills** in the **Skills and Reference Handbook** at the end of your textbook.

| **Facts About Speed and Velocity** Sample answers shown below. | |
|---|---|
| **What Is Important** | **Why It Is Important** |
| Average speed is distance divided by time. | I could use this to calculate various speeds, like the average speed at which I travel getting to school. |
| Instantaneous speed is different from average speed. | You can't use a single speedometer reading to determine how long a trip will take. |
| Velocity is not the same as speed. | This could be useful in giving directions or in describing the path that you take on a walk. |

## Speed (pages 332–334)

1. Define speed. Speed is the ratio of the distance an object moves to the amount of time it moves.

2. The SI units for speed are meters per second (m/s).

3. How is instantaneous speed different from average speed? Instantaneous speed is measured at a particular instant, while average speed is computed for the entire duration of a trip.

4. The equation used for calculating average speed is $v = d/t$.

5. Is the following sentence true or false? You can determine how fast you were going at the midpoint of a trip by calculating average speed for the entire trip. false

6. A student walked 1.5 km in 25 minutes, and then, realizing he was late, ran the remaining 0.5 km in 5 minutes. Calculate his average speed on the way to school.
   $\bar{v}$ = Total distance/Total time = (1.5 km + 0.5 km)/(25 min + 5 min) = 2.0 km/30 min = 2.0 km/0.5 h = 4.0 km/h

7. What type of speed does an automobile's speedometer display?
   A speedometer displays instantaneous speed.

## Graphing Motion (page 334)

8. The slope of a line on a distance-time graph represents speed.

*For questions 9 through 11, refer to the graph below.*

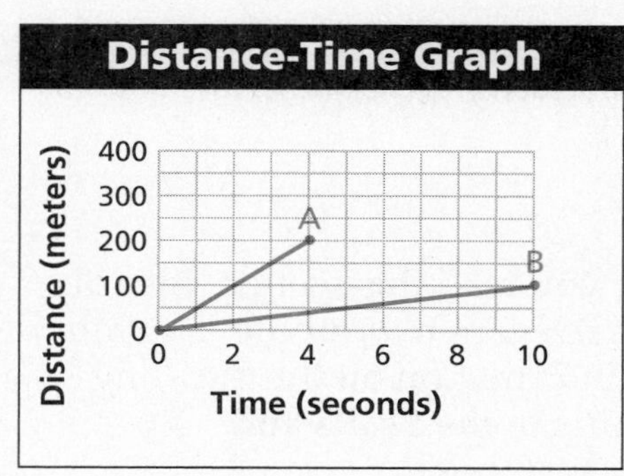


9. Draw a point on the graph that represents 200 m traveled in 4 seconds. Draw a line connecting this point with the origin (0,0). Label this as line A.
10. Draw a point on the graph that represents 100 m traveled in 10 seconds. Draw a line connecting this point with the origin (0,0). Label this as line B.
11. Calculate the average speed (slope) of lines A and B. Be sure to include units. A: $v$ = 200 m/4 s = 50 m/s; B: $v$ = 100 m/10 s = 10 m/s

## Velocity (page 336)

12. How do speed and velocity differ? Speed indicates distance traveled over a given amount of time; velocity describes both speed and direction of motion.
13. Circle the letter of each sentence that describes a change in velocity.
    - (a.) A moving object gains speed.
    - (b.) A moving object changes direction.
    - c. A moving object moves in a straight line at a constant speed.
    - (d.) A moving object slows down.
14. Is the following sentence true or false? If a car travels around a gentle curve on a highway at 60 km/h, the velocity does not change. false

## Combining Velocities (page 337)

15. How do velocities combine? Velocities combine by vector addition.
16. A river flows at a velocity of 3 km/h relative to the riverbank. A boat moves upstream at a velocity of 15 km/h relative to the river. What is the velocity of the boat relative to the riverbank?
    - a. 18 km/h downstream
    - b. 15 km/h upstream
    - (c.) 12 km/h upstream
    - d. 12 km/h downstream

Name ______________________ Class ______________ Date __________



# Section 11.3 Acceleration
## (pages 342–348)

*This section describes the relationships among speed, velocity, and acceleration. Examples of these concepts are discussed. Sample calculations of acceleration and graphs representing accelerated motion are presented.*

## Reading Strategy (page 342)

**Summarizing** Read the section on acceleration. Then complete the concept map to organize what you know about acceleration. For more information on this Reading Strategy, see the **Reading and Study Skills** in the **Skills and Reference Handbook** at the end of your textbook.

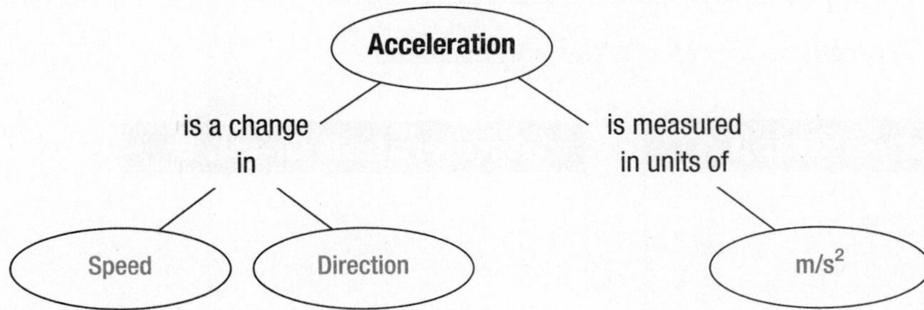


## What Is Acceleration? (pages 342–345)

1. The rate at which velocity changes is called acceleration.
2. In terms of speed and direction, in what ways can an object accelerate? It can change its speed, its direction, or both its speed and direction.
3. Because acceleration is a quantity that has both magnitude and direction, it is a(n) vector.
4. Is the following sentence true or false? Acceleration is the result of increases or decreases in speed. true
5. Ignoring air resistance, a rock in free fall will have a velocity of 39.2 m/s after 4.0 seconds.
6. A horse on a carousel that is moving at a constant speed is accelerating because its direction is constantly changing.
7. Describe constant acceleration. Constant acceleration is a steady change in velocity.

## Calculating Acceleration (pages 345–346)

8. Write the equation used to calculate the acceleration of an object.
Acceleration = Change in velocity/Total time

9. Is the following sentence true or false? When the final velocity is less than the initial velocity of an object, the acceleration is negative. ____true____

10. A skateboarder begins down a ramp at a speed of 1.0 m/s. After 3 seconds, her speed has increased to 4.0 m/s. Calculate her acceleration.

    (a.) 1.0 $m/s^2$ b. 3.0 $m/s^2$
    c. 5.0 $m/s^2$ d. 9.8 $m/s^2$

## Graphs of Accelerated Motion (pages 346–348)

11. A speed-time graph in which the displayed data forms a straight line is an example of a(n) ____linear graph____.

*For questions 12 through 15, refer to the graphs below.*

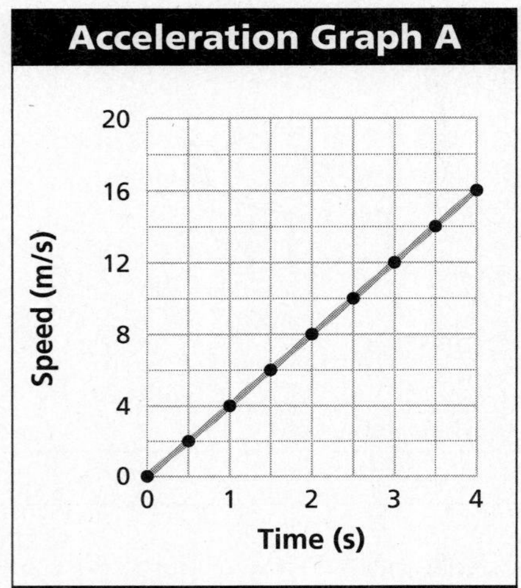


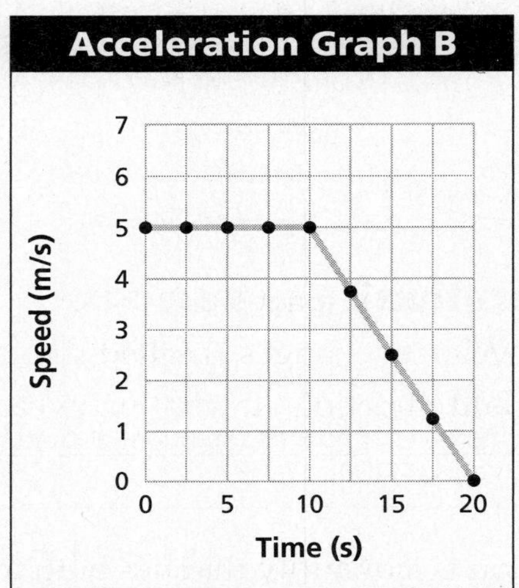


12. Graph A represents the motion of a downhill skier. How fast was the skier moving after traveling down the hill for 2.5 seconds? ____10 m/s____

13. In which graph does an object move at constant speed during the first 4 seconds? ____Graph B____

14. Graph B represents the motion of a mountain biker. What is the biker's speed at times of 10 s and 20 s? ____5 m/s (at 10 s); 0 m/s (at 20 s)____

15. Determine the acceleration of the mountain biker during the 10 second to 20 second time period. Show your work.

    $a = v_f - v_i/t = (0 \text{ m/s} - 5 \text{ m/s})/10 \text{ s} = -0.5 \text{ m/s}^2$

16. The plotted data points representing acceleration in a distance-time graph form a(n) ____curve____.

## Instantaneous Acceleration (page 348)

17. The measure of how fast a velocity is changing at a specific instant is known as ____instantaneous acceleration____.

Name ______________________ Class ________________ Date ____________



# WordWise

*Complete the sentences by using one of the scrambled vocabulary words below.*

| | | |
|---|---|---|
| vrlaeeit oinotm | mefar fo ecrneeefr | gvaeera dspee |
| levotciy | nerlia | centidsa |
| esdep | erfe lafl | aulsettrn crovet |
| atnicoelecar | rotcev | nnilraeon |

An equation for acceleration is $(v_f - v_i)/t$.

A quantity that has both magnitude and direction is called a(n) vector.

The total distance traveled divided by the total time is average speed.

A speed-time graph in which data points form a straight line is an example of a(n) linear graph.

Common units for speed include meters per second (m/s).

In order to accurately and completely describe the motion of an object, a(n) frame of reference is necessary.

You can determine distance by measuring the length of the actual path between two points in space.

Two or more vectors combine to form a(n) resultant vector.

Objects in free fall accelerate at 9.8 $m/s^2$.

A curve often connects data points on a(n) nonlinear graph.

Together, the speed and direction in which an object is moving are called velocity.

Movement in relation to a frame of reference is relative motion.

# Interpreting a Distance-Time Graph

**Math Skill: Line Graphs and Conversion Factors**

You may want to read more about this **Math Skill** in the **Skills and Reference Handbook** at the end of your textbook.

The distance-time graph below illustrates the motion of a car whose speed varied with time during a trip. Calculate the average speed of the car during the first 8 seconds of the trip. Give your answer in km/h.

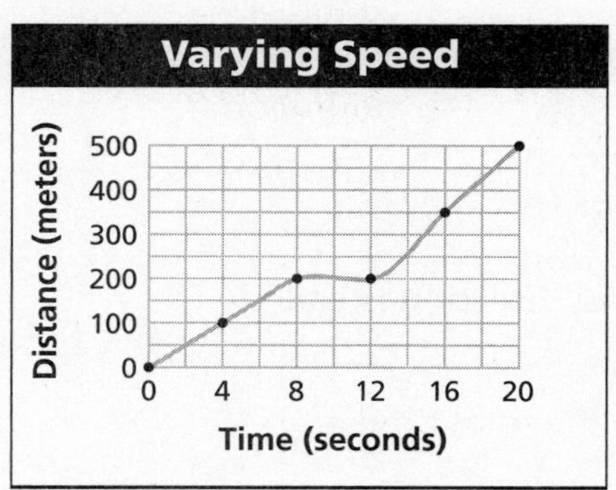


**1. Read and Understand**

*What information are you given?*

A graph of distance versus time.

**2. Plan and Solve**

*How will you determine speed for the time interval referenced in the question?*

1. To determine the distance traveled in 8 s, move your finger up from the 8 s mark on the time axis to the plotted line.
2. Now move your finger horizontally to the left to the distance axis. Read the value from the axis. (200 m)
3. Calculate the average speed using the formula

   Speed = Distance/Time = 200 m/8 s = 25 m/s
4. Convert from m/s to km/h:

   (25 m/s)(3600 s/h)(1 km/1000 m) = 90 km/h

**3. Look Back and Check**

*Is your answer reasonable?*

A quick calculation from the interval of constant speed shows that the car traveled 100 meters in 4 seconds—an average speed of 25 m/s.

## Math Practice

*On a separate sheet of paper, solve the following problems.*

1. How long did it take the car to travel a distance of 350 m? 16 s
2. Determine the speed of the car in km/h during the interval 0 s to 12 s.
   Speed = 200 m/12 s = 16.7 m/s; (16.7 m/s)(3600 s/h)(1 km/1000 m) = 60 km/h

Name ______________ Class ______________ Date ______________



# Section 12.1 Forces
## (pages 356–362)

*This section describes what forces are and explains how forces affect the motion of various objects.*

## Reading Strategy (page 356)

**Relating Text and Visuals** As you read about forces, look carefully at Figures 2, 3, and 5 in your textbook. Then complete the table by describing the forces and motion shown in each figure. For more information on this Reading Strategy, see the **Reading and Study Skills** in the **Skills and Reference Handbook** at the end of your textbook.

| Forces and Motion | | |
|---|---|---|
| **Figure** | **Is Net Force 0?** | **Effect on Motion** |
| 2A | Yes | None |
| 2B | Yes | None |
| 3 | Yes | None |
| 5A | Yes | None |
| 5B | No | Potted plant accelerates |

## What is a Force? (pages 356–357)

**1.** A force is defined as a(n) ____push____ or a(n) ____pull____ that acts on an object.

**2.** Is the following sentence true or false? A force can act to cause an object at rest to move or it can accelerate an object that is already moving. ____true____

**3.** How can a force change the motion of an object that is already moving?

A force can accelerate a moving object by changing its speed, its direction, or both.

**4.** Circle the letter of the best answer. What force causes a 1-kg mass to accelerate at a rate of 1 meter per second each second?

a. 1 kg/m•s$^2$ b. 1 kg/s

c. 1 kg•m (d.) 1 newton

## Combining Forces (pages 357–358)

**5.** The overall force acting on an object after all the forces are combined is the ____net force____.

**6.** How do balanced and unbalanced forces affect the motion of an object?

When balanced forces act on an object, there is no change in the object's motion because the net force is zero. When unbalanced forces act on an object, the net force is not zero, so the object accelerates.

Name ______________________ Class ______________ Date __________



## Friction (pages 359–360)

7. Is the following sentence true or false? Friction is a force that helps objects that are touching move past each other more easily.
   false

8. Circle the letters that identify types of friction.
   - (a.) rolling
   - b. gravity
   - (c.) static
   - (d.) sliding

9. The friction force that acts on objects that are at rest is static friction.

10. Why is less force needed to keep an object moving than to start the object in motion? Sliding friction, which opposes a moving object, is less than the static friction that acts on an object at rest, so less force is needed to keep an object moving.

11. Complete the table below about friction forces.

| Types of Friction Forces | |
|---|---|
| **Friction Force** | **Example** |
| Static | Walking |
| Sliding | Pushing a book along your desk |
| Rolling | In-line skates |

12. Is the following sentence true or false? Fluid friction is a force that opposes the motion of an object through a fluid such as water.
    true

## Gravity (page 361)

13. Gravity is a(n) attractive force that pulls objects together.

14. Is the following sentence true or false? Earth's gravity acts downward toward the center of Earth. true

15. Describe how gravity and air resistance affect the motion of a falling object. Gravity causes an object to accelerate downward, whereas air resistance acts opposite the direction of motion to reduce acceleration.

16. Is the following sentence true or false? Terminal velocity is the constant velocity of a falling object when the force of air resistance equals the force of gravity. true

## Projectile Motion (page 362)

17. The curved path caused by the combination of an initial forward velocity and the downward force of gravity is known as projectile motion.

# Section 12.2 Newton's First and Second Laws of Motion
**(pages 363–369)**

*This section discusses how force and mass affect acceleration. The acceleration due to gravity is defined, and mass and weight are compared.*

## Reading Strategy (page 363)

**Building Vocabulary** As you read this section, write a definition in the table for each vocabulary word you encounter. Use your own words in the definitions. For more information on this Reading Strategy, see the **Reading and Study Skills** in the **Skills and Reference Handbook** at the end of your textbook.

| Matter and Motion | |
|---|---|
| **Vocabulary** | **Definition** |
| Inertia | Inertia is the tendency of an object to resist a change in its motion. |
| Mass | Mass is the amount of matter an object contains as measured by its inertia. |
| Weight | Weight is the force of gravity acting on an object. |

## Aristotle, Galileo, and Newton (pages 363–364)

*Match each scientist with his accomplishment.*

**Accomplishment**

__b__ 1. Italian scientist who did experiments that helped correct misconceptions about force and motion

__c__ 2. Scientist who studied in England and introduced several laws describing force and motion

__a__ 3. An ancient Greek philosopher who made many scientific discoveries through observation and logical reasoning

**Scientist**

a. Aristotle

b. Galileo

c. Newton

## Newton's First Law of Motion (pages 364–365)

4. Is the following sentence true or false? According to Newton's first law of motion, an object's state of motion does not change as long as the net force acting on it is zero. __true__

5. What is inertia? Inertia is the tendency of an object to resist changes in its motion.

6. Is the following sentence true or false? The law of inertia states that an object in motion will eventually slow down and come to a complete stop if it travels far enough in the same direction.
false

## Newton's Second Law of Motion (pages 365–368)

7. According to Newton's second law of motion, acceleration of an object depends upon the mass of the object and the net force acting on it.

*Match each term with its description.*

| | Description | Term |
|---|---|---|
| a | 8. A measure of the inertia of an object | a. mass |
| c | 9. Net force/Mass | b. net force |
| b | 10. Causes an object's velocity to change | c. acceleration |

11. Is the following sentence true or false? The acceleration of an object is always in the same direction as the net force acting on the object. true

12. Is the following sentence true or false? If the same force acts upon two objects with different masses, the acceleration will be greater for the object with greater mass. false

## Weight and Mass (pages 368–369)

13. What is weight? Weight is the force of gravity acting on an object.

14. Write the formula used to calculate the weight of an object.
Weight = Mass × Acceleration due to gravity

15. Is the following sentence true or false? Because the weight formula shows that mass and weight are proportional, doubling the mass of an object will not affect its weight. false

16. Complete the table below by describing the difference between mass and weight.

| Mass and Weight | |
|---|---|
| **Mass** | **Weight** |
| Measure of the inertia of an object | Measure of the force of gravity acting on an object |

17. On the moon, the acceleration due to gravity is only about one sixth that on Earth. Thus, an object will weigh less on the moon than it weighs on Earth.

Name ______________ Class ______________ Date ______________



# Section 12.3 Newton's Third Law of Motion and Momentum

**(pages 372–377)**

*This section describes action-reaction forces and how the momentum of objects is determined.*

## Reading Strategy (page 372)

**Summarizing** As you read about momentum in this section, complete the concept map to organize what you learn. For more information on this Reading Strategy, see the **Reading and Study Skills** in the **Skills and Reference Handbook** at the end of your textbook.

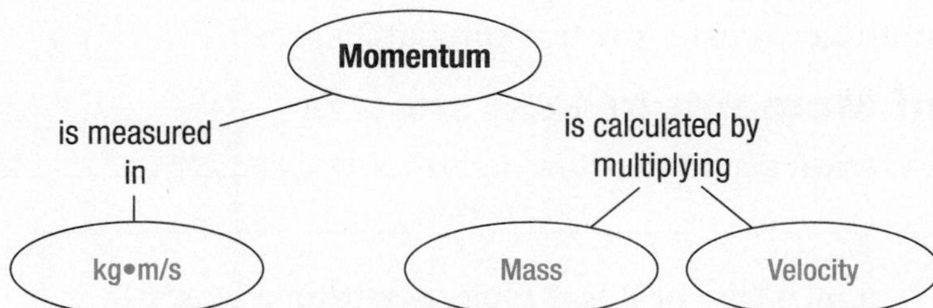


## Newton's Third Law (page 373)

1. According to Newton's third law of motion, what happens whenever one object exerts a force on a second object? The second object exerts an equal and opposite force on the first object.

2. The equal and opposite forces described by Newton's third law are called ___action___ and ___reaction___ forces.

3. Circle the letters that identify each sentence that is true about action-reaction forces.
   a. Newton's second law describes action-reaction forces.
   (b.) Forces always exist in pairs.
   (c.) Action-reaction forces never cancel.
   d. All action-reaction forces produce motion.

4. Is the following statement true or false? Action-reaction forces do not cancel each other because the action force is always greater than the reaction force. ___false___

## Momentum (pages 374–375)

5. Circle the letter of each factor that affects the momentum of a moving object.
   (a.) mass  b. volume  c. shape  (d.) velocity

6. If two identical objects are moving at different velocities, the object that is moving faster will have ___greater___ momentum.

7. Your in-line skates are sitting in a box on a shelf in the closet. What is their momentum? ___zero___

8. Is the following sentence true or false? An object with a small mass can have a large momentum if the object is traveling at a high speed. ___true___

9. Write the momentum formula, including the correct units.
Momentum (kg•m/s) = Mass (kg) × Velocity (m/s)

10. Circle the letter of the object that has the greatest momentum.
   a. a 700-gram bird flying at a velocity of 2.5 m/s
   b. a 1000-kilogram car traveling at 5 m/s
   c. a 40-kilogram shopping cart rolling along at 0.5 m/s
   (d.) a 300-kilogram roller coaster car traveling at 25 m/s

## Conservation of Momentum (pages 376–377)

11. What does conservation of momentum mean? Momentum does not increase or decrease.

12. Is the following sentence true or false? Objects within a closed system can exert forces on one another, but other objects and forces cannot leave or enter the system. ___true___

13. According to the law of conservation of momentum, what happens to the total momentum of a system if no net force acts on the system?
The total momentum does not change.

14. Is the following sentence true or false? In a closed system with two objects, the loss of momentum of one object equals the gain in momentum of the other object. ___true___

*For questions 15 and 16, refer to the graph below.*

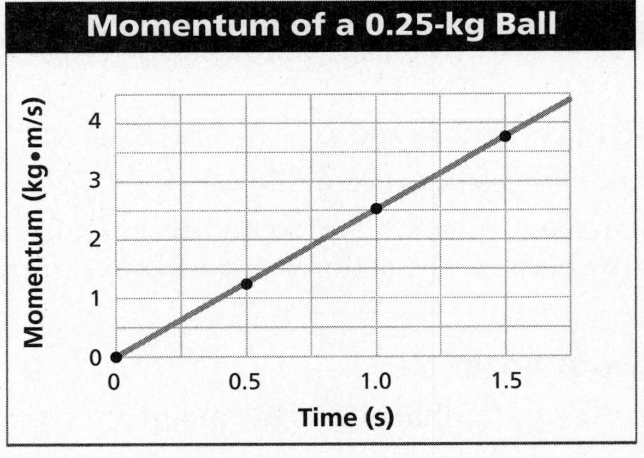


15. The momentum of the ball at one second is ___2.5 kg•m/s___.

16. What is the speed of the ball at 0.5 seconds? Show your calculation. *Hint:* Solve the momentum formula for velocity.
Momentum = Mass × Velocity; 1.25 kg•m/s = 0.25 kg × Velocity; Velocity = $\frac{1.25 \text{ kg•m/s}}{0.25 \text{ kg}}$ = 5 m/s

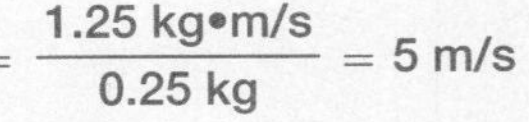

# Section 12.4 Universal Forces
**(pages 378–382)**

*This section defines four forces that exist throughout the universe. Each force is described and its significance is discussed.*

## Reading Strategy (page 378)

**Comparing and Contrasting** As you read this section, compare two universal forces by completing the table. For more information on this Reading Strategy, see the **Reading and Study Skills** in the **Skills and Reference Handbook** at the end of your textbook.

| Universal Nuclear Forces | | | |
|---|---|---|---|
| **Force** | **Acts on Which Particles?** | **Acts Over What Distance?** | **Relative Strength** |
| Strong nuclear | Neutrons and protons | Very short | Very strong (100 times stronger than electrical force) |
| Weak nuclear | All particles | Short | Weaker than the strong force |

**1.** What are the four universal forces?

a. Electromagnetic b. Strong nuclear

c. Weak nuclear d. Gravitational

## Electromagnetic Forces (pages 378–379)

**2.** Is the following sentence true or false? Electromagnetic force is associated with charged particles. true

**3.** Name the only two forces that can both attract and repel. Electric and magnetic forces can both attract and repel.

**4.** Objects with like charges repel one another, and objects with opposite charges attract one another.

**5.** Circle the letters of the sentences that correctly describe magnets or magnetic forces.

(a.) Magnetic forces act on certain metals.

(b.) Magnets have two poles, north and south.

c. Two poles that are alike attract each other.

(d.) Magnetic forces can both attract and repel.

## Nuclear Forces (pages 379–380)

**6.** The force that holds particles in the nucleus together is the strong nuclear force.

**7.** What evidence suggests that nuclear forces have a powerful force of attraction? These forces are strong enough to overcome the electric force of repulsion that acts among the positively charged protons in the nucleus.

8. Circle the letter of the best answer. Over extremely short distances, approximately how many times stronger is the strong nuclear force than the electric force of repulsion?

   a. 10 (b.) 100 c. 1000 d. 10,000

9. Compare and contrast the strong and weak nuclear forces. Both forces act within the nucleus of an atom to hold it together. The strong nuclear force affects only the neutrons and protons in the nucleus and acts over extremely short distances. The weak nuclear force acts over an even shorter distance but affects all particles, not just protons and neutrons.

## Gravitational Force (pages 380–382)

10. State Newton's law of universal gravitation. Every object in the universe attracts every other object.

11. Circle the letter of each sentence that is true about gravitational force.

    a. The closer two objects are to one another, the weaker the gravitational force.

    (b.) The farther apart two objects are, the weaker the gravitational force.

    (c.) The greater the mass of an object, the stronger its gravitational force.

    d. Earth's gravitational force is stronger than the gravitational force of the sun.

12. The gravitational force of attraction between two objects depends on mass and distance.

13. Is the following sentence true or false? Gravity is the weakest universal force, but it is the most effective force over long distances. true

14. The sun's mass is much greater than the mass of Earth, so the sun's gravitational force is much stronger than that of Earth.

15. Why does the moon orbit Earth in a nearly circular path? The moon's inertia and centripetal force from Earth produce the nearly circular path.

16. Is the following sentence true or false? The gravitational pull of the moon is the primary cause of Earth's ocean tides. true

17. Is the following sentence true or false? The pull of Earth's gravity can slow an artificial satellite, causing it to lose altitude and fall from the sky. false

18. List four uses of artificial satellites. Students' answers should include four of the following: Satellites monitor Earth's weather, create detailed radar maps of Earth's surface, use telescopes to gaze into space, study Earth's climate, receive and transmit radio and microwave signals, receive and transmit cell phone and satellite television signals.

Name ______________________ Class ________________ Date ____________



# WordWise

*Complete the sentences using one of the scrambled words below.*

| | | |
|---|---|---|
| nicofirt | vtiyagr | aecmleorntcgeti corfe |
| ssma | raeeaclnocit | hwgeti |
| ten eofrc | lirnetcptae refco | swonten |
| lfudi tnfcriio | kewa cnuarel | teianri |
| mtnmoemu | | |

A measure of an object's inertia is its ___mass___.

The ___weak nuclear___ force affects all particles in a nucleus and acts only over a short range.

A sky diver experiences ___fluid friction___, which opposes the force of gravity.

A change in an object's speed or direction of motion is called ___acceleration___.

The product of an object's mass and its velocity is ___momentum___.

A measure of the force of gravity acting on an object is its ___weight___.

A center-directed ___centripetal force___ continuously changes the direction of an object to make it move in a circle.

A force associated with charged particles is ___electromagnetic force___.

Mass is the measure of the ___inertia___ of an object.

A force that opposes the motion of objects that touch as they move past each other is called ___friction___.

The universal force that causes every object to attract every other object is ___gravity___.

A person's weight on Mars, measured in ___newtons___, is 0.38 times the weight on Earth.

Acceleration equals ___net force___ divided by mass.

# Calculating Acceleration

**Math Skill: Formulas and Equations**

You may want to read more about this **Math Skill** in the **Skills and Reference Handbook** at the end of your textbook.

A car with a mass of 1300 kg accelerates as it leaves a parking lot. If the net force on the car is 3900 newtons, what is the car's *acceleration*?

**1. Read and Understand**

*What information are you given?*

Mass , $m = 1300$ kg

Force, $F = 3900$ N (in the forward direction)

**2. Plan and Solve**

*What unknown are you trying to calculate?*

Acceleration, $a = ?$

*What formula contains the given quantities and the unknown?*

$$a = \frac{F}{m}$$

*Replace each variable with its known value and solve.*

$$a = \frac{3900\text{ N}}{1300\text{ kg}} = 3\,\frac{\text{N}}{\text{kg}} = 3\,\frac{\text{kg}\bullet\text{m/s}^2}{\text{kg}} = 3\text{ m/s}^2$$

$a = 3\text{ m/s}^2$ in the forward direction

**3. Look Back and Check**

*Is your answer reasonable?*

Powerful sports cars can accelerate at 6 m/s$^2$, so a smaller acceleration of 3 m/s$^2$ seems reasonable.

## Math Practice

*On a separate sheet of paper, solve the following problems.*

1. A construction worker pushes a wheelbarrow with a total mass of 50.0 kg. What is the acceleration of the wheelbarrow if the net force on it is 75 N?

$$a = \frac{F}{m}; a = \frac{75\text{ N}}{50.0\text{ kg}} = 1.5\text{ N/kg} = \frac{(1.5\text{ kg}\bullet\text{m/s}^2)}{\text{kg}} = 1.5\text{ m/s}^2\text{, in the forward direction}$$

2. A van with a mass of 1500 kg accelerates at a rate of 3.5 m/s$^2$ in the forward direction. What is the net force acting on the van? (*Hint:* Solve the acceleration formula for force.)

$$a = \frac{F}{m}; F = ma = (3.5\text{ m/s}^2)(1500\text{ kg}) = 5250\text{ kg}\bullet\text{m/s}^2 = 5300\text{ N}$$

3. A $6.0 \times 10^3$ N force accelerates a truck entering a highway at 2.5 m/s$^2$. What is the mass of the truck? (*Hint:* Solve the acceleration formula for mass.)

$$a = \frac{F}{m}; m = \frac{F}{a} = \frac{6.0 \times 10^3\text{ kg}\bullet\text{m/s}^2}{2.5\text{ m/s}^2} = 2400\text{ kg}$$

Name ______________ Class ______________ Date ______________



# Section 13.1 Fluid Pressure
## (pages 390–393)

*This section defines pressure and describes factors that determine fluid pressure. The atmosphere as a fluid is discussed, including how air pressure changes with altitude.*

## Reading Strategy (page 390)

**Using Prior Knowledge** Before reading the section, write a common definition of the word *pressure*. After you have read the section, write the scientific definition of *pressure* and contrast it to your original definition. For more information on this Reading Strategy, see the **Reading and Study Skills** in the **Skills and Reference Handbook** at the end of your textbook.

| Meanings of *Pressure* | |
|---|---|
| Common definition | Definitions will vary and may involve the scientific or the nonscientific definition of pressure. |
| Scientific definition | Pressure is the amount of force per unit area. Students should contrast this definition with their original definition given above. |

## Pressure (pages 390–391)

1. Pressure is the result of a(n) ___force___ distributed over a(n) ___area___.
2. The same force is exerted by each of the following. Which exerts the most pressure?
   a. a foot b. a large book
   c. a fingertip (d.) the tip of a ball-point pen
3. How is pressure calculated? Divide the force acting on an object by the area over which the force acts; Pressure = Force/Area
4. A wooden crate that measures 2.0 m long and 0.40 m wide rests on the floor. If the crate has a weight of 600.0 N, what pressure does it exert on the floor?
   a. 0.80 $m^2$ b. 480 Pa
   c. $3.0 \times 10^3$ N/$m^2$ (d.) 750 Pa

## Pressure in Fluids (pages 391–392)

5. A substance that assumes the shape of its container is called a(n) ___fluid___.
6. List four examples of fluids. Answers should include gases and liquids such as:
   a. ___Air___ b. ___Oil___
   c. ___Oxygen___ d. ___Water___

7. Circle the letter of each sentence that is true about fluid pressure.
   a. Water pressure decreases as depth decreases.
   b. Fluid pressure is exerted only at the base of the container holding the fluid.
   (c.) The pressure in a fluid at any given depth is constant, and it is exerted equally in all directions.
   (d.) The two factors that determine the pressure a fluid exerts are type of the fluid and its depth.
8. Is the following sentence true or false? The pressure at a depth of 2 feet in a large lake is greater than the pressure at the same depth in a swimming pool. ____false____

## Air Pressure and the Atmosphere (pages 392–393)

9. Instead of referring to their depth in the atmosphere, people refer to their ____altitude____ above sea level.

*For questions 10 through 13, refer to the air pressure table below.*

| Changes in Air Pressure with Altitude | | |
|---|---|---|
| **Altitude Above Sea Level (m)** | **Air Pressure (bars)** | **Air Pressure (kPa)** |
| 0 | 1.000 | 101.3 |
| 200 | 0.9971 | 98.97 |
| 400 | 0.9545 | 96.68 |
| 600 | 0.9322 | 94.42 |
| 800 | 0.9103 | 92.21 |
| 1000 | 0.8888 | 90.03 |
| 1200 | 0.8677 | 87.89 |

10. Complete the air pressure columns in the table by converting between units of air pressure. *Hint:* 1 bar = 101.3 kPa.
11. How does air pressure change as a function of altitude?
    Air pressure decreases with increasing altitude.
12. Suppose a hiker is on a mountain ridge 1200 meters above sea level. Approximately what air pressure will she experience?
    87.89 kPa or 0.8677 bars
13. By how much does the air pressure decrease, in bars, from sea level to an altitude of 1200 meters? ____0.1323 bars____
14. Is the following sentence true or false? Air exerts a force of more than 1000 N on top of your head. ____true____
15. What keeps a person from being crushed by air pressure? The pressure inside a person's body balances the air pressure outside, resulting in a net force of zero.

Name ______________________ Class ________________ Date ____________



# Section 13.2 Forces and Pressure in Fluids
**(pages 394–397)**

*This section presents Pascal's and Bernoulli's principles. Examples of each principle from nature and industry are discussed.*

## Reading Strategy (pages 394)

**Predicting** Imagine two small foam balls hanging from strings at the same height with about three centimeters of space between them. Before you read the section, write a prediction about what will happen to the balls when you blow air through the space between them. Identify your reasons. After you have read the section, check the accuracy of your prediction. For more information on this Reading Strategy, see the **Reading and Study Skills** in the **Skills and Reference Handbook** at the end of your textbook.

| Predicting Forces and Pressure in Fluids | |
|---|---|
| **Prediction** | Students will most likely predict that the foam balls will be blown apart from one another. |
| **Reason for Prediction** | Reasons will likely include the force the air exerts on the foam balls as it blows past them. |

## Transmitting Pressure in a Fluid (pages 394–395)

1. In a fluid-filled container, why is the pressure greater at the base of the container? Because the pressure exerted by a fluid increases with depth.

2. Is the following sentence true or false? If you squeeze a container filled with fluid, the pressure within the fluid increases equally throughout the fluid. true

3. According to Pascal's principle, what happens when there is a change in pressure at any point in a fluid? The change in pressure is transmitted equally and unchanged in all directions throughout the fluid.

4. The science of applying Pascal's principle is called hydraulics.

5. In a hydraulic lift system, an increased output force is produced because constant fluid pressure is exerted on the larger area of the output piston.

6. Is the following sentence true or false? In a hydraulic system, the output force is greater than the input force because the pressure acting on the output piston is greater than the pressure acting on the input piston. false

## Bernoulli's Principle (pages 396–397)

7. Circle the letter of the sentence that correctly states Bernoulli's principle.
   a. As the speed of a fluid decreases, the pressure within the fluid decreases.
   b. As the speed of a fluid increases, the pressure within the fluid increases.
   (c.) As the speed of a fluid increases, the pressure within the fluid decreases.
   d. Fluid motion has no effect on pressure within the fluid.
8. Because the air traveling over the top of an airplane wing moves faster than the air passing underneath the wing, the pressure above the wings is ___less___ than the pressure below the wing.
9. What is lift, and how does it relate to an airplane's flight? Lift is an upward force created by the pressure difference between the top and the bottom of a plane's wing. This upward force keeps the airplane aloft.
10. What is a spoiler on a racecar designed to do? It creates a downward force that improves traction.

*For questions 11 through 14, refer to the figure below. Place the correct letter after each phrase.*

**Spray Bottle with Fertilizer**

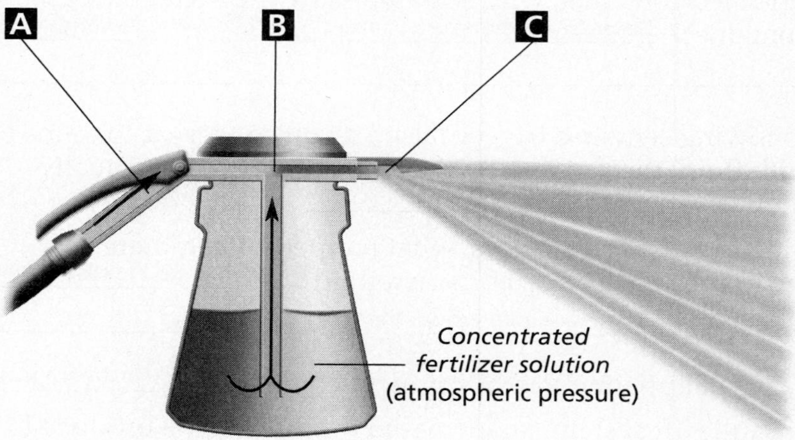


11. Location where the water and fertilizer solution mix. ___B___
12. Location where water enters the sprayer at high speed. ___A___
13. Location where the water-fertilizer mixture exits the sprayer. ___C___
14. Use Bernoulli's principle to explain why the fertilizer solution moves up the tube. The fast-moving water creates a low-pressure area above the tube reaching into the solution chamber. The pressure difference between the solution chamber and the top of the tube forces the fertilizer solution up the tube.

Name ______________________ Class ______________ Date ____________



# Section 13.3 Buoyancy

**(pages 400–404)**

*This section discusses buoyancy and Archimedes' principle of factors that determine whether an object will sink or float in a fluid.*

## Reading Strategy (page 400)

**Summarizing** As you read about buoyancy, write a brief summary of the text following each green heading. Your summary should include only the most important information. For more information on this Reading Strategy, see the **Reading and Study Skills** in the **Skills and Reference Handbook** at the end of your textbook.

| Buoyant Force | Buoyant force is the apparent loss of weight of an object submerged in a fluid. |
|---|---|
| Archimedes' Principle | The buoyant force on an object is equal to the weight of fluid it displaces. |
| Density and Buoyancy | Objects less dense than the fluid they are in, float. Objects denser than the fluid they are in, sink. When the buoyant force is equal to the weight, the object floats or is suspended. When the buoyant force is less than the weight, the object sinks. |

## Buoyant Force (page 400)

1. What is buoyancy? Buoyancy is the ability of a fluid to exert an upward force on an object within it.

2. Circle the letter of the correct answer. In which direction does a buoyant force act?
   a. in the direction of gravity
   b. perpendicular to gravity
   (c.) in the direction opposite of gravity
   d. from above the fluid

3. Is the following sentence true or false? The greater a fluid's density, the greater its buoyant force. true

4. Buoyancy causes an apparent loss of weight of an object immersed in a fluid.

5. Circle the letter of each sentence that is true about buoyancy.
   (a.) Forces pushing up on a submerged object are greater than the forces pushing down on it.
   (b.) Forces acting on the sides of a submerged object cancel each other out.
   c. Gravitational forces work together with buoyant forces.
   d. The net buoyant force is non-vertical.

## Archimedes' Principle (page 401)

6. According to Archimedes' principle, the weight of fluid displaced by a floating object is equal to the ____buoyant force____ acting on that object.

7. Is the following sentence true or false? When an object floats partially submerged in a fluid, it displaces a volume of fluid equal to its own volume. ____false____

## Density and Buoyancy (pages 401–404)

*Match each description with the correct property. Properties may be used more than once.*

| | Description | Property |
|---|---|---|
| __c__ | 8. This property is the ratio of an object's mass to its volume, often expressed in $g/cm^3$. | a. weight |
| __a__ | 9. This force is equal to the force of gravity that acts on a floating object. | b. buoyant force |
| __c__ | 10. When this property is greater for an object than for the fluid it is in, the object sinks. | c. density |
| __a; b__ | 11. These two forces act on every object in a fluid. | |
| __a__ | 12. An object will either float or be suspended when the buoyant force is equal to this. | |

13. Use what you know about density and buoyancy to predict whether each of the substances listed in the table will float or sink in water. The density of water is 1.0 $g/cm^3$.

| Will It Float or Sink? | | |
|---|---|---|
| **Substance** | **Density ($g/cm^3$)** | **Float or Sink?** |
| Gold | 19.3 | Sink |
| Balsa Wood | 0.15 | Float |
| Ice | 0.92 | Float |
| Brick | 1.84 | Sink |
| Milk | 1.03 | Sink |
| Gasoline | 0.70 | Float |

14. How is a heavy steel ship able to float?
   a. Because the density of steel is 7.8 $g/cm^3$.
   (b.) The ship's shape enables it to displace a large volume of water.
   c. Because the density of water is 1 $g/cm^3$.
   d. The ship's effective density is greater than that of water.

Name ______________________ Class ________________ Date ____________

Chapter 13 Forces in Fluids

# WordWise

*Solve the clues to determine which vocabulary words from Chapter 13 are hidden in the puzzle. Then find and circle the terms in the puzzle. The terms may occur vertically, horizontally, or diagonally.*

| | | | | | | | | | | | | | | |
|---|---|---|---|---|---|---|---|---|---|---|---|---|---|---|
| h | y | d | r | a | u | l | i | c | s | y | s | t | e | m |
| v | a | h | u | s | p | i | a | c | f | r | h | y | e | b |
| s | r | q | a | z | f | f | r | e | r | f | v | d | c | q |
| p | c | i | u | y | t | t | p | r | e | s | s | u | r | e |
| t | h | d | f | r | g | s | f | l | u | t | m | a | o | e |
| k | i | u | b | p | l | o | e | k | j | h | t | u | f | z |
| k | m | t | y | u | i | r | f | l | u | i | d | l | t | d |
| v | e | k | p | o | o | p | f | v | b | n | m | i | n | m |
| o | d | k | a | r | p | y | o | i | m | q | c | c | a | f |
| p | e | g | s | y | h | z | a | v | b | n | h | s | y | b |
| p | s | e | c | u | h | n | j | n | m | l | o | m | o | q |
| l | r | i | a | j | u | e | r | t | c | v | f | d | u | a |
| p | o | i | l | m | j | g | b | h | f | y | u | j | b | o |

**Clues** | **Hidden Words**

Mathematician who discovered that the buoyant force on an object equals the weight of the fluid displaced by the object — Archimedes

The result of a force distributed over an area — pressure

Type of substance that assumes the shape of its container — fluid

Ability of a fluid to exert an upward force on an object within it — buoyancy

SI-unit of measure used to express pressure — pascal

Upward force that keeps an aircraft aloft — lift

Device that uses pressurized fluids acting on pistons of different sizes to change a force — hydraulic system

Force that opposes the weight of an object floating in a fluid — buoyant force

Name ______________________ Class ______________ Date __________



# Calculating Pressure

Math Skill: Formulas and Equations

You may want to read more about this **Math Skill** in the **Skills and Reference Handbook** at the end of your textbook.

Each tile on the bottom of a swimming pool has an area of $0.50\ m^2$. The water above each tile exerts a force of 11,000 N on each tile. How much pressure does the water exert on each tile?

**1. Read and Understand**

*What information are you given?*

Force = 11,000 N

Area = $0.50\ m^2$

**2. Plan and Solve**

*What formula contains the given quantities and the unknown?*

$$\text{Pressure} = \frac{\text{Force}}{\text{Area}}$$

*Replace each variable with its known value and solve.*

$$\text{Pressure} = \frac{11{,}000\ \text{N}}{0.50\ \text{m}^2} = 22{,}000\ \text{N/m}^2 = 22{,}000\ \text{Pa} = 22\ \text{kPa}$$

**3. Look Back and Check**

*Is your answer reasonable?*

Because the area of each tile is a half square meter and pressure is defined as force per square meter, the pressure exerted will be double the magnitude of the force. Thus, an 11,000 N force will produce 22,000 Pa of pressure on the tiles. The calculation verifies this result.

## Math Practice

*On a separate sheet of paper, answer the following questions.*

1. The weight of the gasoline in a 55-gallon drum creates a force of 1456 newtons. The area of the bottom of the drum is $0.80\ m^2$. How much pressure does the gasoline exert on the bottom of the drum?

   Pressure = Force/Area = $1456\ N/0.80\ m^2$ = 1820 Pa = 1.8 kPa

2. The weight of a gallon of milk is about 38 N. If you pour 3.0 gallons of milk into a container whose bottom has an area of $0.60\ m^2$, how much pressure will the milk exert on the bottom of the container?

   Force = (3.0 gallons)(38 N/gallon) = 114 N;
   Pressure = Force/Area = $114\ N/0.60\ m^2$ = 190 Pa = 0.19 kPa

3. A company makes garden statues by pouring concrete into a mold. The amount of concrete used to make a statue of a deer weighs 3600 N. If the base of the deer statue is 0.60 meters long and 0.40 meters wide, how much pressure will the statue exert on the ground? (*Hint:* Area is equal to length times width.)

   Area = $0.60\ m \times 0.40\ m = 0.24\ m^2$; Pressure = Force/Area = $3600\ N/0.24\ m^2$ = 15,000 Pa = 15 kPa

Name ______________________ Class ______________________ Date ______________



# Section 14.1 Work and Power
**(pages 412–416)**

*This section defines work and power, describes how they are related, and explains how to calculate their values.*

## Reading Strategy (page 412)

**Relating Text and Visuals** As you read, look carefully at Figures 1 and 2 and read their captions. Complete the table by describing the work shown in each figure. For more information on this Reading Strategy, see the **Reading and Study Skills** in the **Skills and Reference Handbook** at the end of your textbook.

| Figure | Direction of Force | Direction of Motion | Is Work Done? |
|---|---|---|---|
| 1 | Up | None | No |
| 2A | Horizontal | Horizontal | Yes |
| 2B | Diagonal | Horizontal | Yes |
| 2C | Up | Horizontal | No |

## What Is Work? (pages 412–413)

1. In science, work is done when a(n) ___force___ acts on an object in the direction the object moves.
2. Why isn't work being done on a barbell when a weight lifter is holding the barbell over his head? ___Because in order for work to be done on an object, the object must be moving.___
3. Describe what conditions of force and motion result in maximum work done on an object. ___Work is maximized when force is applied in the same direction that the object is moving.___
4. Is the following sentence true or false? A vertical force does work on an object that is moving in a horizontal direction. ___false___

## Calculating Work (pages 413–414)

5. In science, work that is done on an object can be described as the force acting on the object multiplied by the ___distance___ the object moves.
6. Circle the letter of the correct form of the work equation to use when determining the distance an object moves as a result of a force applied to it.

a. Distance = Force × Work

b. $\text{Distance} = \frac{\text{Force}}{\text{Work}}$

c. $\text{Distance} = (\text{Force})^2$

(d.) $\text{Distance} = \frac{\text{Work}}{\text{Force}}$

7. The SI unit of work is the ____joule____.

8. Circle the letter of the amount of work done when a 1 newton force moves an object 1 meter.

 a. 1 newton per second
 (b.) 1 joule
 c. 1 watt
 d. 1 newton per meter

## What Is Power? (pages 414)

9. Is the following sentence true or false? Power is the rate of doing work. ____true____

10. In order to do work faster, more ____power____ is required.

11. Circle the letter of each sentence that is true about power.

 a. Power and work are always equal.
 (b.) You can increase power by doing a given amount of work in a shorter period of time.
 c. When you decrease the force acting on an object, the power increases.
 (d.) When you do less work in a given time period, the power decreases.

## Calculating Power (pages 415)

12. Write a word equation describing how to calculate power. Power equals work divided by time.

13. The SI unit of power is the ____watt____.

14. Circle the letter of the expression that is equivalent to one watt.

 a. one newton per meter
 b. one joule per meter
 c. one newton per second
 (d.) one joule per second

15. How much work does a 100-watt light bulb do when it is lit for 30 seconds? (100 J/s)(30 s) = 3000 J

## James Watt and Horsepower (page 416)

16. Circle the letter of the quantity that is approximately equal to one horsepower.

 a. 746 J
 (b.) 746 W
 c. 7460 N/m
 d. 7460 J

17. Why did James Watt use the power output of a horse to compare the power outputs of steam engines he designed? Horses were a logical choice for comparison as they were the most commonly used source of power in the 1700s.

Name ______________________ Class ______________________ Date ______________

Chapter 14 Work, Power, and Machines

# Section 14.2 Work and Machines
**(pages 417–420)**

*This section describes how machines change forces to make work easier to do. Input forces exerted on and output forces exerted by machines are identified and input work and output work are discussed.*

## Reading Strategy (page 417)

**Summarizing** As you read, complete the table for each machine. After you read, write a sentence summarizing the idea that your table illustrates. For more information on this Reading Strategy, see the **Reading and Study Skills** in the **Skills and Reference Handbook** at the end of your textbook.

| Machine | Increases or Decreases Input Force | Increases or Decreases Input Distance |
|---|---|---|
| Tire jack | Decreases | Increases |
| Lug wrench | Decreases | Increases |
| Rowing oar | Increases | Decreases |
| **Summary:** As input force decreases, the input distance increases. | | |

## Machines Do Work (pages 417–418)

1. Describe what a machine is able to do. A machine makes work easier to do by changing a force.

2. Is the following sentence true or false? A machine can make work easier to do by changing the size of the force needed, the direction of a force, or the distance over which a force acts. true

3. Consider the equation Work = Force × Distance. If a machine increases the distance over which a force is exerted, the force required to do a given amount of work decreases.

4. Give an example of a machine that changes the direction of an applied force. Sample answers may include oars used in rowing.

5. When you make several trips to unload a few heavy items from a car instead of moving them all at once, the total distance over which you exert yourself increases.

## Work Input and Work Output (pages 419–420)

6. The work done by a machine is always less than the work done on a machine because of friction.

7. Circle the letter of the definition for input force.
   a. the amount of force exerted by a machine
   b. the amount of friction slowing the speed of a machine
   c. the amount of work done by a machine
   (d.) the amount of force exerted on a machine

8. Write a word equation that describes work input.
   Work input equals the input force multiplied by the input distance.

9. Is the following sentence true or false? Every machine uses some of its work input to overcome friction. true

10. The force exerted by a machine is called the output force.

11. Circle the letter of the expression that equals the work output of a machine.

   a. $\frac{\text{Input distance}}{\text{Output distance}}$   b. Output distance × Input distance

   c. $\frac{\text{Output distance}}{\text{friction}}$   (d.) Output distance × Output force

12. Is the following sentence true or false? Output work always is less than input work. true

*For questions 13 through 15, refer to the figure below.*

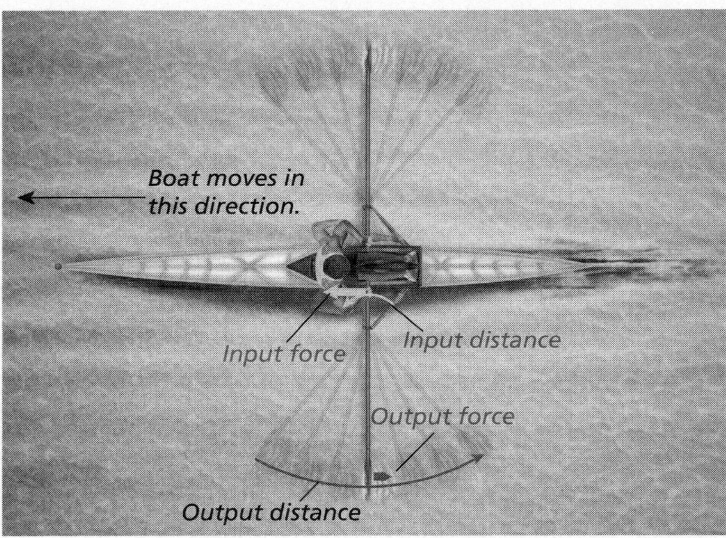


13. Which arrow represents the input force? Label it on the figure.
14. Which arrow represents the input distance? Label it on the figure.
15. Which arrow represents the output force? Label it on the figure.
16. How can you increase a machine's work output? The only way to increase work output is to increase the amount of work put into a machine.

Name ______________ Class ______________ Date ______________



# Section 14.3 Mechanical Advantage and Efficiency

**(pages 421–426)**

*This section describes mechanical advantage and efficiency and how to calculate these values. Ways to maximize mechanical advantage and efficiency are discussed.*

## Reading Strategy (page 421)

**Building Vocabulary** As you read the section, write a definition in the table for each vocabulary term in your own words. For more information on this Reading Strategy, see the **Reading and Study Skills** in the **Skills and Reference Handbook** at the end of your textbook.

| Mechanical Advantage | |
|---|---|
| **Vocabulary** | **Definition** |
| Mechanical advantage | The number of times a machine increases force |
| Actual mechanical advantage | Ratio of output force to input force |
| Ideal mechanical advantage | The mechanical advantage of a machine if there were no friction |
| Efficiency | Percentage of work input that become work output |

## Mechanical Advantage (pages 421–423)

1. The number of times that a machine increases an input force is the mechanical advantage of the machine.

2. For a given input force, what affects the output force that a nutcracker can exert on a nut? The position of the nut in the nutcracker affects the nutcracker's output force.

3. Mechanical advantage describes the relationship between input force and output force.

4. How is the actual mechanical advantage of a machine determined? It is the ratio of the output force to the input force.

5. Greater input force is required to move an object along a ramp with a rough surface, compared to a ramp with a smooth surface, because a greater force is needed to overcome friction.

6. Is the following sentence true or false? A loading ramp with a rough surface has a greater mechanical advantage than one with a smooth surface. false

7. Because friction is always present, the actual mechanical advantage of a machine is never ___greater___ than its ideal mechanical advantage (IMA).
8. A machine's ___ideal mechanical advantage___ is the mechanical advantage in the absence of friction.
9. What type of materials do engineers use to increase the mechanical advantage of a machine?
   They use low-friction materials and lubricants.

## Calculating Mechanical Advantage (pages 424–425)

10. Is the following sentence true or false? To calculate ideal mechanical advantage, divide input distance by output distance, and then divide the result by the force of friction.
    ___false___
11. Is the following sentence true or false? An inclined plane is an example of a machine. ___true___
12. Calculate the IMA of a ramp for the distances given in the table.

| Ideal Mechanical Advantages of Ramps | | |
|---|---|---|
| Horizontal Distance | Vertical Rise | IMA |
| 1.5 meters | 0.5 meters | 3 |
| 12 meters | 1.5 meters | 8 |
| 3.6 meters | 0.3 meters | 12 |

13. Is the following sentence true or false? If the input distance of a machine is greater than the output distance, then the IMA for that machine is greater than one. ___true___

## Efficiency (pages 425–426)

14. Why is the efficiency of a machine always less than 100 percent? Because there is always friction that must be overcome.
15. Is the following sentence true or false? To calculate the efficiency of a machine, divide the work output by work input, and then multiply by 100. ___true___
16. What is a significant factor affecting a car's fuel efficiency?
    ___air resistance___
17. Calculate the efficiency of a machine with a work output of 120 J and a work input of 500 J. ___(120 J / 500 J) × 100 = 24%___
18. Circle the letter of the work input for a machine with a work output of 240 J and an efficiency of 80 percent.
    - (a.) 300 J
    - b. 200 J
    - c. 320 J
    - d. 200 W
19. Reducing friction ___increases___ the efficiency of a machine.

Name ______________________ Class ________________ Date ____________

Chapter 14 Work, Power, and Machines

# Section 14.4 Simple Machines
**(pages 427–435)**

*This section presents the six types of simple machines. A discussion of how each type works and how to determine its mechanical advantage is given. Common uses of simple machines are also described.*

## Reading Strategy (page 427)

**Summarizing** After reading the section on levers, complete the concept map to organize what you know about first-class levers. On a separate sheet of paper, construct and complete similar concept maps for second- and third-class levers. For more information on this Reading Strategy, see the **Reading and Study Skills** in the **Skills and Reference Handbook** at the end of your textbook.

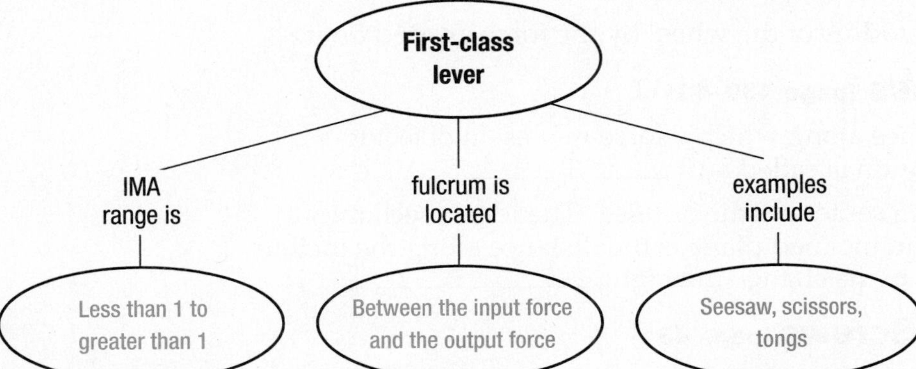


1. List the six types of simple machines.
   a. Lever
   b. Wheel and axle
   c. Inclined plane
   d. Wedge
   e. Screw
   f. Pulley

## Levers (pages 428–429)

2. A screwdriver used to pry the lid off a paint can is an example of a(n) ___lever___.
3. The fixed point that a lever rotates around is called the ___fulcrum___.
4. To calculate the ideal mechanical advantage of any lever, divide the input arm by the ___output arm___.
5. What characteristics distinguish levers as first-class, second-class, or third-class?
   Levers are classified by the relative positions of the fulcrum, input force, and output force.
6. Is the following sentence true or false? First-class levers always have a mechanical advantage that is greater than one.
   ___false___

7. Is the following sentence true or false? All second-class levers have a mechanical advantage greater than one because the input arm is longer than the output arm. true

## Wheel and Axle (page 430)

8. Describe a wheel and axle. A wheel and axle is a simple machine that consists of two disks or cylinders, each one with a different radius.

9. Circle the letter of the sentence that describes how to calculate the IMA of a wheel and axle.
   a. Multiply the area of the wheel by the area of the axle.
   b. Divide input force by output force.
   (c.) Divide the diameter where input force is exerted by the diameter where output force is exerted.
   d. Divide the radius of the wheel by the force exerted on it.

## Inclined Planes (page 430–431)

10. A slanted surface along which a force moves an object to a different elevation is called a(n) inclined plane.

11. Is the following sentence true or false? The ideal mechanical advantage of an inclined plane is the distance along the incline plane divided by its change in height. true

## Wedges and Screws (page 431)

12. A thin wedge of a given length has a(n) greater mechanical advantage than a thick wedge of the same length.

13. Screws with threads that are close together have a greater ideal mechanical advantage.

## Pulleys (pages 432–433)

14. A simple machine consisting of a rope fitted into a groove in a wheel is a(n) pulley.

15. What determines the ideal mechanical advantage of a pulley or pulley system? It is equal to the number of rope sections supporting the load being lifted.

## Compound Machines (page 435)

16. Is the following sentence true or false? A compound machine is a combination of two or more simple machines that operate together. true

17. Circle each letter that identifies a compound machine.
   (a.) a car
   b. a handheld screwdriver
   (c.) a washing machine
   (d.) a watch

Name ______________________ Class ______________________ Date ____________

Chapter 14 **Work, Power, and Machines**

# WordWise

*Answer the question or identify the clue by writing the correct vocabulary term in the blanks. Use the circled letter(s) in each term to find the hidden vocabulary word. Then, write a definition for the hidden word.*

| Clues | Vocabulary Terms |
|---|---|
| $\frac{\text{Work output}}{\text{Work input}} \times 100$ | e f f (i) c i e n c y |
| A mechanical watch is an example of this. | c o m p o u (n) d m a c h i n e |
| One way to determine this is to divide output work by output force. | o u t (p) u t d i s t a n c e |
| This is the SI unit of work. | j o (u) l e |
| On a lever, it is the distance between the fulcrum and the input force. | i n p u (t) a r m |
| The IMA of this machine increases as its thickness decreases relative to its length. | w e (d) g e |
| This is exerted on a jack handle to lift a car. | (i) n p u t f o r c e |
| This unit equals about 746 joules. | h o r (s) e p o w e r |
| This is the distance between the output force and the fulcrum. | o u (t) p u t a r m |
| This SI unit of power is used to describe light bulbs. | w (a) t t |
| The IMA of this machine is the distance along its surface divided by the change in height. | i n c l i (n) e d p l a n e |
| A device that can change the size of the force required to do work. | m a (c) h i n e |
| This quantity is equal to Work/Time. | p o w (e) r |

**Hidden words:** i n p u t d i s t a n c e

**Definition:** The distance the input force acts through.

Name ______________________ Class ________________ Date __________

Chapter 14 **Work, Power, and Machines**

# Calculating Work and Power

**Math Skill: Formulas and Equations**

You may want to read more about this **Math Skill** in the **Skills and Reference Handbook** at the end of your textbook.

Calculate the power of a machine that exerts a force of 800.0 N over a distance of 6.0 m in 2.0 s.

**1. Read and Understand**

*What information are you given?*

Force = 800.0 N

Distance = 6.0 m

Time = 2.0 s

**2. Plan and Solve**

*What variable are you trying to determine?*

Power =?

*What formula contains the given quantities and the unknown?*

$$\text{Power} = \frac{\text{Work}}{\text{Time}} = \frac{\text{Force} \times \text{Distance}}{\text{Time}}$$

$$\text{Power} = \frac{800.0\ \text{N} \times 6.0\ \text{m}}{2.0\ \text{s}}$$

$$\text{Power} = \frac{4800\ \text{J}}{2.0\ \text{s}} = 2400\ \text{J/s} = 2400\ \text{W}$$

**3. Look Back and Check**

*Is your answer reasonable?*

Work = (2400 J/s) $\times$ 2.0 s = 4800 J

This is a reasonable answer. Substituting power and time back into the power equation yields the original value for work.

## Math Practice

*On a separate sheet of paper, solve the following problems.*

1. Suppose 900.0 J of work are done by a light bulb in 15.0 s. What is the power of the light bulb?

   Power = Work/Time = 900.0 J/15.0 s = 60.0 J/s = 60.0 W

2. What is the power of a machine if an output force of 500.0 N is exerted over an output distance of 8.0 m in 4.0 s?

   Power = (Force)(Distance)/Time = (500.0 N $\times$ 8.0 m)/4.0 s = 1000 J/s = 1000 W

3. The power of a machine is $6.0 \times 10^3$ J/s. This machine is scheduled for design improvements. What would its power be if the same work could be done in half the time?

   Power = Work/Time = ($6.0 \times 10^3$ J/s)/0.5 s = $1.2 \times 10^4$ J

Name ______________________ Class ______________ Date ____________

Chapter 15 Energy

# Section 15.1 Energy and Its Forms

## (pages 446–452)

*This section describes how energy and work are related. Kinetic energy and potential energy are defined, and examples are shown for calculating these forms of energy. Examples of various types of energy are discussed.*

## Reading Strategy (page 446)

**Building Vocabulary** As you read, complete the concept map with vocabulary terms and definitions from this section. For more information on this Reading Strategy, see the **Reading and Study Skills** in the **Skills and Reference Handbook** at the end of your textbook.

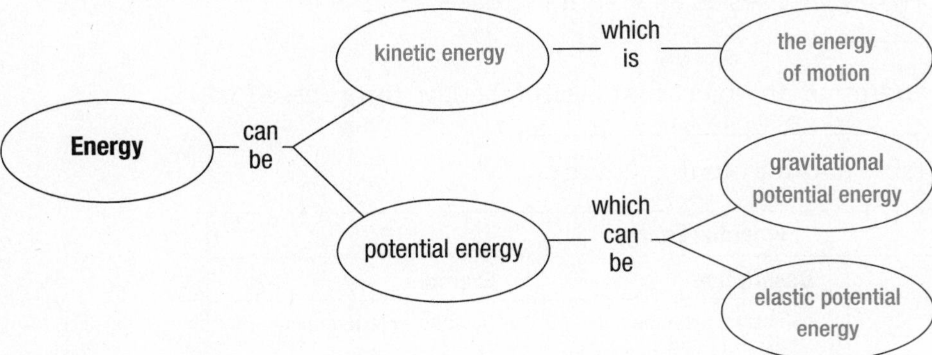


## Energy and Work (page 447)

1. What is energy? Energy is the ability to do work.
2. When work is done on an object, energy is transferred to that object.
3. Circle the letter of each sentence that is true about work and energy.
   - (a.) Energy in food is converted into muscle movement.
   - (b.) Energy is transferred when work is done.
   - (c.) Both work and energy are usually measured in joules.
   - d. One joule equals one meter per newton.

## Kinetic Energy (pages 447–448)

4. The energy of motion is called kinetic energy.
5. Is the following sentence true or false? You can determine the kinetic energy of an object if you know its mass and its volume. false
6. Write the formula used to calculate an object's kinetic energy. Kinetic energy = $1/2\ mv^2$
7. Calculate the kinetic energy of a 0.25-kg toy car traveling at a constant velocity of 2 m/s.
   $KE = 1/2\ mv^2 = 1/2\ (0.25\text{ kg})(2.0\text{ m/s})^2 = 0.5\text{ kg}\bullet\text{m}^2/\text{s}^2 = 0.5\text{ J}$

## Potential Energy (pages 448–450)

8. What is potential energy? It is energy that is stored as a result of position or shape.

9. Is the following sentence true or false? The work done by a rock climber going up a cliff decreases her potential energy.
false

10. An object's gravitational potential energy depends on its mass, its height, and the acceleration due to gravity.

11. Is the following sentence true or false? Gravitational potential energy of an object increases as its height increases.
true

12. The potential energy of an object that is stretched or compressed is known as elastic potential energy.

13. Complete the table about potential energy.

| Potential Energy | | |
|---|---|---|
| **Type** | **Description** | **Example** |
| Gravitational | Objects raised to heights relative to a reference level | Diver on a platform high above the water |
| Elastic | Stretched or compressed objects | A guitar string stretched to one side |

## Forms of Energy (pages 450–452)

*For numbers 14 through 19, write the letter of the form of energy that best matches the description.*

**Descriptions**

b 14. Energy stored in gasoline, coal, and wood

a 15. The sum of an object's potential energy and kinetic energy, excluding atomic-scale movements

e 16. Produces the sun's heat and light

f 17. Travels through space in the form of waves

c 18. Produces lightning bolts

d 19. Increases as atoms within an object move faster

**Forms of Energy**

a. mechanical energy
b. chemical energy
c. electrical energy
d. thermal energy
e. nuclear energy
f. electromagnetic energy

Name ______________________ Class ________________ Date ___________



# Section 15.2 Energy Conversion and Conservation

**(pages 453–459)**

*This section describes how energy is converted from one form to another. The law of conservation of energy also is presented.*

## Reading Strategy (page 453)

**Relating Cause and Effect** As you read, complete the flowchart to explain an energy conversion used by some gulls to obtain food. For more information on this Reading Strategy, see the **Reading and Study Skills** in the **Skills and Reference Handbook** at the end of your textbook.

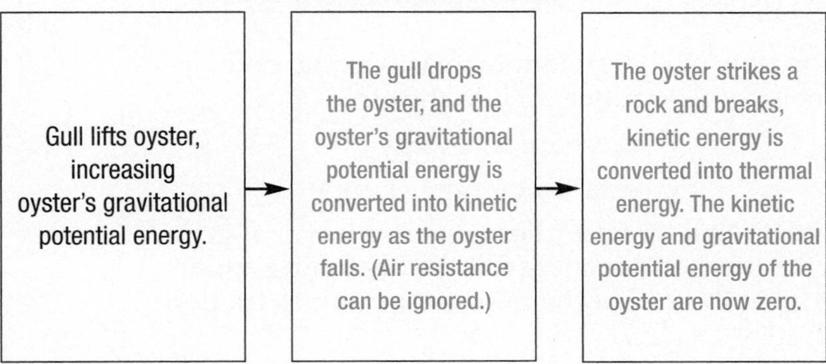


## Energy Conversion (page 454)

1. Is the following sentence true or false? Energy can be converted from one form to another. ___true___
2. When a wind-up toy is set in motion, elastic potential energy that was stored in a compressed spring is converted into the ___kinetic energy___ of the toy's moving parts.
3. Is the following sentence true or false? The action of striking a match shows that stored chemical energy in the match can be converted into thermal energy and electromagnetic energy of the flame in a single step. ___false___

## Conservation of Energy (page 455)

4. What does the law of conservation of energy state? ___Energy cannot be created or destroyed.___
5. Is the following sentence true or false? When an object slows down because of frictional force acting on it, an amount of energy is destroyed that is equivalent to the decrease in kinetic energy of the object. ___false___
6. A moving object slows down because friction causes a continual conversion of kinetic energy into ___thermal energy___.

Name ______________________ Class ________________ Date ____________



## Energy Conversions (pages 456–458)

7. As an object falls, the gravitational potential energy of the object is converted into kinetic energy.

8. Circle the letter of each sentence that is true about pendulums.
   - (a.) A pendulum consists of a weight suspended from a string that swings back and forth.
   - b. The weight at the end of a pendulum reaches maximum kinetic energy at the highest point in the pendulum's swing.
   - (c.) Potential energy and kinetic energy undergo constant conversion as a pendulum swings.
   - d. Frictional forces enable a pendulum to continue swinging without slowing down.

9. At what point during a pole-vaulter's jump is his gravitational potential energy the greatest? It is greatest at the highest point of the jump.

10. Circle the letter of the type of energy that increases as the pole bends before it propels a pole-vaulter up into the air.
    - a. kinetic energy
    - b. mechanical energy
    - c. frictional force
    - (d.) elastic potential energy

11. Is the following sentence true or false? For a mechanical change in an isolated system, the mechanical energy at the beginning equals the mechanical energy at the end of the process, as long as friction is negligible. true

12. Tell whether the following situations illustrate *kinetic energy, potential energy,* or *both.*

| What Type of Energy Is It? | |
|---|---|
| **Situation** | **Form of Energy** |
| A stationary wind-up toy with a compressed spring | Potential energy |
| A descending roller coaster car | Both |
| A skier poised to take off at the top of a hill | Potential energy |
| A car driving on a flat road | Kinetic energy |
| A vibrating guitar string | Both |

## Energy and Mass (page 459)

13. What does Einstein's equation imply about mass and energy? Mass and energy are equivalent, and mass and energy can be converted into each other.

14. Is the following sentence true or false? Einstein's equation, $E = mc^2$, suggests that mass and energy together are conserved. true

# Section 15.3 Energy Resources
**(pages 462–466)**

*This section describes types of energy resources and ways to conserve them.*

## Reading Strategy (page 462)

**Identifying Main Ideas** As you read the section, write the main idea for each heading in the table. For more information on this Reading Strategy, see the **Reading and Study Skills** in the **Skills and Reference Handbook** at the end of your textbook.

| Heading | Main Idea |
|---|---|
| Nonrenewable energy resources | Nonrenewable energy resources include oil, natural gas, and coal. They exist in limited quantities. |
| Renewable energy resources | Renewable energy resources include hydroelectric, solar, geothermal, wind, biomass, and nuclear fusion. |
| Conserving energy resources | Energy resources can be conserved by reducing energy needs and by increasing the efficiency of energy use. |

## Nonrenewable Energy Resources (page 462)

1. What are nonrenewable energy resources? They are resources that exist in limited quantities and, once used, cannot be replaced except over the course of millions of years.

2. List four examples of nonrenewable energy resources.
   a. Oil b. Natural gas
   c. Coal d. Uranium

3. Circle the letter of each resource that is considered to be a fossil fuel.
   a. tree
   b. uranium
   (c.) oil
   (d.) coal

4. Is the following sentence true or false? Although fossil fuels are evenly distributed throughout Earth, they only represent ten percent of total energy consumed. false

5. What are some advantages and disadvantages of using fossil fuels as a source of energy? Fossil fuels are relatively inexpensive and are usually readily available, but their use creates pollution.

## Renewable Energy Resources (pages 463–464)

6. An energy resource that can be replaced in a reasonably short period of time is called a(n) renewable resource.

7. Circle the letter of each sentence that is true about renewable energy resources.
   (a.) Wind and solar energy are both renewable energy resources.
   b. Renewable energy resources are always more efficient than nonrenewable resources.
   (c.) Renewable energy resources can be used to generate electricity and to heat homes.
   d. Magma generates most renewable energy, either directly or indirectly.

8. Describe one energy conversion that takes place during the generation of hydroelectric power. Potential energy of water behind a dam is converted to kinetic energy upon release of the water.

9. Is the following sentence true or false? One disadvantage of hydroelectric power is that it is among the most expensive energy sources. false

*For numbers 10 through 15, match the letter of each renewable energy source to its description.*

| | Description | Renewable Energy Sources |
|---|---|---|
| c | 10. Water pumped below ground is converted to steam. | a. hydroelectric |
| f | 11. The most likely raw material is hydrogen. | b. solar |
| b | 12. Mirrors concentrate sunlight to produce electricity. | c. geothermal |
| d | 13. Kinetic energy of moving air is converted into rotational energy of a turbine. | d. wind |
| a | 14. Energy is obtained from flowing water. | e. biomass |
| e | 15. Chemical energy stored in wood, peat, and agricultural waste can be converted into thermal energy. | f. nuclear fusion |

16. Is the following sentence true or false? Hydrogen fuel cells generate electricity by combining hydrogen with oxygen. true

## Conserving Energy Resources (page 466)

17. What are two ways that energy resources can be conserved? Energy resources can be conserved by reducing energy needs and by increasing the efficiency of energy use.

18. Name two practical ways in which people can conserve energy. Accept reasonable responses, such as carpooling, walking or biking on short trips, using more efficient appliances, developing and driving more fuel-efficient cars.

Name ______________________ Class ________________ Date ____________



# WordWise

*Complete the sentences by using one of the scrambled vocabulary words below.*

| | | |
|---|---|---|
| absoism reegny | ynrege vnsnoorctaie | slisfo sluef |
| rslao eeyngr | neegyr seonoscvri | caurnle rygnee |
| mrelhta eeryng | loptnieat nygeer | gyreen |
| mcelhaci reeyng | ctniiek yenrge | rvtnatgialoai |

When an object is raised to a higher level, its ___gravitational___ potential energy increases.

The motion of microscopic particles in matter partly determines the amount of ___thermal energy___ within it.

As a pole-vaulter springs higher into the air, her kinetic energy decreases as her gravitational potential energy increases. This is an example of ___energy conversion___.

Atomic fission and fusion produce ___nuclear energy___.

When your muscles move, ___chemical energy___ from the cereal you ate for breakfast is converted into ___kinetic energy___.

The ___potential energy___ of a 100-kg boulder perched high on a cliff is greater than that of a 50-kg boulder at the same height.

You can recognize ___energy___ by the changes it causes, such as motion and sound.

Formed from the remains of once-living organisms, ___fossil fuels___ are nonrenewable energy resources.

Photovoltaic cells convert ___solar energy___ into electrical energy.

Methods of ___energy conservation___ include ways to reduce energy needs.

When you sit around a campfire, you are enjoying energy stored in wood—a type of ___biomass energy___.

Name ______________________ Class ________________ Date ____________



# Calculating Potential Energy

**Math Skill: Percents and Decimals**

You may want to read more about this **Math Skill** in the **Skills and Reference Handbook** at the end of your textbook.

A 60.0-kg person is standing on the edge of a pier that is 2.5 m above the surface of a lake. How much higher would the pier have to be to raise the gravitational potential energy of this person by 10 percent?

**1. Read and Understand**

*What information are you given?*

Mass of person = $m$ = 60.0 kg

Height above lake level = $h$ = 2.5 m

Acceleration due to gravity = $g$ = 9.8 m/s$^2$

**2. Plan and Solve**

*What variable are you trying to determine?*

Gravitational potential energy = ?

*What formula contains the given variables?*

Gravitational potential energy (PE) = $mgh$

Initial PE = (60.0 kg)(9.8 m/s$^2$)(2.5 m) = 1500 J

*Determine the 10-percent increase of PE.*

(1500 J)(0.10) = 150 J

Final PE = 1500 J + 150 J = 1650 J

*Rearrange the equation to determine the final height.*

$h$ = PE/$mg$ = 1650 J/(60.0 kg)(9.8 m/s$^2$) = 2.8 m

The height increase for the pier would be 2.8 m − 2.5 m = 0.3 m.

**3. Look Back and Check**

*Is your answer reasonable?*

This is a reasonable answer because 0.3 m is about 10 percent of 2.5 m. A 10-percent increase in $h$ should result in a 10-percent increase in the gravitational PE.

## Math Practice

*On a separate sheet of paper, solve the following problems.*

1. A 300-gram toy car and a 500-gram toy car are sitting on a shelf that is 2 meters higher than the floor. By what percent is the PE of the 500-g car greater than the PE of the 300-g car?

   The percent increase in mass is (0.5 − 0.3)/0.3 = 67 percent.
   The percent increase in PE is therefore also 67 percent.

2. An 80-kg rock climber is standing on a cliff so that his gravitational PE = 10,000 J. What percent increase in height is required to raise his PE by 3500 J?

   35 percent. The percent increase in PE is directly proportional to the percent increase in height.

Name ______________________ Class ___________________ Date ____________



# Section 16.1 Thermal Energy and Matter

**(pages 474–478)**

*This section defines heat and describes how work, temperature, and thermal energy are related to heat. Thermal expansion and contraction of materials is discussed, and uses of a calorimeter are explained.*

## Reading Strategy (page 474)

**Previewing** Before you read, preview the figures in this section and add two more questions in the table. As you read, write answers to your questions. For more information on this Reading Strategy, see the **Reading and Study Skills** in the **Skills and Reference Handbook** at the end of your textbook.

| Thermal Energy and Matter | |
|---|---|
| **Questions About Thermal Energy and Matter** | **Answers** |
| Which has more thermal energy, a cup of tea or a pitcher of juice? | A pitcher of juice |
| Why did Rumford conclude that heat is not a form of matter? (Fig. 1) | The brass was hot enough to make water boil only during drilling, so the heat must be related to the motion of the drill. |
| How is specific heat related to temperature? (Fig. 3) | The lower a material's specific heat, the more its temperature rises when a given amount of energy is absorbed by a given mass. |

## Work and Heat (page 474)

1. Heat is the transfer of thermal energy from one object to another as the result of a difference in ___temperature___.
2. Circle the letter of each sentence that is true about heat.
   a. Heat is a fluid that flows between particles of matter.
   (b.) Heat flows spontaneously from hot objects to cold objects.
   (c.) Friction produces heat.
   (d.) The transfer of thermal energy from one object to another is heat.

## Temperature (page 475)

3. What is temperature? ___Temperature is a measure of how hot or cold an object is compared to a reference point.___
4. Is the following sentence true or false? On the Celsius scale, the reference points for temperature are the freezing and boiling points of water. ___true___

5. Circle the letter of each sentence that explains what happens when an object heats up.
   (a.) Its particles move faster, on average.
   b. The average kinetic energy of its particles decreases.
   c. Its mass increases.
   (d.) Its temperature increases.

## Thermal Energy (page 475)

6. What is thermal energy? Thermal energy is the total potential and kinetic energy of all the particles in an object.

7. Thermal energy depends upon the mass, temperature, and phase of an object.

8. Is the following sentence true or false? Two substances can be the same temperature and have different thermal energies. true

## Thermal Expansion and Contraction (page 476)

9. Is the following sentence true or false? Thermal contraction occurs when matter is heated, because particles of matter tend to move closer together as temperature increases. false

10. Describe thermal expansion and contraction by completing the table below.

| Thermal Expansion and Contraction | | | |
|---|---|---|---|
| Condition | Temperature | Space Between Particles | Volume |
| Thermal expansion | Increases | Increases | Increases |
| Thermal contraction | Decreases | Decreases | Decreases |

## Specific Heat (pages 476–477)

11. The amount of heat needed to raise the temperature of one gram of material by one degree Celsius is called specific heat.

12. Why are you more likely to burn yourself on a metal toy than on a plastic toy if both have been sitting in the sun? The specific heats of metals tend to be lower than the specific heats of plastics. If equal masses of metal and plastic absorb the same thermal energy, the metal's temperature rises more.

## Measuring Heat Changes (page 478)

13. What device is used to measure changes in thermal energy? a calorimeter

14. Is the following sentence true or false? A calorimeter uses the principle that heat flows from a hotter object to a colder object until both reach the same temperature. true

# Section 16.2 Heat and Thermodynamics

**(pages 479–483)**

*This section discusses three kinds of thermal energy transfer and introduces the first, second, and third laws of thermodynamics.*

## Reading Strategy (page 479)

**Build Vocabulary** As you read this section, add definitions and examples to complete the table. For more information on this Reading Strategy, see the **Reading and Study Skills** in the **Skills and Reference Handbook** at the end of your textbook.

| Transfer of Thermal Energy | |
|---|---|
| **Definitions** | **Examples** |
| Conduction: transfer of thermal energy with no net transfer of matter | Frying pan handle heats up |
| Convection: transfer of thermal energy when particles of a fluid move from one place to another | Hot air circulating in an oven |
| Radiation: transfer of energy by waves moving through space | Heating coil of a stove glows |

## Conduction (pages 479–480)

1. The transfer of thermal energy with no overall transfer of matter is called ____conduction____.
2. Why is conduction slower in gases than in liquids and solids? In conduction, thermal energy is transferred by collisions between particles, and there are fewer collisions among particles in a gas than in a liquid or a solid.
3. Is the following sentence true or false? Conduction is faster in metals than in other solids because metals have free electrons that transfer thermal energy. ____true____
4. Circle the letter of each sentence that is true about conduction.
   - (a.) Thermal energy is transferred without transfer of matter.
   - b. Matter is transferred great distances during conduction.
   - c. Conduction can occur between materials that are not touching.
   - (d.) In most solids, conduction takes place as particles vibrate in place.
5. Complete the table about conduction.

| Conduction | | |
|---|---|---|
| **Type of Material** | **Quality of Conduction** | **Two Examples** |
| Thermal conductor | Conducts thermal energy well | Copper; aluminum |
| Thermal insulator | Conducts thermal energy poorly | Wood; air |

Name ______________________ Class ________________ Date ___________



## Convection (pages 480–481)

6. The transfer of thermal energy when particles of a fluid move from one place to another is called ___convection___.

7. Why is temperature higher at the bottom of an oven? When air at the bottom of the oven heats up, it expands, becomes less dense, and cools as it rises. Cooler, denser air sinks and is heated again at the bottom of the oven.

8. When a fluid circulates in a loop as it alternately heats up and cools down, a(n) ___convection current___ occurs.

9. Give three examples of convection currents in nature. Ocean currents, weather systems, and movement of hot rock in Earth's interior are examples of convection currents.

## Radiation (page 481)

10. The transfer of energy by waves moving through space is called ___radiation___.

11. Circle the letter of each sentence that is true about radiation.
    - (a.) Energy is transferred by waves.
    - (b.) All objects radiate energy.
    - c. The amount of energy radiated from an object decreases as its temperature increases.
    - (d.) The farther away you are from a radiating object, the less radiation you receive.

## Thermodynamics (pages 482–483)

12. Thermodynamics is the study of conversions between ___thermal energy___ and other forms of energy.

13. Is the following sentence true or false? Energy cannot be created or destroyed, but it can be converted into different forms. ___true___

14. Thermal energy flows spontaneously from ___hotter___ objects to ___colder___ ones.

15. According to the second law of thermodynamics, what must happen for thermal energy to flow from a colder object to a hotter object? Work must be done on the system.

16. Thermal energy that is not converted into work is called ___waste heat___.

17. Is the following sentence true or false? Scientists have created a heat engine with 100 percent efficiency by reducing the temperature of the outside environment to absolute zero. ___false___

18. Is the following sentence true or false? Matter can be cooled to absolute zero. ___false___

Name ______________________ Class ______________ Date __________



# Section 16.3 Using Heat
**(pages 486–492)**

*This section describes ways in which humans benefit from heat engines, heating systems, and cooling systems. It also discusses how each of these systems works.*

## Reading Strategy (page 486)

**Sequencing** As you read, complete the cycle diagram to show the sequence of events in a gasoline engine. For more information on this Reading Strategy, see the **Reading and Study Skills** in the **Skills and Reference Handbook** at the end of your textbook.

**Sequence of Events in a Gasoline Engine**

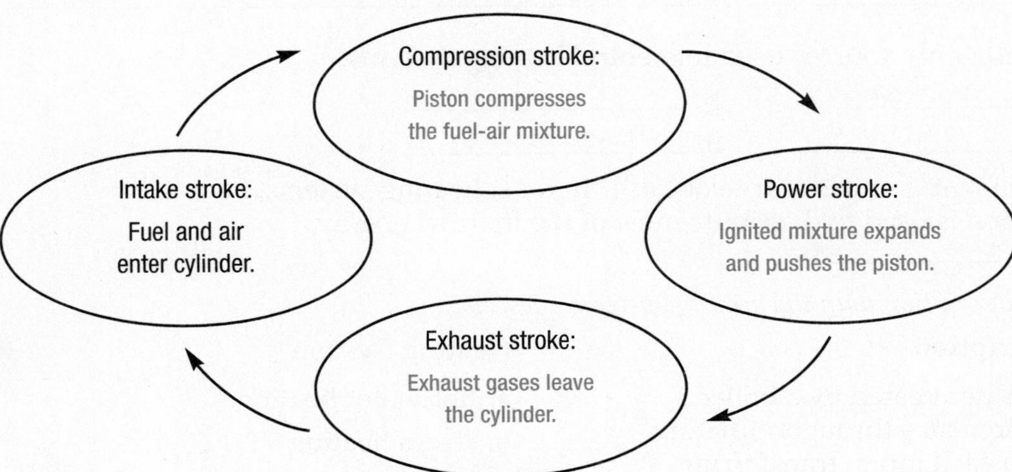


## Heat Engines (pages 486–487)

1. The two main types of heat engines are the external combustion engine and the internal combustion engine.
2. A steam engine is an external combustion engine because it burns fuel outside the engine.
3. Who developed the first practical steam engine?
   a. James Prescott Joule
   (b.) Thomas Newcomen
   c. James Watt
   d. Benjamin Thompson
4. How is heat converted into work in a steam engine? Expanding steam pushes against a piston.
5. A heat engine used by most cars in which fuel burns inside the engine is called a(n) internal combustion engine.
6. Each upward or downward motion of a piston in an internal combustion engine is called a(n) stroke.

7. Is the following sentence true or false? In a typical car, the crankshaft produces a linear motion that turns the wheels.
false

8. Why is it important for an internal combustion engine to have a cooling system? Waste energy produced when the engine does work is transferred to the atmosphere by the cooling system. Without it, the engine would be damaged by thermal expansion.

9. Is the following sentence true or false? Gasoline engines operate very efficiently in converting fuel energy to work.
false

## Heating Systems (pages 489–490)

10. What is a central heating system? It is a system that is used to heat many rooms from one location.

11. List four energy sources used for central heating systems.

a. Natural gas  b. Coal

c. Oil  d. Electrical energy

12. Is the following sentence true or false? In most heating systems, conduction is used to distribute most of the thermal energy.
false

*Match each description with the heating system it describes.*

| | Description | Heating System |
|---|---|---|
| a | 13. Water heated by a boiler circulates through radiators in each room, transferring thermal energy. | a. hot-water heating |
| d | 14. Fans are used to circulate warm air through ducts to the rooms in a building. | b. steam heating |
| c | 15. A hot coil heats air by conduction and radiation. | c. electric baseboard heating |
| b | 16. This system is often used in older buildings or to heat many buildings from a single location. | d. forced-air heating |

## Cooling Systems (pages 490–492)

17. Is the following sentence true or false? Most cooling systems, such as air conditioners and refrigerators, are heat pumps.
true

18. A fluid that vaporizes and condenses inside the tubing of a heat pump is called a(n) refrigerant.

19. How does a heat pump reverse the normal flow of thermal energy? A heat pump must do work on a refrigerant to remove heat from a cold area, such as the inside of a refrigerator.

Name ______________________ Class __________________ Date ____________



# WordWise

*Answer the questions by writing the correct vocabulary term in the blanks. Use the circled letter(s) in each term to find the hidden vocabulary word. Then, write a definition for the hidden word.*

| **Clues** | **Vocabulary Terms** |
|---|---|
| This flows spontaneously from hot objects to cold objects. | h e a (t) |
| Any device that converts heat into work | (h) (e) a t e n g i n e |
| A heat pump does work on this so you can keep your veggies cold. | r e f (r) i g e r a n t |
| The Kelvin scale is used to measure this. | t e (m) p e r a t u r e |
| A device used to determine the specific heat of a material | c (a) (l) o r i m e t e r |
| The transfer of thermal energy when particles of a fluid move from place to place | c o n v e c t (i) o (n) |
| The amount of heat needed to raise the temperature of one gram of a material by one degree Celsius | (s) p e c i f i c h e a t |
| The transfer of thermal energy with no overall transfer of matter | c o n d (u) c t i o n |
| The total potential and kinetic energy of all the particles in an object | t h e r m a (l) e n e r g y |
| The transfer of energy by waves moving through space | r (a) d i a (t) i (o) n |
| According to the first law of thermodynamics, this is conserved. | e n e (r) g y |

**Hidden words:** t h e r m a l i n s u l a t o r

**Definition:** A material that conducts thermal energy poorly

# Calculating with Specific Heat

**Math Skill: Formulas and Equations**

You may want to read more about this **Math Skill** in the **Skills and Reference Handbook** at the end of your textbook.

How much heat is required to raise the temperature of a gold earring from 25.0°C to 30.0°C? The earring weighs 25 grams, and the specific heat of gold is 0.128 J/g•°C.

**1. Read and Understand**

*What information are you given?*

Specific heat = $c$ = 0.128 J/g•°C

Mass = $m$ = 25.0 grams

Change in Temperature = $\Delta T$ = (30.0°C − 25.0°C) = 5.0°C

**2. Plan and Solve**

*What unknown are you trying to calculate?*

Amount of heat needed = $Q$ = ?

*What formula contains the given quantities and the unknown?*

$Q$ = Mass × Specific heat × Change in Temperature

$Q = m \times c \times \Delta T$

*Replace each variable with its known value.*

$Q$ = 25.0 g × 0.128 J/g•°C × 5.0°C = 16 J

**3. Look Back and Check**

*Is your answer reasonable?*

$$\frac{\text{Heat absorbed}}{(m \times c)} = 16\text{ J}/(25.0\text{ g} \times 0.128\text{ J/g}\bullet{}^\circ\text{C}) = 5.0^\circ\text{C}$$

This is a reasonable answer for the heat required to raise the temperature of the earring.

## Math Practice

*On a separate sheet of paper, solve the following problems.*

1. How much heat is required to raise the temperature of 25 grams of water from 25.0°C to 30.0°C? The specific heat of water is 4.18 J/g•°C.

   $Q = m \times c \times \Delta T$ $Q$ = 25 g × 4.18 J/g•°C × 5.0°C = 520 J

   Heat absorbed by the water = $Q$ = 520 J

2. Determine the mass of a sample of silver if 705 J of heat are required to raise its temperature from 25°C to 35°C. The specific heat of silver is 0.235 J/g•°C.

   $m = Q/(c \times \Delta T)$ $m$ = 705 J / (0.235 J/g•°C × 10°C)

   $m$ = 300 g

3. An iron skillet has a mass of 500.0 g. The specific heat of iron is 0.449 J/g•°C. The pan is heated by adding 19,082.5 J of heat. How much does the temperature of the pan increase?

   $\Delta T = Q/(m \times c)$ 19,082.5 J = 500.0g × 0.449 J/g•°C × $\Delta T$

   19,082.5 J /(500.0 g × 0.449 J/g•°C) = $\Delta T$

   $\Delta T$ = 85.0°C

Name ______________ Class ______________ Date ______________



# Section 17.1 Mechanical Waves
**(pages 500–503)**

*This section explains what mechanical waves are, how they form, and how they travel. Three main types of mechanical waves—transverse, longitudinal, and surface waves—are discussed and examples are given for each type.*

## Reading Strategy (page 500)

**Previewing** As you read this section, use Figure 2 on page 501 to complete the web diagram. Then use Figures 3 and 4 to make similar diagrams for longitudinal waves and surface waves on a separate sheet of paper. For more information on this Reading Strategy, see the **Reading and Study Skills** in the **Skills and Reference Handbook** at the end of your textbook.

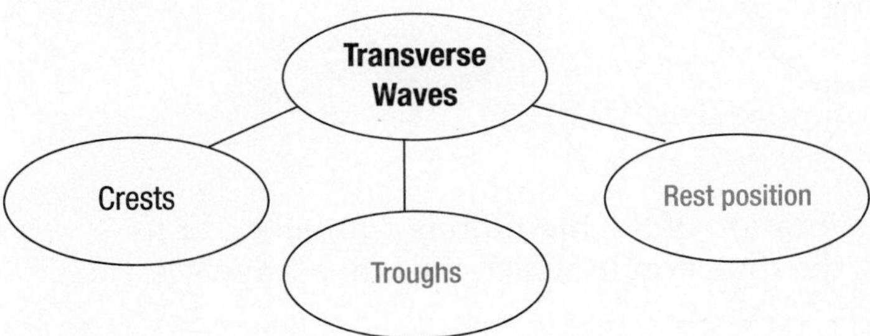


## What Are Mechanical Waves? (page 500)

1. A disturbance in matter that carries energy from one place to another is called a(n) mechanical wave.
2. Is the following sentence true or false? Mechanical waves can travel through empty space. false
3. The material through which a wave travels is called a(n) medium.
4. Is the following sentence true or false? Solids, liquids, and gases all can act as mediums for waves. true
5. What creates a mechanical wave? An energy source causes a vibration to travel through a medium.

## Types of Mechanical Waves (pages 501–503)

6. Is the following sentence true or false? The three main types of mechanical waves are water waves, longitudinal waves, and surface waves. false
7. Circle the letter of the characteristic used to classify a mechanical wave.
   a. the height of its crest
   b. the depth of its trough
   (c.) the way it travels through a medium
   d. the type of medium through which it travels

8. The highest point of a wave above the rest position is the crest and the lowest point below the rest position is the trough.

9. What is a transverse wave? It is a wave that causes the medium to vibrate at right angles to the direction in which the wave travels.

10. Look at the figure below. Label the missing aspects of the wave in the rope.

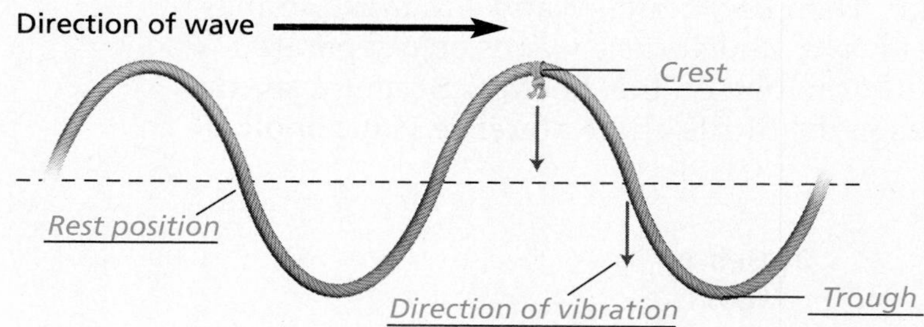


11. A wave in which the vibration of the medium is parallel to, or in the same direction as, the direction in which the wave travels is called a(n) longitudinal wave.

12. When a longitudinal wave carries energy through a spring, the area where the coils of a spring are closer together than they would be in the rest position is called a(n) compression.

13. Is the following sentence true or false? A rarefaction is a region in a longitudinal wave where particles of a medium spread out. true

14. Why is an ocean wave classified as a surface wave? It travels along a surface separating two mediums, air and water.

15. Why do ocean waves transport objects on the surface of the water as they approach shore? In shallow water, friction with the shore slows down the bottom of the waves, causing the waves to topple over themselves and move material toward the shore.

*Match the type of wave to each description below. The type of wave may be used more than once.*

| | Description | Type of Wave |
|---|---|---|
| b | 16. P wave | a. transverse wave |
| a | 17. Direction of travel is perpendicular to vibration direction | b. longitudinal wave |
| b | 18. Rarefactions with particles that are spread out | c. surface wave |
| c | 19. A wave that travels along a boundary separating two mediums | |
| c | 20. An ocean wave | |

# Section 17.2 Properties of Mechanical Waves

**(pages 504–507)**

*This section introduces measurable properties used to describe mechanical waves, including frequency, period, wavelength, speed, and amplitude.*

## Reading Strategy (page 504)

**Build Vocabulary** As you read, write a definition in your own words for each term in the table below. For more information on this Reading Strategy, see the **Reading and Study Skills** in the **Skills and Reference Handbook** at the end of your textbook.

| Properties of Waves | |
|---|---|
| **Vocabulary Term** | **Definition** |
| Period | The time required for one cycle |
| Frequency | The number of complete cycles in a given time |
| Wavelength | The distance between a point on a wave and the same point on the next cycle of the wave |
| Amplitude | The maximum displacement of a medium from its rest position |

## Frequency and Period (page 504)

1. Is the following sentence true or false? A periodic motion repeats at regular time intervals. ___true___
2. The time required for one cycle, a complete motion that returns to its starting point, is called the ___period___.
3. The number of complete cycles in a given period of time is the ___frequency___ of a periodic motion.
4. Circle the letter of each sentence that is true about frequency.
   (a.) Frequency is measured in cycles per second, or hertz.
   (b.) A wave's frequency equals the frequency of the vibrating source producing it.
   c. Five cycles per minute is a frequency of five hertz.
   (d.) Any periodic motion has a frequency.

## Wavelength (page 505)

5. The distance between a point on one wave and the same point on the next cycle of the wave is called ___wavelength___.
6. How is wavelength determined for a longitudinal wave?
   For a longitudinal wave, wavelength is the distance between adjacent compressions or rarefactions.

Name ______________________ Class ________________ Date ____________



## Wave Speed (pages 505–506)

7. Write a formula you can use to determine the speed of a wave.
Speed = Wavelength × Frequency

8. Is the following sentence true or false? The speed of a wave equals its wavelength divided by its period. true

9. What variables can cause the speed of a wave to change? The speed of a wave can change if it enters a new medium or if variables such as temperature and pressure change.

10. Circle the letter of the sentence that tells how wavelength is related to frequency for a wave traveling at a constant speed.
   a. Wavelength is equal to frequency.
   b. Wavelength is directly proportional to frequency.
   (c.) Wavelength is inversely proportional to frequency.
   d. A wave with a higher frequency will have a longer wavelength.

## Amplitude (page 507)

11. What is the amplitude of a wave? Amplitude is the maximum displacement of a medium from its rest position.

12. It takes more energy to produce a wave with higher crests and deeper troughs, so the more energy a wave has, the greater its amplitude.

*Questions 13 through 17 refer to the figure below.*

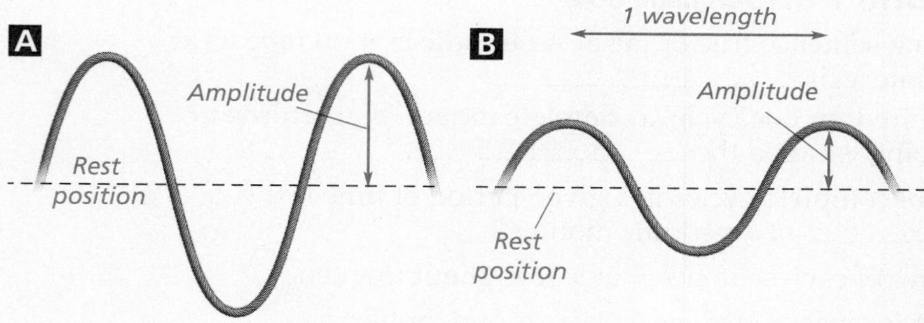


13. The type of waves shown are transverse waves.
14. Label the rest position for waves A and B.
15. Add arrows to the figure to indicate the amplitude of each wave. Which wave has the greater amplitude? wave A
16. Which wave shown has more energy? wave A
17. Add an arrow to indicate one wavelength on wave B.

Name ______________________ Class ______________________ Date ______________



# Section 17.3 Behavior of Waves
## (pages 508–512)

*This section describes different interactions that can occur when a mechanical wave encounters an obstacle, a change in medium, or another wave. These interactions include reflection, refraction, diffraction, and interference.*

## Reading Strategy (page 508)

**Identifying Main Ideas** Complete the table below. As you read, write the main idea of each topic. For more information on this Reading Strategy, see the **Reading and Study Skills** in the **Skills and Reference Handbook** at the end of your textbook.

| Wave Interactions | |
|---|---|
| **Topic** | **Main Idea** |
| Reflection | A wave reflected at a fixed boundary will be flipped upside down. |
| Refraction | Refraction occurs when a wave enters a new medium at an angle because one side of a wave front moves more slowly than the other side. |
| Diffraction | The larger the wavelength is compared to the size of an opening or obstacle, the more a wave diffracts. |
| Interference | The types of interference are constructive and destructive interference. |
| Standing waves | A standing wave forms only if a multiple of one half wavelength fits exactly into the length of the vibrating object. |

## Reflection (page 508)

1. Is the following sentence true or false? Reflection occurs when a wave bounces off a surface that it cannot pass through.
 true

2. Circle the letter of the results that occur when a wave reflects off a fixed boundary.
   (a.) The reflected wave will be turned upside down.
   b. The amplitude will double as it strikes the surface.
   c. The speed of the wave will decrease.
   d. The frequency of the wave will decrease.

## Refraction (page 509)

3. Why does refraction occur when a wave enters a new medium at an angle? Refraction occurs because one side of the wave moves more slowly than the other side.

4. Is the following sentence true or false? Refraction always involves a change in the speed and direction of a wave. true

## Diffraction (page 510)

**5.** What is required in order for diffraction to occur? Waves diffract when they encounter an obstacle or pass through a narrow opening.

**6.** Is the following sentence true or false? A wave diffracts more if its wavelength is small compared to the size of an opening or obstacle. false

## Interference (pages 510–511)

**7.** What causes wave interference? Wave interference occurs when two or more waves overlap and combine.

**8.** Complete the table about interference.

| Interference | | |
|---|---|---|
| **Type** | **Alignment** | **Displacement Change** |
| Constructive | Crests align with crests; troughs align with troughs | Displacements combine to produce an increased amplitude. |
| Destructive | Crests align with troughs | Displacements combine to produce a reduced amplitude. |

**9.** Is the following sentence true or false? Destructive interference can result in wave displacements that are above the rest position. true

**10.** How can an increased depth of a trough be considered constructive interference? When constructive interference occurs, two or more waves combine and their displacements add together, resulting in a wave with greater amplitude.

## Standing Waves (page 512)

**11.** At certain frequencies, interference between a wave and its reflection can produce a(n) standing wave.

**12.** Circle each letter of a sentence that is true about standing waves.

(a.) A node is a point that has no displacement from the rest position.

b. Standing waves appear to move through a medium, such as a string.

c. Complete destructive interference occurs at antinodes.

d. A standing wave will form for any wavelength, as long as two ends of a rope or string are stretched tightly between two points.

**13.** Is the following sentence true or false? If a standing wave occurs in a medium at a given frequency, another standing wave will occur if this frequency is doubled. true

**14.** Give an example of a common standing wave. The vibrations you can see when plucking a stringed instrument are examples of standing waves.

# Section 17.4 Sound and Hearing
## (pages 514–521)

*This section discusses properties of sound waves, how they are produced, and how the ear perceives sound. A description of how music is produced and recorded also is presented.*

## Reading Strategy (page 514)

**Using Prior Knowledge** Before you read, add properties you already know about sound waves to the diagram below. Then add details about each property as you read the section. For more information on this Reading Strategy, see the **Reading and Study Skills** in the **Skills and Reference Handbook** at the end of your textbook.

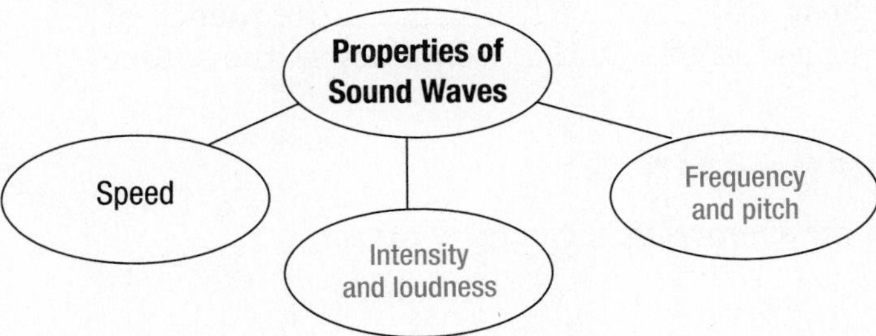


## Properties of Sound Waves (pages 514–515)

1. Circle the letter of each sentence that is true about sound.
   - (a.) Many behaviors of sound can be explained using a few properties.
   - (b.) Sound waves are compressions and rarefactions that travel through a medium.
   - c. Sound waves usually travel more slowly in solids than in gases.
   - d. The speed of sound in air is about 30 meters per second.

*Match each description with one or more sound properties.*

| | Description | Property |
|---|---|---|
| c | 2. This property is measured in units called decibels. | a. loudness |
| b, d | 3. These properties are affected by the length of tubing in a musical instrument. | b. pitch |
| b | 4. This property is the frequency of a sound as your ears perceive it. | c. intensity |
| a, b | 5. These properties depend on factors such as your age and the health of your ears. | d. frequency |
| a | 6. This property is a physical response to the intensity of sound. | |

## Ultrasound (page 516)

7. Is the following sentence true or false? Ultrasound is sound at frequencies that are lower than most people are capable of hearing. false

8. Describe some applications of ultrasound. Ultrasound imaging is an important medical technique; sonar is used to determine the distance to an object under water.

## The Doppler Effect (page 516)

9. Is the following sentence true or false? The Doppler effect is a change in sound frequency caused by motion of the sound source, motion of the listener, or both. true

10. For a stationary observer, as a moving sound source approaches, the observer will first hear a(n) higher frequency of sound and then a(n) lower frequency as the source moves away.

## Hearing and the Ear (page 517)

*Match each description with the appropriate region(s) of the ear.*

| | Description | Region |
|---|---|---|
| a | 11. Sound is gathered and focused here. | a. outer ear |
| c | 12. Nerve endings send signals to the brain. | b. middle ear |
| a, b | 13. The eardrum is located at the boundary between these two regions of the ear. | c. inner ear |
| b | 14. Hammer, anvil, and stirrup are located here. | |
| b | 15. Sound vibrations are amplified. | |

## How Sound Is Reproduced (pages 518–519)

16. How is sound recorded? Sound waves are converted to electronic signals that can be processed and stored in different ways.

17. Sound is reproduced by converting electronic signals back into sound waves.

## Music (page 521)

18. Is the following sentence true or false? Many musical instruments vary pitch by changing the frequency of standing waves. true

19. Theaters are designed to prevent "dead spots" where the volume is reduced by destructive interference of reflected sound waves.

20. The response of a standing wave to another wave of the same frequency is called resonance.

Name ______________________ Class ______________ Date __________



# WordWise

*Test your knowledge of vocabulary terms from Chapter 17 by completing this crossword puzzle.*

**Clues across:**

1. Maximum displacement of a wave
3. The time required for one complete wave cycle
6. An apparent change in frequency of a sound source that moves relative to an observer
8. A point of no displacement in a standing wave
9. Area where particles in a medium are spread out as a longitudinal wave travels through it
10. Distance from one point to the next identical point on a wave

**Clues down:**

2. Type of mechanical wave whose direction of vibration is perpendicular to its direction of travel
4. A unit used to compare sound intensity levels
5. Occurs when waves overlap
6. Occurs when a wave encounters an object or opening that is close in size to its wavelength
7. Lowest point of a wave below the rest position

1 AMPLITUDE
2 TRANSVERSE
3 PERIOD
4 DECIBEL
5 INTERFERENCE
6 DOPPLER EFFECT
6 DIFFRACTION
7 TROUGH
8 NODE
9 RAREFACTION
10 WAVELENGTH

Name ______________________ Class ______________ Date __________



# Calculating Wave Properties

**Math Skill: Formulas and Equations**

You may want to read more about this **Math Skill** in the **Skills and Reference Handbook** at the end of your textbook.

A transverse wave in a rope is traveling at a speed of 3.0 m/s. The period of this mechanical wave is 0.25 s. What is the wavelength?

**1. Read and Understand**

*What information are you given?*

Speed = 3.0 m/s

Period = 0.25 s

**2. Plan and Solve**

*What unknown are you trying to calculate?*

Wavelength = ?

*What formula contains the given quantities and the unknown?*

$$\text{Speed} = \text{Wavelength} \times \text{Frequency} = \frac{\text{Wavelength}}{\text{Period}}$$

$$\text{Wavelength} = \text{Period} \times \text{Speed}$$

*Replace each variable with its known value.*

Speed = 3.0 m/s

Period = 0.25 s

$$\text{Wavelength} = 0.25 \text{ s} \times 3.0 \text{ m/s} = 0.75 \text{ m}$$

**3. Look Back and Check**

*Is your answer reasonable?*

$$\text{Speed} = \text{Wavelength} \times \text{Frequency} = \text{Wavelength} \times \frac{1}{\text{Period}}$$

$$\text{Speed} = 0.75 \text{ m} \times \frac{1}{0.25 \text{ s}} = 3.0 \text{ m/s}.$$

Substituting the calculated wavelength into the equation yields the original speed of 3.0 m/s.

## Math Practice

*On a separate sheet of paper, solve the following problems.*

1. What is the speed, in m/s, of a wave on a cord if it has a wavelength of 4 m and a period of 0.5 s?

   Speed = Wavelength/Period = 4 m × 0.5 s = 8 m/s

2. What is the period of a wave traveling 5 m/s if its wavelength is 20 m?

   Period = Wavelength/Speed = (20 m)/(5 m/s) = 4 s

3. Calculate the frequency, in Hz, of a wave in a string traveling 1.25 m/s, with a wavelength of 0.50 m.

   Frequency = Speed/Wavelength = (1.25 m/s)/0.50 m = 2.5 Hz

# Section 18.1 Electromagnetic Waves
**(pages 532–538)**

*This section describes the characteristics of electromagnetic waves.*

## Reading Strategy (page 532)

**Comparing and Contrasting** As you read about electromagnetic waves, fill in the table below. If the characteristic listed in the table describes electromagnetic waves, write E in the column for Wave Type. Write M for mechanical waves and B for both. For more information on this Reading Strategy, see the **Reading and Study Skills** in the **Skills and Reference Handbook** at the end of your textbook.

| Electromagnetic and Mechanical Waves | |
|---|---|
| Travels through a vacuum | E |
| Travels though medium | B |
| Fits wave model | B |
| Fits particle model | E |
| Transverse wave | B |
| Longitudinal wave | M |

## What Are Electromagnetic Waves? (page 533)

1. What are electromagnetic waves? They are transverse waves that consist of changing electric fields and changing magnetic fields.

2. Electric fields are produced by electrically charged particles and by changing magnetic fields.

3. Magnetic fields are produced by magnets, by changing electric fields, and by vibrating charges.

4. Electromagnetic waves are produced when a(n) electric charge vibrates or accelerates.

5. Circle the letter of each sentence that is true about electric and magnetic fields.
   (a.) An electromagnetic wave occurs when electric and magnetic fields vibrate at right angles to each other.
   b. A magnetic field is surrounded by an electric current.
   (c.) Changing electric and magnetic fields regenerate each other.
   (d.) Electromagnetic waves are produced when an electric charge vibrates.

6. Is the following sentence true or false? Electromagnetic waves need a medium to travel through. false

7. The transfer of energy by electromagnetic waves traveling through matter or across space is called electromagnetic radiation.

## The Speed of Electromagnetic Waves (page 534)

8. As a thunderstorm approaches, you see the lightning before you hear the thunder, because light travels ___faster___ than sound.

9. Is the following sentence true or false? All electromagnetic waves travel at the same speed through a vacuum. ___true___

10. Circle the letter that gives the correct speed of light in a vacuum.

    a. $3.00 \times 10^8$ kilometers per second

    b. $3.00 \times 10^8$ meters per hour

    (c.) $3.00 \times 10^8$ meters per second

    d. $3.00 \times 10^8$ kilometers per hour

## Wavelength and Frequency (page 535)

11. Circle the letter of each sentence that is true about electromagnetic waves.

    (a.) Different electromagnetic waves can have different frequencies.

    b. Wavelength is directly proportional to frequency.

    c. Electromagnetic waves always travel at the speed of light.

    (d.) All electromagnetic waves travel at the same speed in a vacuum.

12. As the wavelengths of electromagnetic waves increase, the frequencies ___decrease___, for waves moving in a(n) ___vacuum___.

## Wave or Particle? (pages 536–537)

13. Electromagnetic radiation behaves sometimes like a(n) ___wave___ and sometimes like a stream of ___particles___.

14. Interference only occurs when two or more waves overlap, so ___Young's___ experiment showed that light behaves like a ___wave___.

15. The emission of electrons from a metal caused by light striking the metal is called the ___photoelectric___ effect.

16. Blue light has a higher frequency than red light, so photons of blue light have ___more___ energy than photons of red light.

## Intensity (page 538)

17. The closer you get to a source of light, the ___brighter___ the light appears.

18. Intensity is the ___rate___ at which a wave's energy flows through a given unit of area.

19. As photons travel farther from the source, the ___intensity___ of light decreases.

Name ______________________ Class ______________ Date __________



# Section 18.2 The Electromagnetic Spectrum

**(pages 539–545)**

*This section identifies the waves in the electromagnetic spectrum and describes their uses.*

## Reading Strategy (page 539)

**Summarizing** Complete the table for the electromagnetic spectrum. List at least two uses for each kind of wave. For more information on this Reading Strategy, see the **Reading and Study Skills** in the **Skills and Reference Handbook** at the end of your textbook.

| The Electromagnetic Spectrum | | |
|---|---|---|
| **Type of Waves** | **Uses** Sample answers: | |
| Radio Waves | Communications | Cooking and radar detection systems |
| Infrared Rays | Detecting heat differences | Keeping food warm |
| Visible Light | Aids in vision | Communication and signaling |
| Ultraviolet Rays | Health (kill microorganisms in heating and cooling systems) | Agriculture (energy source to promote plant growth), Medicine |
| X-rays | Medicine | Transportation industry |
| Gamma Rays | Medicine (kill cancer cells, form images of the brain) | Industry (inspection tool) |

## The Waves of the Spectrum (pages 539–540)

1. Is the following sentence true or false? William Herschel determined that the temperature of colors of light was higher at the blue end and lower at the red end. false

2. Herschel's curiosity led him to conclude there must be invisible radiation beyond the red end of the color band.

3. Is the following sentence true or false? The full range of frequencies of electromagnetic radiation is called the electromagnetic spectrum. true

4. Name each kind of wave in the electromagnetic spectrum, from the longest to shortest wavelength.

   a. Radio waves b. Infrared rays

   c. Visible light d. Ultraviolet rays

   e. X-rays f. Gamma rays

Name ______________________ Class ________________ Date ____________



## Radio Waves (pages 540–542)

5. Circle the letter of each way that radio waves might be used.
   a. x-ray machines
   (b.) microwave ovens
   (c.) radio technology
   (d.) television technology
6. What is the difference between amplitude modulation (AM) and frequency modulation (FM)? In amplitude modulation, the amplitude of the wave is varied and the frequency remains the same. In frequency modulation, the frequency of the wave is varied and the amplitude remains the same.
7. How far do microwaves generally penetrate food? Microwaves penetrate food a few centimeters.
8. How is the Doppler effect used to detect the speed of a vehicle? Radio waves are sent from a stationary source toward a moving car. The faster a car is moving toward the source, the higher the frequency of the radio waves returning to the source.

## Infrared Rays (page 543)

9. Circle the letter of each way infrared rays are used.
   a. source of light
   (b.) to discover areas of heat differences
   (c.) source of heat
   d. to discover areas of depth differences
10. Thermograms show variations in ___temperature___ and are used to find places where a building loses heat to the environment.

## Visible Light (page 543)

11. Is the following sentence true or false? One use for visible light is to help people communicate with one another. ___true___

## Ultraviolet Rays (page 544)

12. Ultraviolet radiation has applications in ___health and medicine___ and ___agriculture___.
13. Is the following sentence true or false? Ultraviolet radiation helps your skin produce vitamin D. ___true___

## X-rays (page 544)

14. Is the following sentence true or false? X-rays have higher frequencies than ultraviolet rays. ___true___
15. Why are X-rays helpful? They are used in medicine, industry, and transportation to make pictures of the inside of solid objects.

## Gamma Rays (page 545)

16. Gamma rays have the highest ___frequencies___ and therefore the most ___energy___ and the greatest penetrating ability of all the electromagnetic waves.
17. How is gamma radiation used in medicine? Gamma radiation is used to kill cancer cells and to make pictures of the brain.

# Section 18.3 Behavior of Light

**(pages 546-549)**

*This section discusses the behavior of light when it strikes different types of materials.*

## Reading Strategy (page 546)

**Monitoring Your Understanding** As you read, complete the flowchart to show how different materials affect light. For more information on this Reading Strategy, see the **Reading and Study Skills** in the **Skills and Reference Handbook** at the end of your textbook.

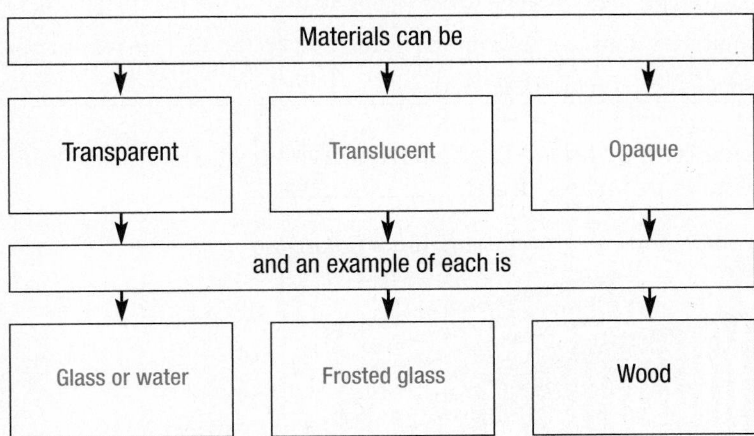


## Light and Materials (pages 546–547)

1. Is the following sentence true or false? Without light, nothing is visible. ____true____

*Match each term to its definition.*

| | Term | Definition |
|---|---|---|
| b | 2. transparent | a. Material that absorbs or reflects all of the light that strikes it |
| a | 3. opaque | b. Material that transmits light |
| c | 4. translucent | c. Material that scatters light |

## Interactions of Light (pages 547–549)

5. Is the following sentence true or false? Just as light can affect matter, matter can affect light. ____true____

6. When light strikes a new medium, it can be ____reflected____, ____absorbed____, or ____transmitted____.

Name ______________________ Class ________________ Date ____________



7. When light is transmitted, it can be refracted, polarized, or scattered.

8. A copy of an object formed by reflected or refracted light waves is known as a(n) image.

9. When parallel light waves strike an uneven surface and reflect off it in the same direction, regular reflection occurs.

10. When parallel light waves strike a rough, uneven surface and reflect in many different directions, diffuse reflection occurs.

11. Light bends, or refracts, when it passes at an angle from one type of medium into another.

12. Explain why a mirage occurs. Light travels faster in hot air than in cooler, denser air. On a hot day, light is gradually refracted as it moves into layers of hotter and hotter air. This refraction causes some of the light to follow a curved path to the ground.

13. Is the following sentence true or false? Light with waves that vibrate in only one plane is polarized light. true

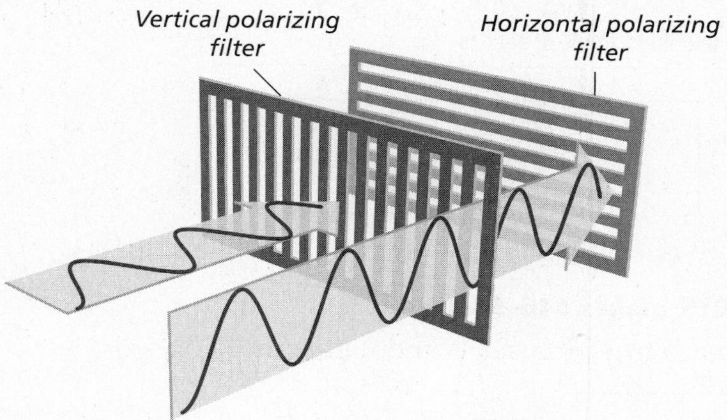


14. Refer to the drawing and complete the table on polarizing filters.

| Polarizing Filters | | |
|---|---|---|
| **Direction of Light Vibration** | **Filter Type** | **Action** |
| Horizontal wave | Vertically polarizing filter | Light is blocked. |
| Vertical wave | Vertically polarizing filter | Light passes through. |

15. How do sunglasses block glare? The vertically polarized filters of the sunglasses block the horizontally polarized light being reflected.

16. The effect when light is redirected as it passes through a medium is called scattering.

17. Explain why the sun looks red at sunset and sunrise. Small particles in the atmosphere scatter shorter-wavelength blue light more than light of longer wavelengths. Longer wavelengths of orange and red light reach the eyes.

Name ______________________ Class ________________ Date ____________



# Section 18.4 Color
**(pages 550–553)**

*This section explains how a prism separates white light. It also discusses factors that influence the various properties of color.*

## Reading Strategy (page 550)

**Venn Diagram** As you read, label the Venn diagram for mixing primary colors of light. For more information on this Reading Strategy, see the **Reading and Study Skills** in the **Skills and Reference Handbook** at the end of your textbook.

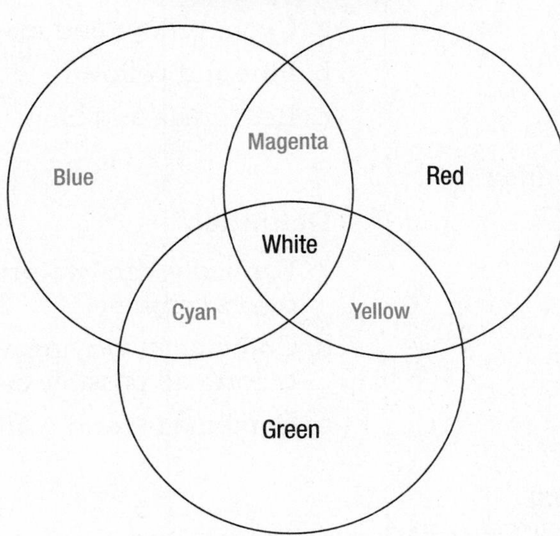


## Separating White Light Into Colors (page 551)

1. What did Isaac Newton's experiments with a prism in 1666 show? They showed that white sunlight is made up of all the colors of the visible spectrum.

2. What happens when white light passes through a prism? Shorter wavelengths refract more than longer wavelengths, and the colors separate.

3. Circle the letter of the process in which white light is separated into the colors of the rainbow.
   a. reflection
   b. dispersion (circled)
   c. absorption
   d. polarization

4. How does a rainbow form? Water droplets act like prisms and separate sunlight into the spectrum.

Name ______________________ Class ______________ Date __________



## The Colors of Objects (pages 551–552)

5. List two factors that determine the color of an object seen by reflected light.
   a. What the object is made of
   b. The color of light that strikes the object

6. Is the following sentence true or false? I see a red car in sunlight because the color of light reaching my eyes is mostly red light.
   true

## Mixing Colors of Light (page 552)

*Match the colors of light with the correct type of color.*

| Type of Color | Colors of Light |
|---|---|
| c 7. primary colors | a. Cyan, yellow, and magenta |
| a 8. secondary colors | b. Blue and yellow |
| b 9. complementary colors | c. Red, green and blue |

*Match each color of light to its definition.*

| Type of Color | Definition |
|---|---|
| b 10. primary colors | a. Formed when two primary colors combine |
| a 11. secondary colors | b. Combine in varying amounts to form all possible colors |
| c 12. complementary colors | c. Combine to form white light |

## Mixing Pigments (page 553)

13. What is a pigment? A pigment is a material that absorbs some colors of light and reflects other colors.

14. List four natural sources of pigments.
   a. Metal oxide compounds   b. Minerals
   c. Plants   d. Animals

15. The primary colors of pigments are cyan, yellow, and magenta.

*Match the primary colors of pigment to the color they produce when combined.*

| Primary Colors | Color Produced |
|---|---|
| c 16. Cyan and magenta | a. green |
| a 17. Cyan and yellow | b. red |
| b 18. Yellow and magenta | c. blue |

19. Any two colors of pigments that combine to make black pigment are complementary colors of pigments.

Name ______________________ Class ______________ Date ____________



# Section 18.5 Sources of Light
**(pages 558–562)**

*This section discusses the major sources of light and their uses.*

## Reading Strategy (page 558)

**Flowchart** Complete the incandescent bulb flowchart. For more information on this Reading Strategy, see the **Reading and Study Skills** in the **Skills and Reference Handbook** at the end of your textbook.

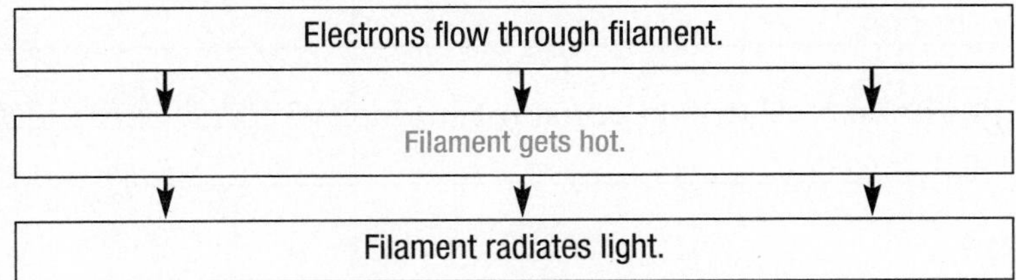


1. Objects that give off their own light are luminous.
2. List six common sources of light.
   a. Incandescent bulbs
   b. Fluorescent bulbs
   c. Laser
   d. Neon
   e. Tungsten-halogen bulbs
   f. Sodium-vapor bulbs

## Incandescent Light (page 558)

3. The light produced when an object gets hot enough to glow is incandescent.
4. As electrons flow through an incandescent light bulb, the filament heats up.
5. Is the following sentence true or false? To increase the life of the filament, incandescent light bulbs contain oxygen at very low pressure. false
6. Most of the energy given off by incandescent bulbs is in the form of heat.

## Fluorescent Light (page 559)

7. What happens in the process of fluorescence? A material absorbs light at one wavelength and then emits light at a longer wavelength.
8. A solid material that can emit light by fluorescence is called a(n) phosphor.
9. Fluorescent bulbs emit most of their energy in the form of photons.
10. Is the following sentence true or false? Incandescent bulbs are more energy efficient than fluorescent bulbs. false

## Laser Light (page 560)

**11.** A laser is a device that generates a beam of coherent light.

**12.** The letters in the word *laser* stand for

l light

a amplification

s stimulated

e emission

r radiation.

**13.** What is coherent light? Coherent light is light in which waves have the same wavelength, and the crests and troughs are lined up.

**14.** Why does coherent light have a relatively constant intensity? Coherent light doesn't spread out significantly from its source.

## Neon Light (page 561)

**15.** How is neon light emitted? Neon light is emitted when electrons move through a gas or a mixture of gases inside glass tubing.

**16.** List three gases used to produce neon light.

a. Helium

b. Argon

c. Krypton

**17.** Why do different types of neon light glow in different colors? Each kind of gas emits photons of different energies and color. The different photons combine to give each glowing gas a distinctive color. The color of the glass tube also affects the color of the light.

## Sodium-Vapor Light (page 562)

**18.** Sodium-vapor lights contain a mixture of neon and argon gases and a small amount of solid sodium.

**19.** Explain what happens when an electric current passes through a sodium-vapor bulb. The electric current ionizes the gas mixture, which warms up. The heat causes the sodium to change from a solid into a gas.

## Tungsten-Halogen Light (page 562)

**20.** Explain how a tungsten-halogen light bulb works. The bulb is filled with a halogen gas. Electrons flow through a tungsten filament. The filament gets hot and emits light.

Name ______________________ Class ______________________ Date ______________



# WordWise

*Complete the sentences using one of the scrambled words below.*

| | | |
|---|---|---|
| nrcteleos | tarfes | qucreynef |
| treclefs | rigehh | kabcl |
| mefailnt | riotrafecn | ratenemypocml |
| yrecurm | snohpot | dairo |
| sifdel | culstantren | otehcern |

Electromagnetic waves consist of changing electric and changing magnetic fields.

You hear thunder from a distant lightning bolt a few seconds after you see the lightning because light travels much faster than sound.

If you know the wavelength of an electromagnetic wave in a vacuum, you can calculate its frequency.

Although light behaves as a wave, the photoelectric effect shows that light also consists of bundles of energy called photons.

Antennas use radio waves to send signals to television receivers.

Ultraviolet rays have a higher frequency than waves of violet light.

If you can look through a material but what you see is not clear or distinct, then the material is said to be translucent.

When a beam of light enters a new medium at an angle, it changes direction, and refraction occurs.

A truck appears red in the sunlight because its paint reflects mainly red light.

A color of light mixed equally with its complementary color of light yields white light.

Complementary colors of pigments combine to form black pigment.

An incandescent bulb produces light by using an electric current to heat a(n) filament.

Inside a fluorescent bulb, an electric current passes through mercury vapor and produces ultraviolet light.

Light that consists of a single wavelength of light with its crests and troughs lined up is called coherent light.

Neon lights emit light when electrons flow through gas in a tube.

# Calculating Wavelength and Frequency

**Math Skill: Multiplication and Division of Exponents**

You may want to read more about this **Math Skill** in the **Skills and Reference Handbook** at the end of your textbook.

A particular AM radio station broadcasts at a frequency of 1030 MHz. What is the wavelength of the transmitted radio wave assuming it travels in a vacuum?

**1. Read and Understand**

*What information are you given?*

Speed $= c = 3.00 \times 10^8$ m/s

Frequency $=$ 1030 kHz $= 1030 \times 10^3$ Hz

**2. Plan and Solve**

*What unknown are you trying to calculate?*

Wavelength = ?

*What formula contains the given quantities and the unknown?*

Speed = Wavelength × Frequency

$$\text{Wavelength} = \frac{\text{Speed}}{\text{Frequency}}$$

*Replace each variable with its known value.*

$$\text{Wavelength} = \frac{3.00 \times 10^8 \text{ m/s}}{1030 \text{ Hz} \times 10^8 \text{ Hz}}$$

$$= \frac{3.00 \times 10^8 \text{ m/s}}{1.030 \times 10^6 \text{ 1/s}} = 291 \text{ m}$$

**3. Look Back and Check**

*Is your answer reasonable?*

Radio waves have frequencies greater that 1 mm, so 291 m is a reasonable wavelength for a radio wave.

## Math Practice

*On a separate sheet of paper, solve the following problems.*

1. In a vacuum, the wavelength of light from a laser is 630 nm ($630 \times 10^{-9}$ m). What is the frequency of the light?

$$\text{Frequency} = \frac{\text{Speed}}{\text{Wavelength}} = \frac{3.0 \times 10^8 \text{ m/s}}{630 \times 10^{-9} \text{ m}} = 4.8 \times 10^{14} \text{ Hz}$$

2. If a radio wave vibrates at 80.0 MHz, what is its wavelength?

$$\text{Wavelength} = \frac{\text{Speed}}{\text{Frequency}} = \frac{3.0 \times 10^8 \text{ m/s}}{80.0 \times 10^6 \text{ Hz}} = 3.8 \text{ m}$$

3. A radio station broadcasts at 780 kHz. The wavelength of its radio waves is 385 m. Verify that the radio wave travels at the speed of light.

Speed = Wavelength × Frequency $= 385 \text{ m} \times (780 \times 10^3 \text{ Hz}) = 3.0 \times 10^8$ m/s

Name ______________________ Class ______________ Date ____________



# Section 19.1 Mirrors

**(pages 570–573)**

*This section describes the law of reflection and explains how images are formed by plane, concave, and convex mirrors. Uses of mirrors are also described.*

## Reading Strategy (page 570)

**Comparing and Contrasting** After reading this section, compare mirror types by completing the table. For more information on this Reading Strategy, see the **Reading and Study Skills** in the **Skills and Reference Handbook** at the end of your textbook.

| Mirror Types | | |
|---|---|---|
| **Mirror** | **Shape of Surface** | **Image (virtual, real, or both)** |
| Plane | Flat | Virtual |
| Concave | Inside curved surface | Both |
| Convex | Outside curved surface | Virtual |

## The Law of Reflection (pages 570–571)

1. A ray diagram shows how rays change direction when they strike mirrors and pass through lenses.
2. Is the following sentence true or false? On a ray diagram, the angle of incidence is the angle that a reflected ray makes with a line drawn perpendicular to the surface of a mirror. false
3. Circle the letter of the sentence that best answers the following question. What does a ray diagram of the law of reflection show?
   a. The angle of incidence is greater than the angle of reflection.
   b. The angle of reflection is greater than the angle of incidence.
   (c.) The angle of incidence is equal to the angle of reflection.
   d. The angle of incidence increases as the angle of reflection decreases.

## Plane Mirrors (page 571)

4. A mirror with a flat surface is known as a(n) plane mirror.
5. Circle the letter of each sentence that is true about plane mirrors.
   (a.) Plane mirrors always produce virtual images.
   (b.) Plane mirrors produce right-left reversed images of objects.
   c. Light rays reflect from a mirror at an angle that is twice as large as the angle of incidence.
   (d.) Your image appears to be the same distance behind a mirror as you are in front of it.

6. What type of image is a copy of an object formed at the location from which the light rays appear to come?

   a. reversed image   (b.) virtual image
   c. real image   d. reflected image

## Concave and Convex Mirrors (pages 572–573)

7. Circle the letter of the object that is most like the shape of a concave mirror.

   (a.) the inside of a shallow bowl   b. the bottom of a bucket
   c. the outside surface of a ball   d. a glass window pane

8. What is the focal point? When a concave mirror reflects light rays that are parallel to the optical axis, the curved reflecting surface causes the light rays to come together at the focal point.

9. Is the following sentence true or false? A real image is a copy of an object formed at the point where light rays actually meet.
   true

*For questions 10 through 12, refer to the diagrams below.*

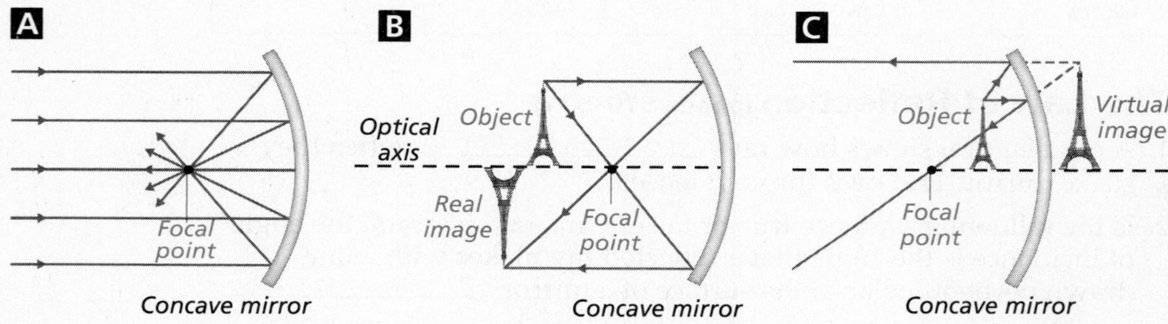


10. Label the focal point on each diagram.
11. In B and C, label the object and image locations and identify the image as real or virtual. *Hint:* The object is always right-side up and in front of the reflecting surface of the mirror.
12. What determines whether a concave mirror produces a real image or a virtual image?

    a. the size of the object
    b. the shape of the object
    (c.) the position of the object relative to the focal point
    d. the location of the optical axis

13. A curved mirror whose outside surface is the reflecting surface is called a(n) convex mirror.
14. Why do convex mirrors always form virtual images? Because the light rays spread out as they reflect from the curved surface of the mirror.
15. Is the following sentence true or false? The image formed by a convex lens is always upright and smaller than the object.
    true

Name ______________________ Class ____________________ Date ______________

Chapter 19 Optics

# Section 19.2 Lenses
## (pages 574–578)

*This section defines index of refraction and discusses how it is related to the way light behaves upon entering different materials. Image formation in concave and convex lenses are presented.*

## Reading Strategy (page 574)

**Building Vocabulary** As you read the section, define in your own words each vocabulary word listed in the table. For more information on this Reading Strategy, see the **Reading and Study Skills** in the **Skills and Reference Handbook** at the end of your textbook.

| Refraction and Reflection | |
|---|---|
| **Vocabulary Term** | **Definition** |
| Index of refraction | Ratio of the speed of light in a vacuum to the speed of light in the material |
| Critical angle | Angle of incidence that produces an angle of refraction of 90 degrees |
| Total internal reflection | The complete reflection of a light ray back into its original medium |

## Index of Refraction of Light (pages 574–575)

1. Circle the letter of the sentence about the speed of light through media that is true.
   a. Once light passes from a vacuum into any medium, it speeds up.
   (b.) Compared to other media, air slows the speed of light only slightly.
   c. The speed of light is greater in water than in air.
   d. The speed of light in a new medium depends on the size of the new medium.
2. What determines how much a light ray bends when it passes from one medium to another? The amount of refraction depends upon the difference between the speeds of light in the two media.
3. The ratio of the speed of light in a vacuum to the speed of light in a particular material is known as the index of refraction of that material.

## Concave and Convex Lenses (pages 576–577)

4. An object made of transparent material that has one or two curved surfaces that can refract light is called a(n) lens.
5. Two properties of a lens that affect the way it refracts light are curvature and thickness.
6. A lens that is curved inward at the center and is thickest at the outside edges is called a(n) concave lens.

Name ______________________ Class ______________ Date __________



7. Concave lenses always cause light rays to spread out or diverge.

8. Circle the letter of each sentence that is true about convex lenses.
   a. Convex lenses are diverging lenses.
   (b.) Fly eyes have many facets shaped like the surface of convex lenses.
   (c.) Convex lenses can form either real or virtual images.
   d. Convex lenses are shaped somewhat like the inside of a bowl.

9. What determines whether a convex lens will form a real image or a virtual image? The type of image depends upon the position of the object with respect to the focal point and the lens.

*For questions 10 and 11, refer to the diagrams below.*

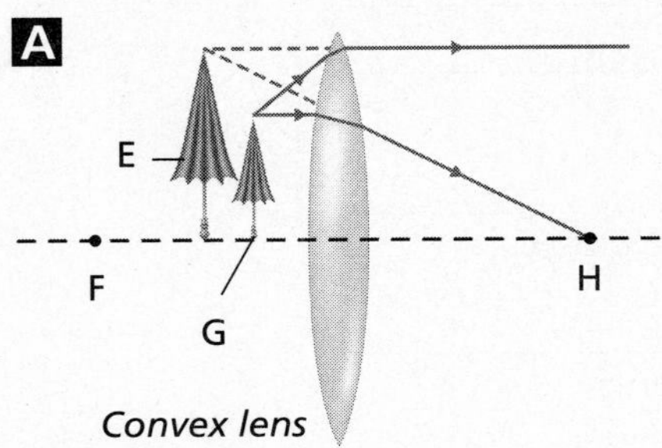


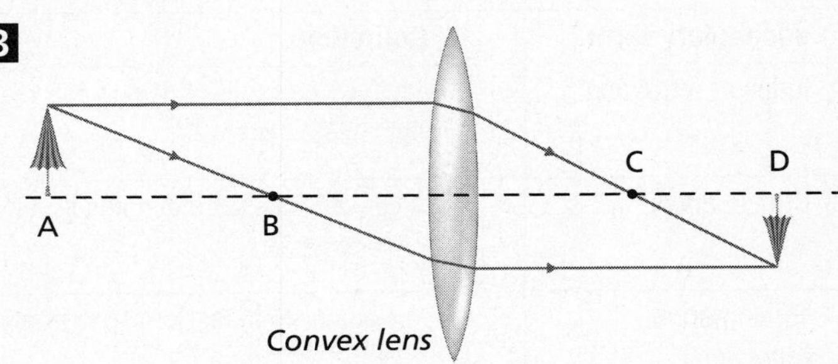


10. In each diagram identify the labeled items as the object, focal point, or image. Also, identify the image as virtual or real.

| | | | |
|---|---|---|---|
| A. | Object | B. | Focal point |
| C. | Focal point | D. | Real image |
| E. | Virtual image | F. | Focal point |
| G. | Object | H. | Focal point |

11. Which diagram shows the formation of a virtual image?
Diagram A

## Total Internal Reflection (page 578)

12. Circle each letter of a sentence that is true about the critical angle.
    (a.) At the critical angle, light refracts along the surface between two media.
    b. All the light is reflected back into the first medium at the critical angle.
    c. Only concave lenses have critical angles.
    (d.) All the light is reflected back into the second, denser medium when the critical angle is exceeded.

13. Is the following sentence true or false? Materials that have small critical angles, such as the glass used in fiber optics, cause most of the light entering them to be totally internally reflected. true

Name ______________________ Class ________________ Date ____________



# Section 19.3 Optical Instruments

**(pages 580–585)**

*This section describes optical instruments, including telescopes, cameras, and microscopes. The basic principles of image formation by these instruments are explained.*

## Reading Strategy (page 580)

**Using Prior Knowledge** Add the names and descriptions of other optical instruments you know to the diagram. Revise the diagram after you read the section. For more information on this Reading Strategy, see the **Reading and Study Skills** in the **Skills and Reference Handbook** at the end of your textbook.

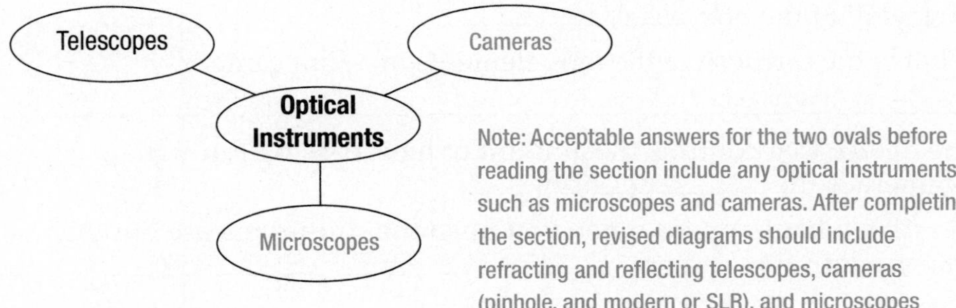


## Telescopes (pages 580–581)

1. Circle the letter that best describes the amount of time it takes light from the most distant stars to reach Earth.

   a. seconds
   b. hours
   c. millions of years
   (d.) billions of years

2. An instrument that uses lenses or mirrors to collect and focus light from distant objects is called a(n) ___telescope___.

3. Complete the table about telescopes.

| Telescopes | | |
|---|---|---|
| **Type** | **Parts That Collect and Focus Light** | **Description of How Image Is Formed** |
| Reflecting telescope | Mirrors and convex lenses | A concave mirror focuses light from a distant object, and this light is reflected by an angled mirror to form a real image; the convex lens of the eyepiece enlarges the image. |
| Refracting telescope | Convex lenses | Light from a distant object passes through a convex lens, which forms a real image inside the telescope; another convex lens in the eyepiece forms an upside down virtual image of the real image. |

Name ______________________ Class ______________ Date ___________

Chapter 19 Optics

## Cameras (pages 582–584)

4. Describe what a camera does. A camera is an optical instrument that records an image of an object.

5. Circle the letter of each sentence that describes how cameras form or record images.
   - (a.) An image is recorded on film or by a sensor.
   - b. Light rays are focused to form virtual images.
   - (c.) Light rays enter through an opening.
   - (d.) Light rays are focused by the opening or lens.

6. Is the following sentence true or false? In a simple pinhole camera made from a box, an upside-down, real image is formed on the back wall of the box. true

7. What is the purpose of the lens elements in a film camera? They focus incoming rays of light.

8. The device that controls the amount of light passing through a camera is the diaphragm.

9. Describe what happens when you push the shutter release button on a modern film camera. The mirror flips up and the shutter briefly opens to let the focused light rays strike the film.

10. How is the position of the lens of a modern film camera used to bring an object into focus? The lens is moved toward or away from the film.

## Microscopes (page 584)

11. An optical instrument that uses two convex lenses to magnify small objects is called a(n) compound microscope.

12. Circle the letter that describes the path light rays follow through a compound microscope.
   - a. Light rays from the objective lens pass through the object and then pass through the light source.
   - b. Light rays from above pass up through the object and then pass through the objective lens.
   - (c.) Light rays from below pass up through the object, the objective lens, and the eyepiece lens.
   - d. Light rays from below pass up through the object, the concave lens, and the objective lens.

13. Is the following sentence true or false? When you look through the eyepiece of a compound microscope you see an enlarged, virtual image of the object. true

Name ______________________ Class ________________ Date ____________



# Section 19.4 The Eye and Vision
**(pages 588–592)**

*This section describes the eye as an optical instrument. Parts of the eye and their functions are defined. Vision problems and how they can be corrected are also described.*

## Reading Strategy (page 588)

**Outlining** As you read, make an outline of the important ideas in this section. Use the green headings as the main topics and the blue headings as subtopics. For more information on this Reading Strategy, see the **Reading and Study Skills** in the **Skills and Reference Handbook** at the end of your textbook.

**Section 19.4 Outline**

I. The Eye and Vision
  A. Structure of the Eye
    1. Cornea
    2. Pupil and Iris
    3. Lens
    4. Retina
    5. Rods and Cones
  B. Correcting Vision Problems
    1. Nearsightedness
    2. Farsightedness
    3. Astigmatism

## Structure of the Eye (pages 588–590)

*Write the letter of the part of the eye that best matches each description.*

**Description**

c 1. Its curved surface helps to focus light entering the eye.

e 2. It focuses light onto sensor cells at the back of the eye.

a 3. This opening allows light to pass through the eye.

d 4. This expands and contracts to control the amount of light entering the eye.

c 5. This is the transparent outer coating of the eye.

b 6. Its surface has rods and cones.

**Part of Eye**

a. pupil
b. retina
c. cornea
d. iris
e. lens

Name ______________ Class ______________ Date ______________



7. Is the following sentence true or false? Nerve endings called rods and cones convert light into electrical signals that are sent to the brain through the optic nerve. true

8. Where on the retina does a blind spot occur? A blind spot occurs in the area of the retina where the nerve endings come together to form the optic nerve.

## Correcting Vision Problems (pages 590–592)

*For questions 9 and 10, refer to the figures below.*

Problem: Nearsightedness (Eyeball is too long.)

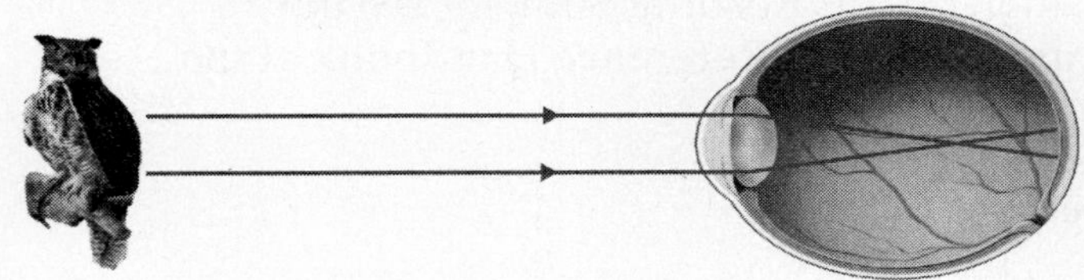

Correction:

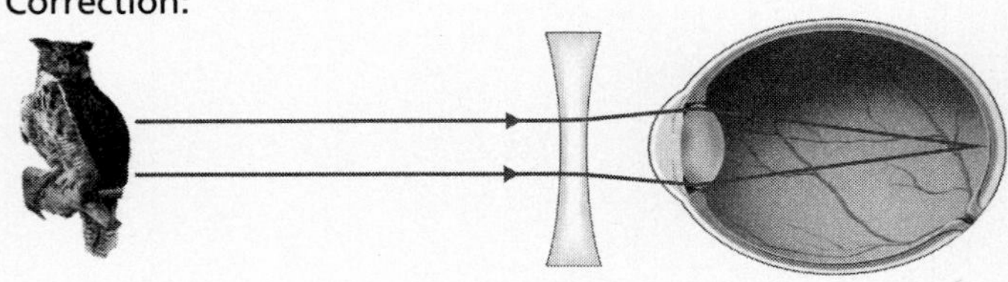

9. Circle the letter of the location where the image forms when nearsightedness occurs.

a. on the retina
b. behind the retina
(c.) before it reaches the retina
d. on the lens

10. Nearsightedness can be corrected by placing a(n) diverging concave lens in front of the eye.

*Match each type of vision problem to its definition.*

| Vision Problem | Definition |
|---|---|
| b 11. astigmatism | a. A condition that causes distant objects to appear blurry because the cornea is too curved or the eyeball is too long |
| c 12. farsightedness | b. A condition that causes objects at any distance to appear blurry because the cornea or lens is misshapen |
| a 13. nearsightedness | c. A condition that causes nearby objects to appear blurry because the cornea is not curved enough or the eyeball is too short |

# WordWise

*Use the clues below to identify vocabulary terms from Chapter 19. Write the terms below, putting one letter in each blank. When you finish, the term enclosed in the diagonal will reveal a term that is important in the study of optics.*

**Clues**

1. Shows how the paths of light rays change when they strike mirrors or pass through lenses
2. Transparent material with one or two curved surfaces that can refract light
3. A mirror with a flat surface
4. An instrument that uses lenses or mirrors to collect and focus light from distant objects
5. Expands and contracts to control the amount of light entering the eye
6. An optical instrument that records an image of an object
7. Transparent outer layer of the eye
8. When the cornea is misshapen, this vision problem can result.
9. Type of lens that causes light rays to diverge

1. r a y d i a g r a m
2. l e n s
3. p l a n e m i r r o r
4. t e l e s c o p e
5. i r i s
6. c a m e r a
7. c o r n e a
8. a s t i g m a t i s m
9. c o n c a v e l e n s

**Hidden Word:** r e a l i m a g e

**Definition:** A copy of an object that forms where light rays converge

Name ______________________ Class ______________ Date __________



# Calculating Index of Refraction

**Math Skill: Ratios and Proportions**

You may want to read more about this **Math Skill** in the **Skills and Reference Handbook** at the end of your textbook.

The speed of light in the mineral halite, NaCl, is approximately $1.95 \times 10^8$ m/s. Calculate the index of refraction for halite. (Recall that the speed of light in a vacuum is $3.00 \times 10^8$ m/s.)

**1. Read and Understand**

*What information are you given?*

Speed of light in halite = $1.95 \times 10^8$ m/s

Speed of light in vacuum = $3.00 \times 10^8$ m/s

**2. Plan and Solve**

*What variable are you trying to determine?*

Index of refraction = ?

*What formulas contain the given variables?*

$$\text{Index of refraction} = \frac{\text{Speed of light}_{\text{vacuum}}}{\text{Speed of light}_{\text{material}}} = \frac{(3.00 \times 10^8 \text{ m/s})}{(1.95 \times 10^8 \text{ m/s})} = 1.54$$

**3. Look Back and Check**

*Is your answer reasonable?*

Speed of light in vacuum = $(1.95 \times 10^8 \text{ m/s})(1.54) = 3.00 \times 10^8$ m/s

Yes, the answer is reasonable. Substituting the calculated index of refraction for halite back into the equation yields the value of the speed of light in a vacuum.

## Math Practice

*On a separate sheet of paper, solve the following problems.*

1. The mineral uvarovite has an index of refraction of 1.86. Calculate the speed of light in this sample of uvarovite.

   Speed of light $_{\text{uvarovite}} = (3.00 \times 10^8 \text{m/s})/(1.86) = 1.61 \times 10^8$ m/s

2. What is the index of refraction of a sample of opal, if the speed of light passing through it is $2.05 \times 10^8$ m/s?

   Index of refraction = $(3.00 \times 10^8 \text{m/s})/(2.05 \times 10^8 \text{m/s}) = 1.46$

3. Because its atomic structure varies with direction, a sample of the mineral calcite has an index of refraction of 1.486 along one direction in the crystal, while another direction has an index of refraction of 1.658. Which index represents the faster speed of light through the calcite? Explain your answer.

   1.486; The lower the index of refraction, the greater the speed of light moving through the calcite, as indicated by the reciprocal relationship between the index of refraction and the speed of light.

# Section 20.1 Electric Charge and Static Electricity
## (pages 600–603)

*This section explains how electric charge is created and how positive and negative charges affect each other. It also discusses the different ways that electric charge can be transferred.*

## Reading Strategy (page 600)

**Identifying Main Ideas** Copy the table on a separate sheet of paper. As you read, write the main ideas. For more information on this Reading Strategy, see the **Reading and Study Skills** in the **Skills and Reference Handbook** at the end of your textbook.

| Characteristics of Electric Charge | |
|---|---|
| **Topic** | **Main Idea** |
| Electric Charge | An excess or shortage of electrons produces a net electric charge. |
| Electric Forces | Like charges repel and opposite charges attract. |
| Electric Fields | The strength of a field depends on the net charge and distance from the charge. |
| Static Electricity | Charge can be transferred by friction, contact, and induction. |



## Electric Charge (pages 600–601)

1. What are the two types of electric charge?

   a. Positive b. Negative

2. Is the following sentence true or false? In an atom, negatively charged electrons surround a positively charged nucleus. true

3. Is the following sentence true or false? If a neutral atom gains one or more electrons, it becomes a positively charged ion. false

4. What is the SI unit of electric charge? The coulomb

## Electric Forces (page 601)

5. Circle the letter of each sentence that is true about electric force.

   a. Like charges attract and opposite charges repel.

   (b.) Electric force is the attraction or repulsion between electrically charged objects.

   c. Electric force is inversely proportional to the amount of charge.

   (d.) Electric force is inversely proportional to the square of the distance between two charges.

6. Which are stronger inside an atom, electric forces or gravitational forces? Electric forces are stronger.

7. Is the following sentence true or false? Electric forces cause friction and other contact forces. true

## Electric Fields (page 602)

8. A charge's electric field is the effect the charge has on other charges in the space around it.

9. Circle the letters of the factors that the strength of an electric field depends on.
   a. the direction of the field
   b. whether the charge is positive or negative
   (c.) the amount of charge that produces the field
   (d.) the distance from the charge

10. Is the following sentence true or false? The field of a negative charge points away from the charge. false

## Static Electricity and Charging (pages 602–603)

11. Static electricity is the study of the behavior of electric charges.

12. Is the following sentence true or false? Charge can be transferred by friction, by contact, and by induction. true

13. What is the law of conservation of charge? The total charge in an isolated system is constant.

14. Rubbing a balloon on your hair is an example of charging by friction.

15. A charge transfer between objects that touch each other is called charging by contact.

16. Circle the letter of each sentence that is true about charging.
   (a.) When you rub a balloon on your hair, your hair loses electrons and becomes positively charged.
   b. The sphere of a Van de Graaff generator transfers all of its charge to you when you touch it.
   (c.) Induction occurs when charge is transferred without contact between materials.
   d. Static charges cannot move.

## Static Discharge (page 603)

17. Is the following sentence true or false? Static discharge occurs when a pathway through which charges can move forms suddenly. true

18. How does lightning occur? Negative charge in the lower part of a storm cloud induces a positive charge in the ground below the cloud. Eventually the air becomes charged, forming a pathway for the electrons to travel from the cloud to the ground.

Name ______________ Class ______________ Date ______________



# Section 20.2 Electric Current and Ohm's Law

**(pages 604–607)**

*This section discusses electric current, resistance, and voltage. It also uses Ohm's Law to explain how voltage, current, and resistance are related.*

## Reading Strategy (page 604)

**Predicting** Before you read, write a prediction of what electric current is in the table below. After you read, if your prediction was incorrect or incomplete, write what electric current actually is. For more information on this Reading Strategy, see the **Reading and Study Skills** in the **Skills and Reference Handbook** at the end of your textbook.

| Electric Current | |
|---|---|
| **Electric Current Probably Means** | **Electric Current Actually Means** |
| Sample answer: Current is moving charge. | Electric current is a continuous flow of charge. |

## Electric Current (page 604)

1. What is electric current? Electric current is a continuous flow of charge.

2. Complete the following table about electric current.

| Electric Current | | |
|---|---|---|
| **Type of Current** | **How Charge Flows** | **Examples** |
| Direct | One direction | Flashlight |
| Alternating | Two directions | Home or school |

3. Electrons flow in the wire from a(n) negative terminal to a(n) positive terminal.

## Conductors and Insulators (page 605)

4. What is an electrical conductor? An electrical conductor is material through which charge can easily flow.

5. What is an electrical insulator? An electrical insulator is material through which charge cannot easily flow.

6. Is the following sentence true or false? Metals are good conductors because they do not have freely moving electrons.
false

Name ______________ Class ______________ Date ______________



*Match each material to the category of a conductor or insulator.*

| | Material | Category |
|---|---|---|
| a | 7. Copper | a. conductor |
| b | 8. Plastic | b. insulator |
| b | 9. Rubber | |
| a | 10. Silver | |
| b | 11. Wood | |

## Resistance (page 605)

12. Explain why the current is reduced as electrons move through a conductor. The electrons collide with electrons and ions. These collisions convert some kinetic energy into thermal energy, leaving less energy to move the electrons.

13. Circle the letter of each factor that affects a material's resistance.
    - (a.) its length
    - (b.) its temperature
    - c. its velocity
    - (d.) its thickness

14. What is a superconductor? A superconductor is a material that has almost zero resistance when it is cooled to low temperatures.

## Voltage (page 606)

*Match each term to its definition.*

| | Definition | Term |
|---|---|---|
| c | 15. A device that converts chemical energy to electrical energy | a. flow of charge |
| a | 16. Requires a complete loop | b. voltage |
| b | 17. The difference in electrical potential energy between two places in an electric field | c. battery |

18. Is the following sentence true or false? Three common voltage sources are batteries, solar cells, and generators. true

## Ohm's Law (page 607)

19. Is the following sentence true or false? According to Ohm's law, the voltage in a circuit equals the product of the energy and the resistance. false

20. Doubling the voltage in a circuit doubles the current if resistance is held constant.

21. Is the following sentence true or false? Doubling the resistance in a circuit will halve the current if voltage is held constant. true

# Section 20.3 Electric Circuits
**(pages 609–613)**

*This section describes circuit diagrams and types of circuits. It also explains calculation of electric power and electric energy and discusses electrical safety.*

## Reading Strategy (page 609)

**Relating Text and Visuals** As you read about household circuits, complete the table by listing three things the diagram in Figure 13 helps you understand about circuits. For more information on this Reading Strategy, see the **Reading and Study Skills** in the **Skills and Reference Handbook** at the end of your textbook.

| Understanding a Circuit Diagram |
| --- |
| **What Can Be Seen in the Circuit Diagram?** |
| Wire bringing current from outside<br>Grounding wire<br>Separate circuit for the lights<br>Separate circuit for the dryer |

## Circuit Diagrams (pages 609–610)

1. Circuit diagrams use ___symbols___ to represent parts of a circuit, including a source of electrical energy and devices that are run by the electrical energy.

*Match each symbol to what it indicates on a circuit diagram.*

| | Symbol | What Symbol Indicates |
| --- | --- | --- |
| c | 2. + | a. The direction of current |
| b | 3. – | b. A negative terminal |
| a | 4. ⟶ | c. A positive terminal |

## Series Circuits (page 610)

5. Is the following sentence true or false? In a series circuit, if one element stops functioning, then none of the elements can operate. ___true___

6. Explain why the bulbs shine less brightly when more bulbs are added to a series circuit. ___Adding more bulbs increases the resistance, which decreases the current.___

## Parallel Circuits (page 610)

7. Is the following sentence true or false? Circuits in a home are rarely wired in parallel. ___false___

8. If one element stops functioning in a parallel circuit, the rest of the elements ___can still operate___.

## Power and Energy Calculations (pages 611–612)

9. The rate at which electrical energy is converted to another form of energy is called ___electric power___.

10. The SI unit of electric power is the joule per second, or ___watt___, which is abbreviated ___W___.

11. Is the following sentence true or false? Electric power is calculated by multiplying current times voltage. ___true___

12. Write the formula for calculating electrical energy.

    ___$E = P \times t$___

13. The unit of energy usually used by electric power companies is the ___kilowatt-hour___.

## Electrical Safety (pages 612–613)

14. Circle the letters of what could happen if the current in a wire exceeds the circuit's safety limit.

    (a.) The wire could overheat. b. The wire could get cooler.

    (c.) A fire could start. (d.) A fuse could blow.

15. Explain how a fuse prevents current overload in a circuit. ___A wire in the center of the fuse melts, which stops the flow of charge in the circuit.___

16. A switch that opens to prevent overloads when current in a circuit is too high is called a(n) ___circuit breaker___.

17. Explain why touching an electrical device with wet hands is dangerous. ___Your hands conduct electricity more readily when they are wet.___

18. Is the following sentence true or false? A ground-fault circuit interrupter shuts down the circuit if the current flowing through the circuit and current returning to ground are equal.

    ___false___

19. The transfer of excess charge through a conductor to Earth is called ___grounding___.

20. Complete the following table about equipment used to prevent electrical accidents.

| Equipment to Prevent Current Overload | Equipment to Protect People from Shock | Equipment to Prevent Short Circuits |
|---|---|---|
| a. Fuse<br>Circuit breaker | b. Insulation<br>c. Three-prong plug<br>Grounding wire<br>d. Ground-fault circuit interrupter | e. Insulation |

Name ______________________ Class __________________ Date ____________



# Section 20.4 Electronic Devices
**(pages 618–622)**

*This section discusses how various electronic devices operate and what they are used for.*

## Reading Strategy (page 618)

**Summarizing** Copy the table on a separate sheet of paper. As you read, complete the table to summarize what you learned about solid-state components. For more information on this Reading Strategy, see the **Reading and Study Skills** in the **Skills and Reference Handbook** at the end of your textbook.

| Solid–State Components | | |
|---|---|---|
| **Solid-State Component** | **Description** | **Uses** |
| Diode | Electrons flow from an n-type to a p-type semiconductor. | Change alternating current to direct current |
| Transistor | A small current flows through the middle layer of three layers of semiconductors, changing the resistance. | Switch, amplifier |
| Integrated Circuit | A thin slice of silicon that contains many solid-state components | Mobile phones, pagers, computers |

## Electronic Signals (pages 618–619)

*Match each term to its definition.*

**Definition**

c 1. Information sent as patterns in the controlled flow of electrons through a circuit

a 2. The science of using electric current to process or transmit information

b 3. A smoothly varying signal produced by continuously changing the voltage or current in a circuit

d 4. A signal that encodes information as a string of 1's and 0's

**Term**

a. electronics
b. analog signal
c. electronic signal
d. digital signal

5. Which type of signal is usually used by an AM radio station?
Analog signals are used by AM radio stations.

6. Is the following sentence true or false? Analog signals are more reliable than digital signals. false

Name ______________________ Class ______________ Date ____________



## Vacuum Tubes (page 619)

7. Circle the letter of each item that is a true about vacuum tubes.
   (a.) can change alternating current to direct current
   b. never burn out
   (c.) can increase the strength of a signal
   (d.) can turn a current on or off

8. Is the following sentence true or false? An image is produced in a CRT when phosphors glow red, green, and blue in response to electron beams. true

## Semiconductors (page 621)

9. What is a semiconductor? A semiconductor is a crystalline solid that conducts current only under certain conditions.

10. Name the two types of semiconductors.
    a. P-type b. N-type

11. Circle the letter of each sentence that is true about a p-type semiconductor.
    (a.) It can be made by adding a trace amount of boron to a silicon.
    (b.) Electrons are attracted to positively charged holes at each boron atom.
    (c.) As the electrons jump from hole to hole, it looks like a flow of positive charge.
    d. Boron atoms provide weakly bound electrons that can flow.

12. Is the following sentence true or false? In an n-type semiconductor, weakly bound electrons can conduct a current. true

## Solid-State Components (pages 621–622)

*Match each term to its definition.*

| | Term | Definition |
|---|---|---|
| c | 13. diode | a. A solid-state component with three layers of semiconductors |
| a | 14. transistor | b. A thin slice of silicon that contains many solid-state components |
| b | 15. integrated circuit | c. A solid-state component that combines an n-type and p-type semiconductor |

16. A chip or microchip is another name for a(n) integrated circuit.

## Communications Technology (page 622)

17. Why is it useful for communication devices to use microchips? Microchips make them more portable, reliable, and affordable.

18. A mobile phone can store data such as phone numbers because capacitors store electric charge.

Name ______________ Class ______________ Date ______________



# WordWise

*Match each definition with the correct term in the grid and then write its number under the appropriate term. When you have filled in all the boxes, add up the numbers in each column, row, and the two diagonals. What is surprising about the sums?* They all equal 34.

**Definitions**

1. A property that causes subatomic particles such as protons and electrons to attract or repel other matter
2. The attraction or repulsion between electrically charged objects
3. Charge transfer without contact between materials
4. Law that total charge in an isolated system is constant
5. A continuous flow of electric charge
6. Material through which charge can easily flow
7. Material through which a charge cannot easily flow
8. The opposition to the flow of charges in a material
9. A circuit in which the charge has only one path through which it can flow
10. An electric circuit with two or more paths through which charge can flow
11. A switch that opens when current in a circuit is too high
12. Information sent as patterns in the controlled flow of electrons through a circuit
13. A smoothly varying signal produced by continuously changing the voltage or current in a circuit
14. A complete path through which a charge can flow
15. A solid-state component with three layers of semiconductors
16. A thin slice of silicon that contains many solid-state components

| | | | | Diagonal = 34 |
|---|---|---|---|---|
| integrated circuit<br>16 | induction<br>3 | electric force<br>2 | analog signal<br>13 | = 34 |
| electric current<br>5 | parallel circuit<br>10 | circuit breaker<br>11 | resistance<br>8 | = 34 |
| series circuit<br>9 | electrical conductor<br>6 | electrical insulator<br>7 | electronic signal<br>12 | = 34 |
| law of conservation of charge<br>4 | transistor<br>15 | electric circuit<br>14 | electric charge<br>1 | = 34 |
| = 34 | = 34 | = 34 | = 34 | Diagonal = 34 |

Name ______________________ Class ______________ Date __________



# Power, Voltage, and Current

**Math Skill: Formulas and Equations**

You may want to read more about this **Math Skill** in the **Skills and Reference Handbook** at the end of your textbook.

The power rating on an electric soldering iron is 40.0 watts. If the soldering iron is connected to a 120-volt line, how much current does it use?

**1. Read and Understand**

*What information are you given in the problem?*

Power = $P$ = 40.0 watts

Voltage = $V$ = 120 volts

**2. Plan and Solve**

*What unknown are you trying to calculate?*

Current = $I$ =?

*What formula contains the given quantities and the unknown?*

$$P = I \times V; I = \frac{P}{V}$$

*Replace each variable with its known value.*

$$I = \frac{40.0 \text{ watts}}{120 \text{ volts}} = 0.33 \text{ amps}$$

**3. Look Back and Check**

*Is your answer reasonable?*

The answer is reasonable because a soldering iron needs a relatively low current to generate heat.

## Math Practice

*On a separate sheet of paper, solve the following problems.*

**1.** A steam cleaner has a power rating of 1100 watts. If the cleaner is connected to a 120-volt line, what current does it use?

$P = I \times V; I = P/V$ = 1100 watts/120 volts = 9.2 amps

**2.** A coffee maker uses 10.0 amps of current from a 120-volt line. How much power does it use?

$P = I \times V$ = 10.0 amps × 120 volts = 1200 watts

**3.** A power mixer uses 3.0 amps of current and has a power rating of 360 watts. What voltage does this appliance require?

$P = I \times V; V = P/I$ = 360 watts/3.0 amps = 120 volts

Name ______________ Class ______________ Date ______________



# Section 21.1 Magnets and Magnetic Fields

**(pages 630–633)**

*This section describes magnetic forces and magnetic fields. Characteristics of magnetic materials also are discussed.*

## Reading Strategy (page 630)

**Using Prior Knowledge** Before you read, copy the diagram below and add what you already know about magnets to the diagram. After you read, revise the diagram based on what you learned. For more information on this Reading Strategy, see the **Reading and Study Skills** in the **Skills and Reference Handbook** at the end of your textbook.

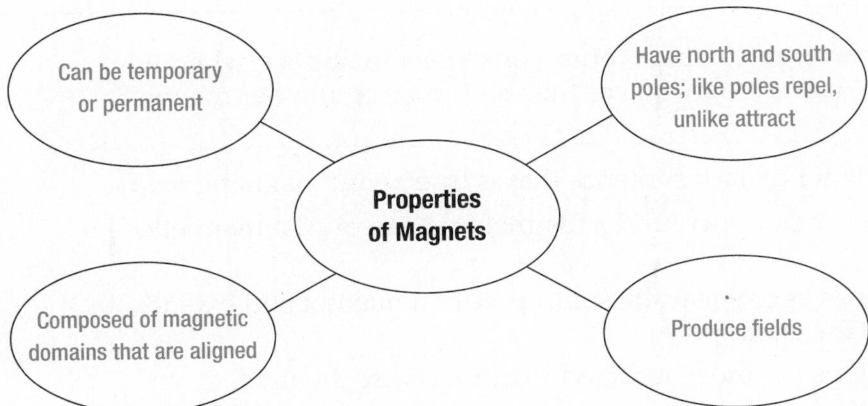


1. In the year 1600, William Gilbert published a book explaining the properties of ____magnets____.

## Magnetic Forces (page 630)

2. Is the following sentence true or false? Magnetic force can be exerted on moving charges, as well as on iron or on another magnet. ____true____

3. What did William Gilbert discover when he used a compass to map forces around a magnetic sphere? ____He discovered that the force is strongest at the poles.____

4. Circle the letter of each sentence that is true about magnetic force.
   (a.) Two magnets that approach each other may attract or repel.
   b. Magnetic forces do not vary with distance.
   c. Opposite magnetic poles repel one another.
   (d.) Magnetic forces act over a distance.

Name ______________________ Class ________________ Date ____________



## Magnetic Fields (pages 631–632)

*For questions 5 and 6, refer to the figure below.*

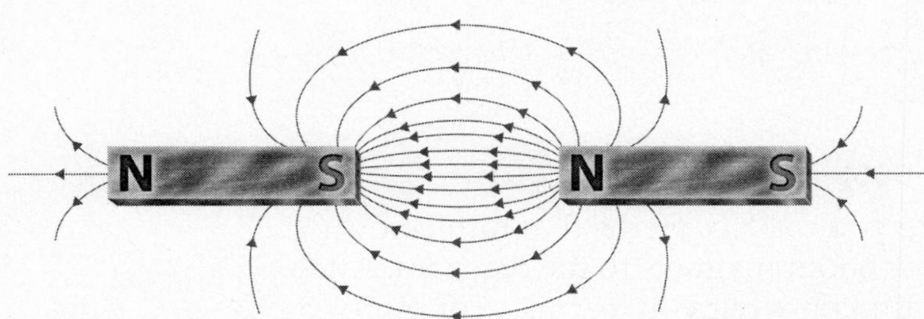


5. Where is the magnetic field the strongest? The field in the gap between the magnets is very strong, where field lines are close together.

6. Based on this figure, what would you expect to happen when the north pole of one magnet faces the south pole of another magnet?
Opposite poles will attract.

7. Circle the letter of each sentence that is true about magnetic fields.
   (a.) Magnetic fields surround a magnet and can exert a magnetic force.
   b. Field lines begin near the south pole of a magnet and extend toward the north pole.
   (c.) Iron filings are most attracted to areas where the field is strongest.
   (d.) A magnetic field is strongest near the north and south poles of a magnet.

8. The area that is influenced by the magnetic field surrounding Earth is called the magnetosphere.

## Magnetic Materials (pages 632–633)

*Match each term with its description.*

| | Description | Term |
|---|---|---|
| a | 9. Can be magnetized because it has many domains | a. ferromagnetic material |
| c | 10. Has randomly oriented domains | b. magnetic domain |
| b | 11. Region that has many atoms with aligned magnetic fields | c. nonmagnetized material |

12. What can cause the realignment of magnetic domains in a material?
Heat, a jarring impact, or moving a material relative to a magnet can cause realignment of magnetic domains.

# Section 21.2 Electromagnetism

**(pages 635–639)**

*This section describes how electricity and magnetism are related. Uses of solenoids and electromagnetic devices are discussed, and a description of how these devices work is presented.*

## Reading Strategy (page 635)

**Identifying Main Ideas** Copy the table on a separate sheet of paper. As you read, write the main idea of the text that follows each topic in the table. For more information on this Reading Strategy, see the **Reading and Study Skills** in the **Skills and Reference Handbook** at the end of your textbook.

| Electromagnetism | |
|---|---|
| **Topic** | **Main Idea** |
| Electricity and magnetism | Electricity and magnetism are different aspects of a single force known as the electromagnetic force. |
| Direction of magnetic fields | Moving charges create a magnetic field. |
| Direction of electric currents | A charge moving in a magnetic field will be deflected in a direction perpendicular to both the magnetic field and the velocity of the charge. |
| Solenoids and electromagnets | Changing the current in an electromagnet controls the strength and direction of its magnetic field. |
| Electromagnetic devices | Electromagnetic devices such as galvanometers, electric motors, and speakers change electrical energy into mechanical energy. |

1. In 1820 Hans Oersted discovered a connection between electricity and ___magnetism___.

## Electricity and Magnetism (pages 635–636)

2. Electricity and magnetism are different aspects of a single force known as the ___electromagnetic___ force.

3. Both aspects of the electromagnetic force are caused by ___electric charges___.

4. Is the following sentence true or false? Moving electric charges create a magnetic field. ___true___

5. Is the following sentence true or false? The vibrating charges that produce an electromagnetic wave also create a magnetic field. ___true___

6. A charge moving in a magnetic field will be deflected in a direction that is ___perpendicular___ to both the magnetic field and to the velocity of the charge.

Name ______________________ Class ______________ Date __________



## Solenoids and Electromagnets (pages 637–638)

7. Is the following sentence true or false? The strength of the magnetic field through the center of a coil of current-carrying wire is calculated by adding together the fields from each turn of the coil. true

8. A coil of current-carrying wire that produces a magnetic field is called a(n) solenoid.

9. What is an electromagnet? An electromagnet is a solenoid with a core made of ferromagnetic material.

10. Circle the letter of each sentence that is true about electromagnets.
    a. Placing an iron rod in a solenoid reduces the strength of its magnetic field.
    (b.) Devices that utilize electromagnets include doorbells and telephones.
    (c.) A magnetic field can be turned on and off with an electromagnet.
    (d.) An electromagnet can control the direction of a magnetic field.

11. List three factors that determine the strength of an electromagnet.
    a. Type of ferromagnetic core
    b. Number of turns in the solenoid coil
    c. Current in the solenoid

12. Is the following sentence true or false? Decreasing the current in the solenoid decreases the strength of an electromagnet. true

13. What types of solenoid cores make stronger electromagnets? Cores that are easily magnetized, such as "soft" iron, make stronger electromagnets.

## Electromagnetic Devices (pages 638–639)

14. Electromagnetic devices change electrical energy into mechanical energy.

15. Complete the following table about electromagnetic devices.

| Description | Device |
|---|---|
| Uses electromagnets to convert electrical signals into sound waves | Loudspeaker |
| Uses a rotating electromagnet to turn an axle | Electric motor |
| Uses an electromagnet to measure small amounts of current | Galvanometer |

Name ______________________ Class ________________ Date ____________



# Section 21.3 Electrical Energy Generation and Transmission

**(pages 642–647)**

*This section describes how electricity is generated and transmitted for human use. A description of how generators and transformers function is given.*

## Reading Strategy (page 642)

**Sequencing** As you read the section, complete the flowchart to show how a step-up transformer works. Then make a similar flowchart for a step-down transformer. For more information on this Reading Strategy, see the **Reading and Study Skills** in the **Skills and Reference Handbook** at the end of your textbook.

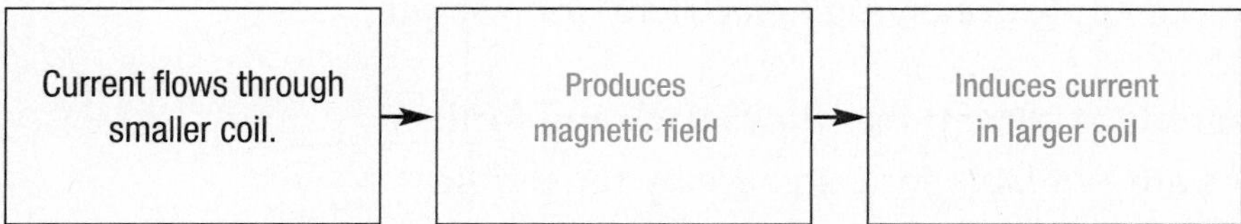


## Generating Electric Current (pages 642–643)

1. Is the following sentence true or false? A magnetic field can be used to produce an electric current. ____true____
2. Circle the letter for the name of the process of generating a current by moving an electrical conductor relative to a magnetic field.
   a. electromagnetic force
   b. electromagnetic field
   (c.) electromagnetic induction
   d. electromagnetic conduction
3. Electrical charges can easily flow through materials known as ____conductors____.
4. Why is the discovery of electromagnetic induction significant? ____It opened the way for practical uses of electromagnetism.____
5. According to Faraday's law, electric current can be induced in a conductor by ____a changing magnetic field____.
6. Is the following sentence true or false? Moving a magnet relative to a coil of wire induces a current in the wire if the coil is part of a complete circuit. ____true____

Name ______________ Class ______________ Date ______________



## Generators (pages 643–644)

7. A generator converts mechanical energy into electrical energy.

8. Circle the letter that best describes how most of the electrical energy used in homes and businesses is produced.
   a. with DC generators
   (b.) using AC generators at large power plants
   c. with small magnets moving inside coils
   d. by rotating a magnetic field around a coil of wire

9. Is the following sentence true or false? In an alternating current produced by an AC generator, the flow direction of charges switches back and forth. true

10. Circle the letter of each sentence that is true about generators.
   (a.) Small generators can produce enough electricity for a small business.
   b. DC generators produce current that flows back and forth.
   (c.) Small generators are available for purchase by the public.
   d. Most modern power plants use DC generators.

## Transformers (pages 644–645)

11. A device that increases or decreases voltage and current of two linked AC circuits is called a(n) transformer.

12. How does a transformer change voltage and current? It induces a changing magnetic field in one coil, which then induces an AC current in a nearby coil with a different number of turns.

13. Why are transformers necessary for home electrical service? They are needed to transmit power at high voltage so power loss can be reduced.

14. Is the following sentence true or false? To prevent overheating wires, voltage is decreased for long-distance transmission. false

15. How is voltage calculated in a transformer? Dividing the number of turns in the secondary coil by the number of turns in the primary coil gives the ratio of the output voltage to the input voltage.

16. Is the following sentence true or false? A step-down transformer decreases voltage and increases current. true

## Electrical Energy for Your Home (pages 646–647)

17. Name at least three sources used to produce electrical energy in the United States. Answers may include coal, water (hydroelectric), nuclear energy, wind, natural gas, and petroleum.

18. A device with fanlike blades that can convert energy from various sources into electrical energy is called a(n) turbine.

**Chapter 21 Magnetism**

# WordWise

*Solve the clues to determine which vocabulary words from Chapter 21 are hidden in the puzzle. Then find and circle the terms in the puzzle. The terms may occur vertically, horizontally, or diagonally. Some terms may be spelled backwards.*

| f | g | d | e | l | o | p | c | i | t | e | n | g | a | m |
|---|---|---|---|---|---|---|---|---|---|---|---|---|---|---|
| e | a | a | t | s | o | r | m | e | v | r | p | e | a | b |
| r | r | q | l | z | f | f | r | e | r | e | v | g | c | t |
| r | c | i | u | v | t | t | c | h | n | g | n | r | r | r |
| o | s | d | o | m | a | i | n | i | u | e | t | a | o | a |
| m | o | u | b | p | l | n | b | k | t | n | u | u | f | n |
| a | l | t | y | o | i | r | o | o | n | e | r | m | t | s |
| g | e | k | p | o | u | d | s | m | a | r | b | i | n | f |
| n | n | k | a | t | p | p | o | i | e | a | i | c | a | o |
| e | o | g | o | y | h | z | a | v | b | t | n | s | y | r |
| t | i | e | e | e | h | n | j | n | m | o | e | m | o | m |
| i | d | i | r | j | u | e | r | t | c | r | f | r | u | e |
| c | t | e | z | z | w | y | n | r | p | e | r | j | b | r |

**Clues** | **Hidden Words**

Region where a magnetic field is strongest — magnetic pole

Nickel is a(n) _____ material. — ferromagnetic

Current-carrying wire with a loop in it — solenoid

Uses an electromagnet to measure small amounts of current — galvanometer

Device with fanlike blades that converts energy from various sources to electrical energy — turbine

Area influenced by Earth's magnetic field — magnetosphere

Converts mechanical energy into electrical energy — generator

Aligned magnetic fields — domain

Step-down or step-up — transformer

Name ______________________ Class ______________ Date __________



# Calculating Voltage

A step-down transformer has a primary coil with 500 turns of wire, and a secondary coil with 50 turns. If the input voltage is 120 V, what is the output voltage?

**Math Skill: Ratios and Proportions**

You may want to read more about this **Math Skill** in the **Skills and Reference Handbook** at the end of your textbook.

**1. Read and Understand**

*What information are you given?*

Input Voltage = 120 V

Primary Coil: 500 turns

Secondary Coil: 50 turns

**2. Plan and Solve**

*What unknown are you trying to calculate?*

Output Voltage = ?

*What formula contains the given quantities and the unknown?*

$$\frac{\text{Secondary Coil turns}}{\text{Primary Coil turns}} = \frac{\text{Output Voltage}}{\text{Input Voltage}}$$

*Replace each variable with its known value.*

$$\frac{50 \text{ turns}}{500 \text{ turns}} = \frac{\text{Output Voltage}}{120 \text{ V}}$$

$$\text{Output Voltage} = \frac{50 \text{ turns}}{500 \text{ turns}} \times 120 \text{ V} = 12 \text{ V}$$

**3. Look Back and Check**

*Is your answer reasonable?*

The ratio of secondary to primary turns is 1 : 10. 12 V is one tenth of 120 V, so the answer is reasonable.

## Math Practice

*On a separate sheet of paper, solve the following problems.*

1. What is the ratio of turns for the secondary to primary coils in a step-down transformer, if the input voltage from a substation is 7200 V, and the output voltage to a home is 240 V?

   $\frac{240 \text{ V}}{7200 \text{ V}}$ = 0.033. The ratio of the secondary to primary turns is 1 : 30.

2. The input voltage from a generating plant to a transformer is 11,000 V. If the output voltage from the transformer to high-voltage transmission lines is 240,000 V, what is the ratio of secondary to primary turns in this step-up transformer?

   $\frac{240{,}000 \text{ V}}{11{,}000 \text{ V}}$ = 21.8. The ratio of turns in the secondary to primary coils is about 22 : 1.

3. A step-down transformer has 200 turns of wire in its primary coil. How many turns are in the secondary coil if the input voltage = 120 V, and the output voltage = 6 V?

   (6 V/120 V) × 200 turns = 10 turns

Name ______________________ Class ________________ Date ____________

Chapter 22 Earth's Interior

# Section 22.1 Earth's Structure

**(pages 660–663)**

*This section explains what geologists study. It describes the main layers of Earth.*

## Reading Strategy (page 660)

**Building Vocabulary** Copy the table on a separate sheet of paper and add more rows as needed. As you read the section, define each vocabulary term in your own words. For more information on this Reading Strategy, see the **Reading and Study Skills** in the **Skills and Reference Handbook** at the end of your textbook.

| Earth's Structure | |
|---|---|
| **Vocabulary Term** | **Definition** |
| Geologist | A scientist who studies Earth and the processes that have shaped Earth over time |
| Uniformitarianism | The concept that geologic processes that are occurring today also occurred in the past |
| Crust | Earth's rocky outer layer |

## The Science of Geology (pages 660–661)

1. The study of planet Earth, including its composition and structure is called ______geology______.

2. Is the following sentence true or false? People who study Earth and the processes that have shaped Earth over time are called geologists. ______true______

3. What is uniformitarianism? Uniformitarianism is the idea that the geologic processes that operate today also operated in the past.

## A Cross Section of Earth (pages 661–663)

4. Circle the letters of the major layers of Earth's interior.
   - (a.) crust
   - b. atmosphere
   - (c.) mantle
   - (d.) core

5. Scientists divide Earth's interior into the crust, mantle, and core based on the ______materials in each layer______.

6. Much of the Earth's crust is made up of ______silicates______.

*Match each type of crust to its characteristics. Each type of crust will have more than one characteristic.*

| | Crust | Characteristic |
|---|---|---|
| a, d, e | 7. oceanic crust | a. Averages about 7 kilometers thick |
| b, c, f | 8. continental crust | b. Consists mainly of less-dense rocks |
| | | c. Averages 40 kilometers in thickness |
| | | d. Composed mostly of dense rocks |
| | | e. Makes up the ocean floor |
| | | f. Makes up the continents |

9. The layer of Earth called the ___mantle___ is found directly below the crust.
10. Circle the letters of each sentence that is true about Earth's mantle.
    - (a.) It is the thickest layer of Earth.
    - (b.) It is divided into layers based on the physical properties of rock.
    - c. It is less dense than the crust.
    - (d.) It is made mainly of silicates.
11. The lithosphere includes the uppermost part of Earth's mantle and Earth's ___crust___.
12. Is the following sentence true or false? Rock flows slowly in the asthenosphere. ___true___
13. The stronger, lower part of the mantle is called the ___mesosphere___.
14. The sphere of metal inside Earth is called the ___core___.
15. Is the following sentence true or false? The outer core of Earth is liquid. ___true___
16. Label the main layers of Earth's interior in the diagram below.

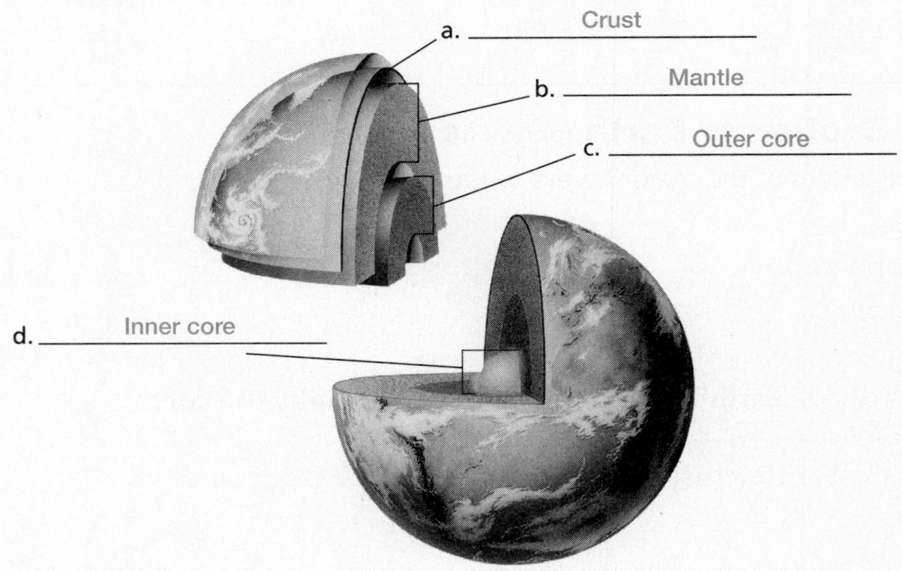

Name ______________________ Class ______________ Date ____________



# Section 22.2 Minerals
**(pages 664–669)**

*This section describes minerals and rocks found on Earth and their different properties.*

## Reading Strategy (page 664)

**Outlining** Copy the outline on a separate sheet of paper and add more lines as needed. Before you read, make an outline of this section. Use the green headings as main topics and the blue headings as subtopics. As you read, add supporting details. For more information on this Reading Strategy, see the **Reading and Study Skills** in the **Skills and Reference Handbook** at the end of your textbook.

**Minerals**

I. Minerals and Rocks
II. The Properties of Minerals
  A. Crystal Structure
  B. Color
  C. Streak
  D. Luster

## Minerals and Rocks (page 665)

1. A solid combination of minerals or mineral materials is a(n) rock.
2. Is the following sentence true or false? A mineral is a naturally occurring, inorganic solid with a crystal structure and a characteristic chemical composition. true
3. A material is called inorganic if it is not produced from a living thing.
4. Circle the letters of sentences that are true about minerals.
   (a.) Within each mineral, chemical composition is nearly constant.
   b. Minerals are organic.
   c. There are about 4000 known minerals.
   (d.) Minerals are the building blocks of rocks.

## The Properties of Minerals (pages 666–669)

5. Is the following sentence true or false? Minerals such as sulfur can sometimes be identified by color. true
6. What could cause two samples of the same mineral to have different colors?
   Slight changes in the mineral's composition could cause the two samples to have different colors.
7. Is the following sentence true or false? The color of a mineral's streak is not always the same color as the mineral. true

8. How is a mineral's streak found? A mineral's streak is usually found by scraping it on a streak plate.

9. The density of a mineral depends on its chemical composition.

10. Is the following sentence true or false? The hardness of a mineral is the way in which its surface reflects light. false

11. To determine the hardness of a mineral, geologists use scratch tests.

12. Is the following sentence true or false? The fracture of a mineral is how it breaks. true

13. A type of fracture in which a mineral splits evenly is called cleavage.

14. Complete the table about the properties by which minerals can be identified.

| Minerals and Properties | |
|---|---|
| **Property** | **Description** |
| Crystal Structure | The particular geometric shape that the atoms of a mineral are arranged in |
| Streak | The color of a mineral's powder |
| Luster | The way in which a mineral's surface reflects light |
| Density | A mineral's mass divided by its volume |
| Hardness | The resistance of a mineral to scratching |
| Fracture | How a mineral breaks |
| Cleavage | A type of fracture where a mineral splits along regular, well-defined flat surfaces where the bonds are weakest |

*Match each mineral to its property.*

| | **Mineral** | **Property** |
|---|---|---|
| e | 15. calcite | a. Gives off visible light under an ultraviolet light |
| c | 16. Iceland spar | b. Becomes electrically charged when heated |
| d | 17. magnetite | c. Refracts light into two separate rays |
| b | 18. tourmaline | d. Is attracted by a magnet |
| a | 19. fluorite | e. Easily dissolved by acids |

Name ______________________ Class ______________ Date ____________

Chapter 22 Earth's Interior

# Section 22.3 Rocks and the Rock Cycle

**(pages 670–675)**

*This section describes how rocks are classified. It also explains how rocks change form in the rock cycle.*

## Reading Strategy (page 670)

**Comparing and Contrasting** After you read, compare groups of rocks by completing the table. For more information on this Reading Strategy, see the **Reading and Study Skills** in the **Skills and Reference Handbook** at the end of your textbook.

| Groups of Rocks | | |
|---|---|---|
| **Rock Group** | **Formed by** | **Example** |
| Igneous | Cooling of magma or lava | Possible answers include granite, basalt, and gabbro. |
| Sedimentary | Compression and cementing together of sediment | Sandstone |
| Metamorphic | Heat and pressure | Possible answers include slate, schist, and gneiss. |

## Classifying Rocks (page 670)

1. Circle the letters of the major groups into which rocks are classified.
   (a.) sedimentary (b.) igneous
   c. calcite (d.) metamorphic
2. Scientists divide rocks into groups based on how they form.

## Igneous Rock (page 671)

3. A rock that forms from magma is called a(n) igneous rock.
4. A mixture of molten rock and gases that forms underground is called magma.
5. What is lava? Lava is magma that flows onto the surface.
6. Is the following sentence true or false? Igneous rock is formed when molten material cools and solidifies either inside Earth or at the surface. true

*Match each type of igneous rock to its characteristics. Each type of crust will have more than one characteristic.*

| | Igneous Rock | Characteristic |
|---|---|---|
| a, d, f | 7. intrusive rock | a. Forms underground |
| b, c, e | 8. extrusive rock | b. Forms at Earth's surface |
| | | c. Has a fine-grained texture |
| | | d. Has a coarse-grained texture |
| | | e. Cools quickly |
| | | f. Cools slowly |

## Sedimentary Rock (pages 672–673)

9. The process of ___weathering___ breaks down rock at Earth's surface.

10. When sediment is squeezed and cemented together, ___sedimentary___ rocks are formed.

11. Circle the groups into which geologists classify sedimentary rocks.
   - (a.) clastic rocks
   - b. foliated rocks
   - (c.) organic rocks
   - (d.) chemical rocks

12. Sedimentary rocks formed from broken fragments of other rocks are called ___clastic___ rocks.

13. Is the following sentence true or false? Clastic rocks are classified mainly based on the number of fragments they have. ___false___

14. Minerals that precipitate out of solution form ___chemical sedimentary rocks___.

## Metamorphic Rock (page 674)

15. Circle the ways a rock can be transformed into a metamorphic rock.
   - (a.) by heat
   - b. by precipitation
   - (c.) by pressure
   - (d.) by chemical reaction

16. Where do most metamorphic rocks form? ___Most metamorphic rocks form deep underground.___

17. Is the following sentence true or false? Metamorphism can change the mineral content and texture of a rock. ___true___

18. Metamorphic rocks with crystals arranged in parallel bands or layers are called ___foliated___ rocks.

## The Rock Cycle (pages 674-675)

19. Circle the letters of the sentences that are true about the rock cycle.
   - (a.) A metamorphic rock that melts and cools to form a new rock becomes an igneous rock.
   - (b.) Forces within Earth and at the surface cause rocks to change form in the rock cycle.
   - (c.) In the rock cycle, rocks may wear away, undergo metamorphism, or melt and form new igneous rock.
   - (d.) The rock cycle is a series of processes in which rocks change from one type to another continuously.

Name ______________________ Class ________________ Date ____________



# Section 22.4 Plate Tectonics

**(pages 676–683)**

*This section describes the theory of plate tectonics. It also examines sea-floor spreading, plate boundaries, and mountain building.*

## Reading Strategy (page 676)

**Previewing** Before you read this section, rewrite the headings as how, why, and what questions about plate tectonics. As you read, write answers to the questions. For more information on this Reading Strategy, see the **Reading and Study Skills** in the **Skills and Reference Handbook** at the end of your textbook.

| Plate Tectonics |
|---|
| **Questions on Plate Tectonics** |
| What is the hypothesis of continental drift? Students' questions may include: |
| What is the process of sea-floor spreading? |
| What is the mid-ocean ridge? |
| How does oceanic crust form? |

1. Is the following sentence true or false? According to the theory of plate tectonics, Earth's plates move about quickly on top of the crust. false

2. What does the theory of plate tectonics explain about Earth's plates? It explains their formation and movement.

## Continental Drift (page 677)

3. Explain Alfred Wegener's hypothesis about the continents. The continents were once joined in a single supercontinent, which then broke into pieces that moved apart.

4. The process by which the continents move slowly across Earth's surface is called continental drift.

## Sea-floor Spreading (pages 678–679)

5. The world's longest mountain chain is the underwater chain called the mid-ocean ridge.

6. Is the following sentence true or false? The theory of sea-floor spreading explains why rocks of the ocean floor are youngest near the mid-ocean ridge. true

7. Is the following sentence true or false? Old oceanic plates sink into the mantle at mid-ocean ridges in a process called subduction. false

8. A depression in the ocean floor where subduction takes place is called a(n) trench.

9. Circle the letter that completes the sentence. Sea-floor spreading _____ new oceanic crust at mid-ocean ridges.

   (a.) creates  b. destroys

10. The process called subduction destroys old oceanic crust at subduction zones.

## The Theory of Plate Tectonics (pages 679–680)

11. Is the following sentence true or false? The concept of sea-floor spreading supports the theory of plate tectonics by providing a way for the pieces of Earth's crust to move. true

12. Heat from Earth's interior causes convection currents in Earth's mantle.

13. Circle the sentences that are true about the theory of plate tectonics.

    (a.) The ocean floor sinks back into the mantle at subduction zones.

    b. The heat that drives convection currents comes from solar energy.

    (c.) Hot rock rises at mid-ocean ridges, cools and spreads out as ocean sea floor.

    (d.) Plate motions are the surface portion of mantle convection.

14. Describe the two sources of the heat in Earth's mantle.

    a. Earth was very hot when it formed and some of the heat is from its gradual cooling.

    b. As radioactive isotopes decay in the mantle and crust, they produce heat.

## Plate Boundaries (pages 681–682)

15. Identify each type of plate boundary.

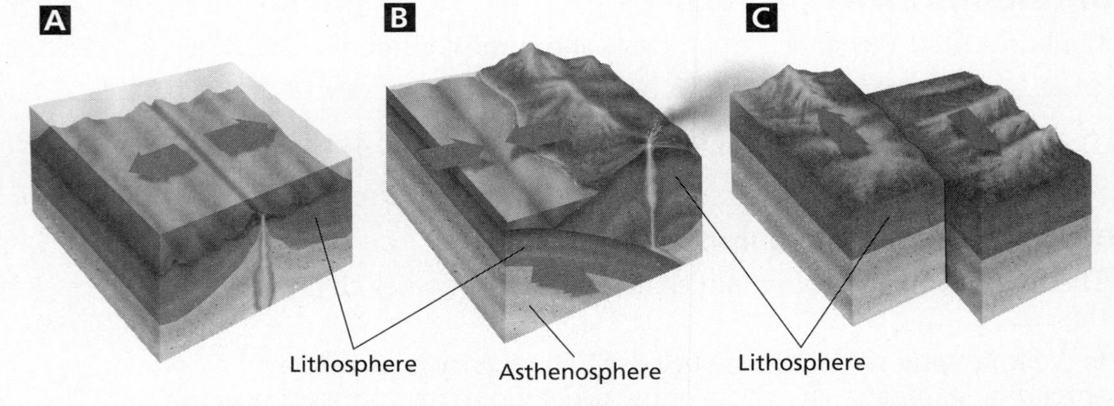


a. Divergent boundary  b. Convergent boundary  c. Transform boundary

## Mountain Building (page 683)

16. Is the following sentence true or false? Most mountains form along plate boundaries. true

17. Describe how the Himalayan Mountains were formed. The Indo-Eurasian plate and the Eurasian plate collided and buckled to form the Himalayan Mountains.

Name ______________________ Class ________________ Date ____________



# Section 22.5 Earthquakes
**(pages 684–689)**

*This section explains what earthquakes are, what causes them, and their effects.*

## Reading Strategy (page 684)

**Building Vocabulary** Copy the table on a separate sheet of paper and add more rows as needed. As you read, define each term for this section in your own words. For more information on this Reading Strategy, see the **Reading and Study Skills** in the **Skills and Reference Handbook** at the end of your textbook.

| Earthquake Terms | |
|---|---|
| **Vocabulary Terms** | **Definitions** |
| Earthquake | A movement of Earth's lithosphere that occurs when rocks in the lithosphere suddenly shift, releasing energy |
| Seismic waves | Vibrations caused by an earthquake that carry the earthquake's energy away |
| Stress | A force within Earth that either squeezes rocks together, pulls them apart, or pushes them in different directions |

**1.** An earthquake releases ___stored (or potential)___ energy that is carried by vibrations called ___seismic waves___.

## Stress in Earth's Crust (page 685)

**2.** Name three ways that stress can affect rocks.

a. It can squeeze them together.

b. It can stretch or pull them apart.

c. It can push them in different directions.

**3.** Is the following sentence true or false? Stress from moving tectonic plates produces faults and folds in Earth's crust. ___true___

*Match each result of stress to its characteristics. Each result will have more than one characteristic.*

| | Result of Stress | Characteristic |
|---|---|---|
| b,c | **4.** fault | a. A bend in layers of rock |
| a,d | **5.** fold | b. Many occur along plate boundaries |
| | | c. A break in a mass of rock where movement happens |
| | | d. Forms where rocks are squeezed but do not break |

**6.** Is the following sentence true or false? Rocks tend to fold instead of break under low temperature or pressure. ___false___

Name ______________________ Class ______________ Date ____________



## Earthquakes and Seismic Waves (pages 686–687)

7. Why do earthquakes occur? They happen because underground stress forces have exceeded the strength of rock.

8. Is the following sentence true or false? The location underground where an earthquake begins is called the focus. true

9. The location on Earth's surface directly above the focus of an earthquake is called the epicenter.

10. Circle the sentences that are true about the physics of earthquakes.
    - (a.) Stress builds in areas where rocks along fault lines snag and remain locked.
    - (b.) In an earthquake, rocks break and grind past each other, releasing energy.
    - (c.) Potential energy is transformed into kinetic energy in the form of seismic waves.
    - d. Potential energy increases as rocks break and move.

*Match each type of seismic wave to its characteristic.*

| | Seismic Waves | Characteristic |
|---|---|---|
| c | 11. P waves | a. Transverse waves that cannot travel through liquids |
| a | 12. S waves | b. Slowest moving type of wave that develops when seismic waves reach Earth's surface |
| b | 13. surface waves | c. Longitudinal waves similar to sound waves that cause particles in the material to vibrate in the direction of the waves' motion |

14. Typically, the first seismic waves to be detected at a distance are P waves.

## Measuring Earthquakes (page 687)

15. What devices do geologists use to record seismic waves? They use a seismograph.

## Seismographic Data (page 689)

16. Most earthquakes are concentrated along plate boundaries.

17. Is the following sentence true or false? Some earthquakes will occur in the interior of plates. true

18. Is the following statement true or false? When seismic waves interact with boundaries between different kinds of rock within Earth, they can be reflected, refracted, or diffracted. true

# Section 22.6 Volcanoes
**(pages 690–696)**

*This section describes volcanoes, how they form, and the different ways they erupt. It also describes the different types of volcanoes and other features created by magma.*

## Reading Strategy (page 690)

**Sequencing** As you read, complete the flowchart to show how a volcano forms. For more information on this Reading Strategy, see the **Reading and Study Skills** in the **Skills and Reference Handbook** at the end of your textbook.

**Formation of a Volcano**

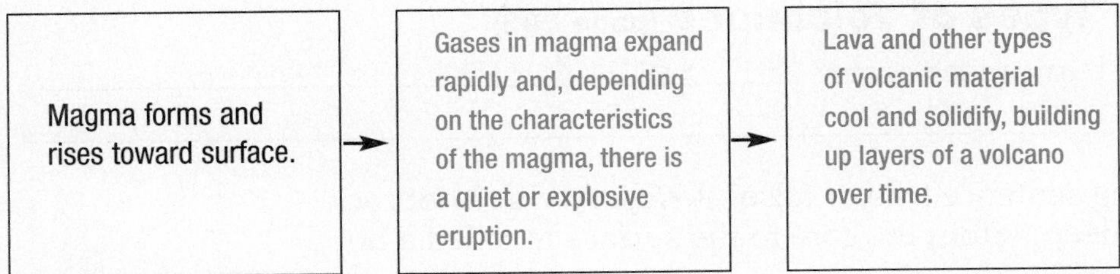


1. A mountain that forms when magma reaches the surface is called a(n) ____volcano____.

## Formation of a Volcano (page 691)

2. Is the following sentence true or false? Liquid magma is formed when small amounts of mantle rock melt. ____true____

3. Describe how a volcano forms. Liquid magma rises upward through the crust and erupts at the surface as a volcano.

4. Describe how a volcano erupts. When the expanding gases in magma bubble out through a crack in the crust, magma is propelled to the surface.

5. Magma collects in a pocket called the ____magma chamber____ before a volcanic eruption.

*Match each feature of a volcano to its correct description.*

| | Feature | Description |
|---|---|---|
| a | 6. pipe | a. A narrow, vertical channel where magma rises to the surface |
| b | 7. vent | b. An opening in the ground where magma escapes to the surface |
| d | 8. crater | c. A huge depression created if the shell of the magma chamber collapses |
| e | 9. magma chamber | d. A bowl-shaped pit at the top of a volcano |
| c | 10. caldera | e. A pocket where the magma collects |

## Quiet and Explosive Eruptions (page 692)

11. Is the following sentence true or false? How easily magma flows depends on its viscosity. true

12. List three factors that determine the viscosity of magma.
    a. Temperature
    b. Water content
    c. Silica content

13. Is the following sentence true or false? Magma with higher temperatures has higher viscosity. false

14. Hot, fast-moving lava is called pahoehoe and cooler, slow-moving lava is called aa.

## Location and Types of Volcanoes (page 693)

15. Where do most volcanoes occur? Most volcanoes occur along plate boundaries or at hot spots in Earth's crust.

16. Is the following sentence true or false? A region where hot rock extends from deep within the core to the surface is called a hot spot. false

17. Is the following sentence true or false? A composite volcano is produced by a quiet eruption of low-viscosity lava. false

18. An eruption of ash and cinders will produce a volcano called a(n) cinder cone.

19. Is the following sentence true or false? A composite volcano is formed from an explosive eruption of lava and ash. true

## Other Igneous Features (page 696)

20. Circle the letters of the igneous features that are formed by magma.
    a. dikes
    b. sills
    c. volcanic necks
    d. batholiths

21. The largest type of intrusive igneous rock mass is called a(n) batholith.

22. Is the following sentence true or false? A crack that has been filled in by magma and hardens parallel to existing rock layers is called a dike. false

Name ______________________ Class ________________ Date ____________



# WordWise

*Use the clues below to identify vocabulary terms from Chapter 22. Write the terms below, putting one letter in each blank. When you finish, the term enclosed in the diagonal will reveal an important process on Earth.*

## Clues

1. A solid combination of minerals or mineral materials
2. The central layer of Earth
3. A type of fracture in which a mineral tends to split along regular, well-defined planes
4. A movement of Earth's lithosphere that occurs when rocks shift suddenly, releasing stored energy
5. A region where plates collide
6. The type of rock that forms when small pieces of sediment are squeezed together
7. A mountain that forms when magma reaches the surface
8. A bend in layers of rock
9. Wegener's hypothesis in which continents move slowly across Earth's surface

## Vocabulary Terms

1. (r) o c k
2. c (o) r e
3. (c) l e a v a g e
4. e a r t h q u a (k) e
5. (c) o n v e r g e n t  b o u n d a r y
6. s e d i m e n t a r (y)  r o c k
7. v o l (c) a n o
8. f o (l) d
9. c o n t i n (e) n t a l  d r i f t

**Hidden Word:** r o c k  c y c l e

**Definition:** A series of processes in which rocks continuously change from one type to another

Name ______________________ Class ______________ Date __________



# Calculating Wavelength and Frequency

**Math Skill: Line Graphs**

You may want to read more about this **Math Skill** in the **Skills and Reference Handbook** at the end of your textbook.

An earthquake occurs 1000 km from seismograph station B. What is the difference in time between the arrivals of the first P wave and the first S wave at station B?

**1. Read and Understand**

*What information are you given in the problem?*

Station B is 1000 km from where an earthquake occurred.

**2. Plan and Solve**

*What does the question ask you to find?*

The difference in time between the arrivals of the first P wave and the first S wave at station B

*Find the amount of time it took the first P wave to reach station B by following the 1000-km line up to where it meets the P wave curve.*

2 minutes

*Find the amount of time it took the first S wave to reach station B by following the 1000-km line up to where it meets the S wave curve.*

4 minutes

*Subtract the amount of time it took the P wave to travel to station B from the amount of time it took the S wave to travel to station B.*

4 minutes − 2 minutes = 2 minutes

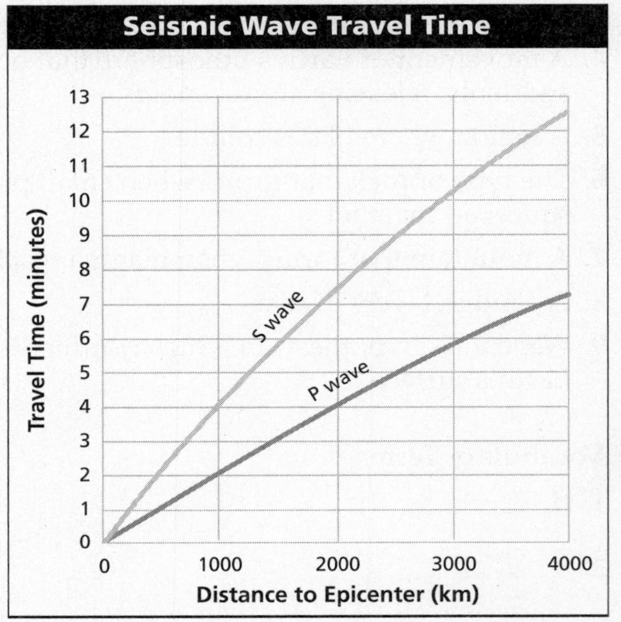


**3. Look Back and Check**

*Is your answer reasonable?* Yes, because S waves move slower than P waves.

## Math Practice

*On a separate sheet of paper, solve the following problems. Use the graph.*

1. An earthquake occurs 500 km from seismograph station B. What is the difference in time between the arrivals of the first P waves and the first S waves?
   S wave arrival takes about 2 minutes and P wave arrival takes about 1 minute, so about 2 minutes − about one minute = about one minute

2. Station C is 2000 km from the epicenter of the earthquake. If P waves arrived there at 4:37 a.m., at approximately what time did the earthquake occur?
   P waves take 4 minutes to travel 2000 km, so the earthquake occurred 4 minutes before 4:37 a.m., at 4:33 a.m.

Name ______________________ Class ________________ Date ____________



# Section 23.1 Fresh Water
**(pages 704–708)**

*This section describes where water is found on Earth. It also explains the water cycle.*

## Reading Strategy (page 704)

**Build Vocabulary** Copy the table on a separate sheet of paper. As you read, add terms and definitions from this section to the table. For more information on this Reading Strategy, see the **Reading and Study Skills** in the **Skills and Reference Handbook** at the end of your textbook.

| Earth's Fresh Water | |
|---|---|
| **Vocabulary Term** | **Definition** |
| Groundwater | Fresh water found underground among particles of rock and soil |
| Water cycle | The continuous movement of water among the oceans, atmosphere, and land |
| Transpiration | The process by which water evaporates from the leaves of trees and other plants and enters the atmosphere |

1. Water found underground in soil and within cracks in rocks is called groundwater.

## The Water Cycle (pages 705–706)

2. Name five major processes of the water cycle.
   a. Evaporation
   b. Condensation
   c. Return of flowing water to oceans
   d. Transpiration
   e. Precipitation

*Match each process with its correct description.*

| | **Description** | **Process** |
|---|---|---|
| d | 3. When water droplets or ice crystals fall to the ground | a. evaporation |
| a | 4. The process through which a liquid changes into a gas | b. transpiration |
| c | 5. The process that forms clouds | c. condensation |
| b | 6. When water is released from a plant's leaves | d. precipitation |

7. What is a glacier? A glacier is a large mass of moving ice and snow.

Name ______________________ Class ______________ Date __________

Chapter 23 Earth's Surface

## Fresh Water (pages 706–708)

8. Circle the letters of the places where portions of Earth's fresh water are located.
   - (a.) in streams
   - (b.) in the atmosphere
   - c. in the oceans
   - (d.) in lakes

9. Most of Earth's fresh water is located in groundwater and glaciers.

10. What is runoff? Runoff is water that flows over Earth's surface.

11. A smaller stream that flows into a river is called a(n) tributary.

12. Circle the letters of the sentences that are true about watersheds.
   - (a.) Watersheds are areas of land that contribute water to a river system.
   - (b.) Watersheds can be large or small.
   - (c.) The Mississippi River watershed drains most of the central United States.
   - (d.) Watersheds are also called drainage basins.

13. Where do lakes and ponds form? Lakes and ponds form in depressions in the land.

14. Is the following sentence true or false? Ponds usually form in large, deep depressions, but lakes form in smaller depressions. false

15. An area underground where the pore spaces are entirely filled with water is called the saturated zone.

16. Is the following sentence true or false? The water table is found at the bottom of the saturated zone. false

17. Water cannot pass through impermeable rocks.

18. Circle the letters of the sentences that are true about aquifers.
   - (a.) They are permeable rock layers that are saturated with water.
   - (b.) They are recharged or refilled as rainwater seeps into them.
   - c. They are often made of shale and unbroken granite.
   - (d.) Many people rely on aquifers for drinking water.

19. Where do glaciers form? Glaciers form in areas where more snow falls than melts each year.

20. Circle the letter of each word that describes how ice is removed from a glacier.
   - (a.) melting
   - (b.) sublimation
   - c. precipitation
   - (d.) formation of icebergs

21. A large piece of ice that breaks off when a glacier reaches the ocean is called a(n) iceberg.

Name ______________________ Class ________________ Date ____________



# Section 23.2 Weathering and Mass Movement
## (pages 709–712)

*This section describes how land is changed by weathering and erosion. It also discusses mass movement.*

## Reading Strategy (page 709)

**Concept Map** As you read, complete the concept map showing the key factors which affect the rate of weathering. For more information on this Reading Strategy, see the **Reading and Study Skills** in the **Skills and Reference Handbook** at the end of your textbook.

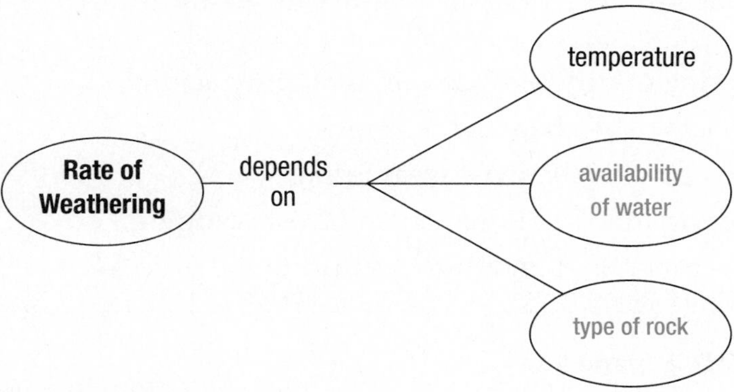


## Erosion (page 709)

**1.** The process that wears down and carries away rock and soil is called ______erosion______.

**2.** Circle the letters of the sentences that are true about erosion.

a. It acts through hoodoos.

(b.) It acts through weathering.

(c.) It acts through the force of gravity.

(d.) It acts through the movement of glaciers, wind, or waves.

**3.** Is the following sentence true or false? The end product of erosion is sediment. ______true______

## Weathering (pages 710–711)

**4.** The process by which rocks are chemically changed or physically broken into fragments is called ______weathering______.

**5.** Circle the letters of the sentences that are true about weathering.

(a.) It can be mechanical.

(b.) It can be chemical.

c. It only breaks down soft rocks.

(d.) It can break down rocks into fragments.

6. Circle the letters of the sentences that are true about mechanical weathering.
   a. It occurs through frost wedging.
   b. It occurs from acidic rain.
   c. It occurs through rusting.
   d. It occurs through abrasion.

7. Is the following sentence true or false? Abrasion happens when rocks scrape against each other. true

8. In the process of chemical weathering, rock is broken down by chemical reactions.

9. Circle the letters of the sentences that are true about chemical weathering.
   a. Chemical weathering occurs because rain is slightly acidic.
   b. Rocks are broken down by chemical reactions.
   c. Water is the main agent of chemical weathering.
   d. Chemical weathering involves abrasion and frost wedging.

10. What happens to the minerals found in rocks during the process of chemical weathering? They are changed into new minerals.

## Rates of Weathering (page 711)

11. What factors determine the rate at which mechanical and chemical weathering take place?
    a. Temperature
    b. The availability of water
    c. The type of rock

12. The kind of weathering that most likely occurs in places where temperature conditions alternate between freezing and thawing is mechanical weathering.

## Mass Movement (page 712)

13. In mass movement, rocks and soil move downhill because of gravity.

*Match each type of mass movement with its correct description.*

| | Description | Mass Movement |
|---|---|---|
| c | 14. Rapid mass movement of soil and other sediment mixed with water | a. creep |
| d | 15. The rapid movement of large amounts of rock and soil | b. slumping |
| b | 16. Weak layers of soil or rock suddenly moving down a slope as a single unit | c. mudflow |
| a | 17. Soil gradually moving down a slope | d. landslide |

Name ______________________ Class ________________ Date ____________



# Section 23.3 Water Shapes the Land
**(pages 713–717)**

*This section describes how water erodes the land. It also describes features created by water erosion and water deposition.*

## Reading Strategy (page 713)

**Concept Map** As you read, complete the concept map showing how moving water shapes the land. For more information on this Reading Strategy, see the **Reading and Study Skills** in the **Skills and Reference Handbook** at the end of your textbook.

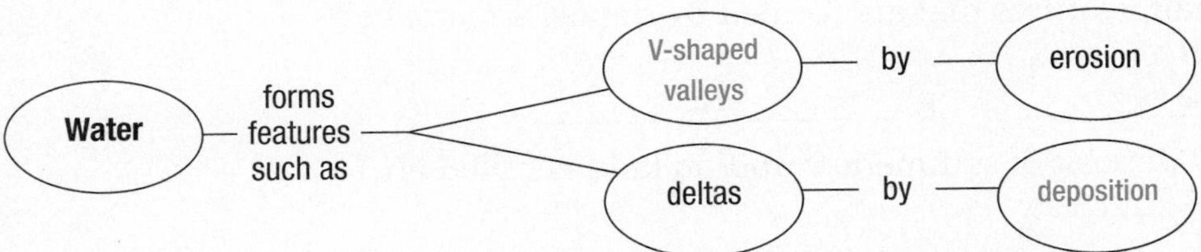


Answers may also include other features formed by erosion such as waterfalls, flood plains, meanders, or oxbow lakes.

1. The process through which sediment is laid down in new locations is called deposition.

## Running Water Erodes the Land (pages 714–715)

*Match each method that sediment is transported in streams with its correct description.*

| | Description | Method of Transportation |
|---|---|---|
| b | 2. Dissolved sediment is carried this way | a. in suspension |
| d | 3. Large boulders can be moved this way during floods | b. in solution |
| a | 4. Tiny sediment grains move along with the water in a stream | c. by saltation |
| c | 5. Large particles bounce along the bottom of a stream | d. pushed or rolled |

6. What does a stream's ability to erode mainly depend on? It depends mainly on the stream's speed.

## Features Formed by Water Erosion (pages 715–716)

7. A(n) V-shaped valley is formed by a fast-moving stream.

8. Is the following sentence true or false? A waterfall may develop where a stream crosses layers of rock that differ in hardness. true

9. A flat area alongside a stream or river that is covered by water only during times of flood is called a(n) flood plain.

10. A loop-like bend in a river is called a(n) meander.

11. Is the following sentence true or false? Oxbow lakes form when an old meander is cut off from the rest of a river. true

12. Circle the letters of features that are formed by water erosion.
   (a.) oxbow lakes
   (b.) V-shaped valleys
   (c.) meanders
   (d.) waterfalls

## Features Formed by Water Deposition (page 716)

13. Name two main features that are formed by deposits made by flowing water.
   a. Alluvial fans
   b. Deltas

14. A fan-shaped deposit of sediment found on land is called a(n) alluvial fan.

15. Is the following sentence true or false? Deltas are masses of sediment that form where rivers enter large bodies of water. true

## Groundwater Erosion (page 717)

16. What type of weathering causes groundwater erosion? chemical weathering

17. Name two features that are formed by groundwater erosion.
   a. Caves
   b. Sinkholes

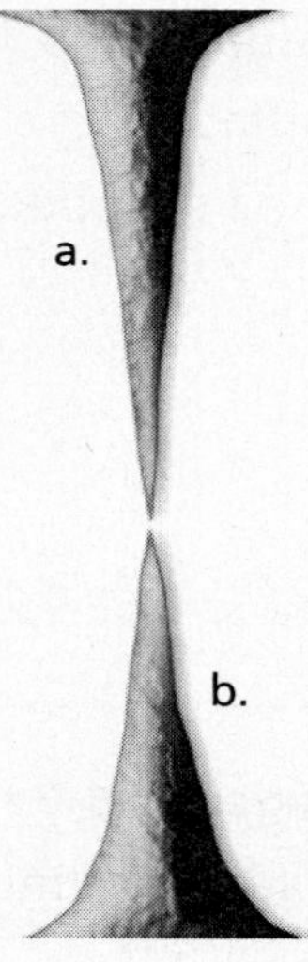


18. Identify the two types of cavern formations shown in the figure above.
   a. Stalactite
   b. Stalagmite

Name ______________ Class ______________ Date ______________



# Section 23.4 Glaciers and Wind
**(pages 719–724)**

*This section describes how glaciers form and how landscape features are created. It also describes wind erosion and deposition.*

## Reading Strategy (page 719)

**Sequencing** As you read, complete the flowchart to show how a glacier forms and moves, and how it erodes and deposits sediment. For more information on this Reading Strategy, see the **Reading and Study Skills** in the **Skills and Reference Handbook** at the end of your textbook.

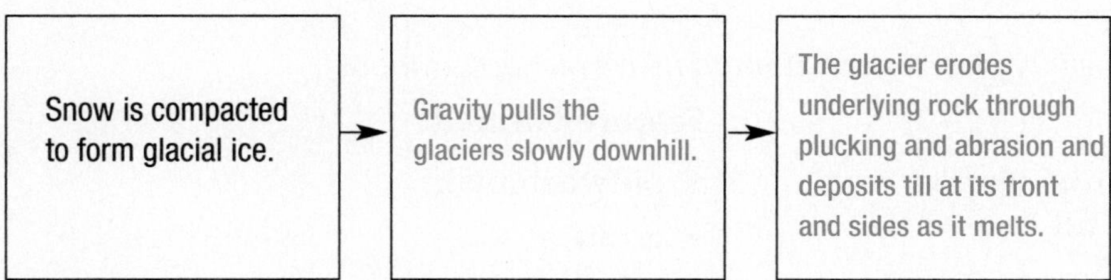


## How Glaciers Form and Move (page 719)

1. Glaciers form in places where snow melts ___faster___ than it falls.

*Match the type of glacier to its description.*

| | Description | Glacier Type |
|---|---|---|
| ___a___ | 2. Found in high mountain valleys | a. valley glacier |
| ___b___ | 3. Covers a continent or large island | b. continental glacier |

## Glacial Erosion and Deposition (page 720–722)

4. What are the two ways through which glaciers erode rock?

   a. ___Abrasion___ b. ___Plucking___

5. Circle the letters of the sentences that are true about glacial erosion.

   (a.) Glacial ice widens cracks in bedrock beneath a glacier.

   b. Pieces of loosened rock stick to the top of a glacier.

   (c.) Rocks stuck to the bottoms and sides of a glacier act like sandpaper, scraping rock and soil.

   d. As a glacier moves, it gently brushes the rocks and soil underneath it.

6. What are four distinctive features caused by glacial erosion?

   a. ___Cirques___

   b. ___Horns or ridges___

   c. ___U-shaped valleys___

   d. ___Glacial lakes___

7. Large bowl-shaped valleys carved high on a mountainside are called cirques.

8. How does a U-shaped valley form? It forms when a glacier flows through and erodes a V-shaped valley.

9. Is the following sentence true or false? Continental glaciers fill depressions in the surface with water, where they create cirques. false

10. How does a glacier create landforms? As it moves, it transports rock and soil, and when it melts, it deposits this load of sediment.

11. Mounds of sediment at the downhill end of a glacier are called moraines.

*Match each feature formed by glacial deposition to its correct description.*

| | Description | Feature Formed |
|---|---|---|
| d | 12. Long teardrop-shaped mounds of till | a. outwash plain |
| a | 13. A flat plain made of particles of rock that were deposited from glacial streams | b. erratics |
| e | 14. A lake formed where large blocks of glacial ice become buried and melt | c. eskers |
| c | 15. Ridges made from sand and gravel that were deposited in the bed of a glacial stream | d. drumlins |
| b | 16. Boulders that a glacier has carried away from their place of origin | e. kettle lake |

## Wind Erosion and Deposition (pages 723–724)

17. Name two ways that wind erodes the land.

a. Deflation b. Abrasion

18. Is the following sentence true or false? Deflation happens when the wind picks up and carries away loose surface material. true

19. Circle the letters of the features deposited by wind.

a. cirques b. glacial lakes
(c.) sand dunes (d.) loess deposits

20. Is the following sentence true or false? Deposits formed from windblown dust are called loess deposits. true

Name ______________________ Class __________________ Date ____________



# Section 23.5 The Restless Oceans
**(pages 725–729)**

*This section describes the oceans and ocean currents. It also describes water erosion and deposition in the oceans.*

## Reading Strategy (page 725)

**Relating Cause and Effect** Copy the table on a separate sheet of paper. After you read, complete the table to compare ways that ocean water can move. For more information on this Reading Strategy, see the **Reading and Study Skills** in the **Skills and Reference Handbook** at the end of your textbook.

| Ways Ocean Water Moves | | |
|---|---|---|
| **Movement Type** | **Causes** | **Effects** |
| Surface current | Winds | Warm water generally flows away from the equator along the east side of continents; cold water generally flows away from polar regions along the west side of continents. |
| Density current | Differences in ocean water density | Responsible for slow mixing of water between the surface and deep ocean |
| Upwelling | Warm water is blown aside by winds and currents, allowing colder water to rise from the deep ocean. | Nutrients are brought up from the deep ocean, providing a food source for algae, which serve, in turn, as food for fish. |
| Longshore drift | Waves carrying sediment approach a beach at an angle. | Sand can be moved great distances along a beach. |

## Exploring the Ocean (pages 725–726)

1. The proportion of dissolved salts in water is called ___salinity___.

2. Is the following sentence true or false? Salt is removed from the ocean by animals and plants and through deposition as sediment. ___true___

3. Circle the letters of the conditions that decrease with the ocean's depth.
   a. pressure
   (b.) light
   (c.) temperature
   d. salinity

4. What is the continental shelf? The continental shelf is the gentle sloping plain that forms an apron of shallow water around most continents.

Chapter 23 Earth's Surface

## Ocean Currents (pages 726–728)

*Match each type of ocean current with its correct description.*

| Description | Ocean Current |
|---|---|
| b 5. A current responsible for a slow mixing of water between the surface and deeper ocean | a. surface current |
| c 6. Movement of water from the deep ocean to the surface | b. density current |
| a 7. A large stream of ocean water that moves continuously in about the same path near the surface | c. upwelling |

8. What causes the continuous flow of surface currents? Winds blowing across the surface of the ocean cause the continuous flow of surface currents.

9. Winds blow warm surface water aside, allowing cold water to rise, in the process of upwelling.

10. What does each letter in the diagram below represent?

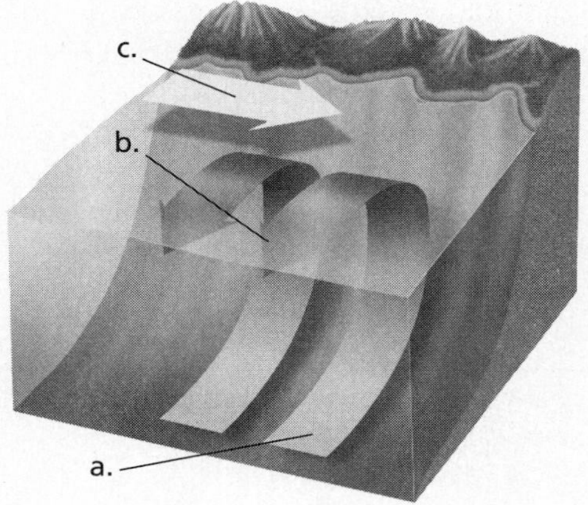


a. Cold water upwelling b. Warm surface water c. Surface wind

## Wave Erosion and Deposition (pages 728–729)

11. What are two hydraulic processes that can be responsible for wave erosion?

a. Hydraulic action b. Abrasion

12. Circle the letters of the sentences that are true about hydraulic action.

(a.) A wave fills a crack with water.

b. Hydraulic action causes no changes to earth's coastlines.

(c.) Waves compress air as they slam into cracked rocks.

(d.) Pressure from waves causes cracks in rocks to get bigger.

13. Is the following sentence true or false? The process that moves sand along a shore is called hydraulic action. false

Name ______________________ Class ______________________ Date ______________

Chapter 23 Earth's Surface

# Section 23.6 Earth's History

**(pages 732–738)**

*This section explains how scientists determine the age of rocks and how they use these methods to develop a time line for the history of Earth. It also describes the four major divisions of Earth history.*

## Reading Strategy (page 732)

**Previewing** Before you read, examine Figures 34 and 36 to help you understand geologic time. Write at least two questions about them in the table. As you read, write answers to your questions. For more information on this Reading Strategy, see the **Reading and Study Skills** in the **Skills and Reference Handbook** at the end of your textbook.

| Questions on Geologic Time |
|---|
| Students' questions may include:<br>What events mark the beginning and end of each geologic era? |
| When did the dinosaurs live? |

1. What are fossils? Fossils are preserved traces of once living things.

## Determining the Age of Rocks (pages 732–734)

2. Is the following sentence true or false? The relative age of a rock is its age compared to the ages of rocks above or below it. true

3. Circle the letter that identifies the direction in which layers of sedimentary rocks form.
   a. vertically
   (b.) horizontally
   c. diagonally
   d. randomly

4. Circle the letter of the sentence that is true about the law of superposition.
   (a.) Younger rocks lie above older rocks if the layers are undisturbed.
   b. Older rocks lie above younger rocks if the layers are undisturbed.
   c. Rock layers are never disturbed.
   d. The youngest rock layers are typically at the bottom.

5. How do geologists use the law of superposition to determine the relative age of rocks?
   a. From the sequence of rock layers
   b. From the fossils within each layer

6. Organize and write the letters of the layers of rock in the diagram from oldest to youngest. If two rock layers are the same age, write them as a pair. D, C, B and E, A and F, G

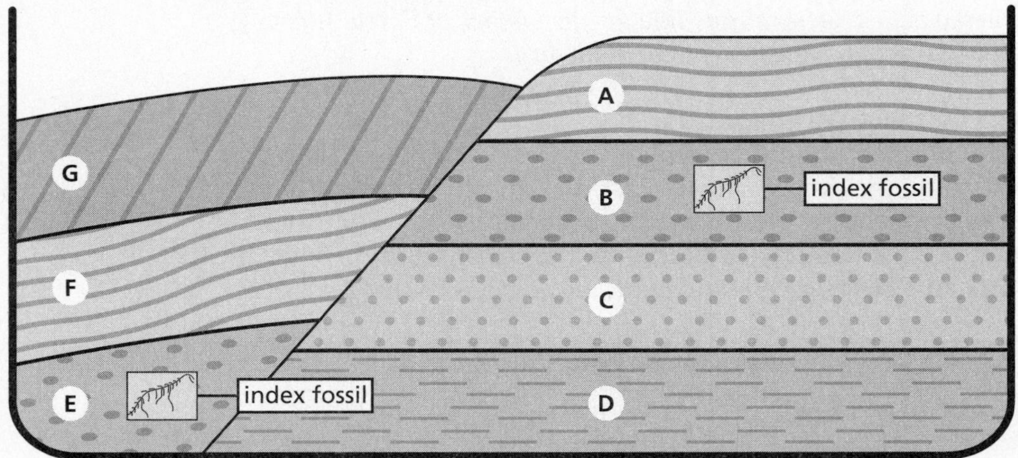


7. Circle the letters of the sentences that are true about index fossils.
   - (a.) They can be easily identified.
   - (b.) They help to determine the relative ages of rocks.
   - (c.) The organisms that formed them occurred over a large area.
   - (d.) The organisms that formed them lived during a well-defined time period.

8. Geologists use radioactive dating to determine the absolute age of rocks.

## A Brief History of Earth (pages 734–738)

9. What is the geologic time scale based on?
   a. Relative ages of rock layers b. Absolute ages of rock

10. What is a mass extinction? A mass extinction is when many different kinds of organisms become extinct in a relatively short time.

*Match each division of Earth's history to its correct description.*

| | Description | Time |
|---|---|---|
| b | 11. Dinosaurs appeared. | a. Precambrian time |
| d | 12. Fishes and other animals first developed in the oceans. | b. Mesozoic Era |
| c | 13. Humans first appeared in Africa. | c. Cenozoic Era |
| a | 14. Earth was formed. | d. Paleozoic Era |

Name ____________________ Class ________________ Date ____________



# WordWise

*Solve the clues to determine which vocabulary terms from Chapter 23 are hidden in the puzzle. Then find and circle the terms in the puzzle. The terms may occur vertically, horizontally, or diagonally.*

t a v f n o l k w e f r z h
g b i m e t l o e s s k d r
s i y b r r w f a d u o l u
b a x a s a d q t w i d m j
p r l l c n p t h r p e p d
s j e i n s g i e a q p y e
u a k p n p j p r u n o f f
p x l v c i b x i a b s c l
w g i t q r t c n s f i p a
e z e f a a z y g q a t j t
l n b o r t x f o s s i l i
l f p j g i i o p d f o g o
i d a n b o l o e m k n c n
n z g d e n r q n i g f s d
g l j q c i s o n a z l x j
m a s s m o v e m e n t n a

| Clues | Hidden Words |
|---|---|
| When water is released from the leaves of plants | transpiration |
| Water that flows over Earth's surface | runoff |
| The process by which rocks are broken down into fragments | weathering |
| The downward movement of rock and soil due to gravity | mass movement |
| The process through which sediment is laid down in new locations | deposition |
| The process wherein pieces of sediment bounce and skip | saltation |
| When wind picks up and carries away loose surface material | deflation |
| Deposits formed from windblown dust | loess |
| The proportion of dissolved salts in water | salinity |
| The movement of water from the deep ocean to the surface | upwelling |
| A preserved remain or trace of a once living thing | fossil |
| A smaller unit of an era | period |

# Exploring Radioactive Dating

**Math Skill: Fractions**
You may want to read more about this **Math Skill** in the **Skills and Reference Handbook** at the end of your textbook.

A fossil contains 100.0 milligrams of Thorium-232, which has a half-life of 14.0 billion years. How much Thorium-232 will remain after three half-lives?

## 1. Read and Understand

*How many milligrams of Thorium-232 does the fossil contain?*

100.0 milligrams

*What is the half-life of Thorium-232?* 14.0 billion years

*What are you asked to find?* the amount of Thorium-232 that will remain in the fossil after three half-lives

## 2. Plan and Solve

*During a half-life, one half of the original amount of a radioisotope decays. To find the amount of Thorium-232 left in the fossil after three half-lives, begin by multiplying $\frac{1}{2}$ by the number of half-lives.*

$$\frac{1}{2} \times \frac{1}{2} \times \frac{1}{2} = \frac{1}{8}$$

*This is the fraction of Thorium-232 that will be left in the fossil after three half-lives. Multiply this fraction by the original amount of Thorium-232 to find the amount of Thorium-232 that will remain.*

$$100.0 \text{ milligrams} \times \frac{1}{8} = 12.5 \text{ milligrams}$$

## 3. Look Back and Check

*Is your answer reasonable?*

To check your answer, divide the number of milligrams in the fossil after three half-lives by the fraction of Thorium-232 left after three half-lives. Your answer should equal the original amount of Thorium-232 in the fossil. 100.0 milligrams

# Math Practice

*On a separate sheet of paper, solve the following problems.*

1. A fossil contains 40.0 milligrams of Uranium-238, which has a half-life of 4.5 billion years. How much Uranium-238 will remain after two half-lives?

$$40.0 \text{ milligrams} \times \frac{1}{4} = 10.0 \text{ milligrams}$$

2. How long will it take for 50.0 milligrams of Thorium-232 in a rock to decay to 25.0 milligrams?

$\frac{25.0 \text{ milligrams}}{50.0 \text{ milligrams}} = .50$; A half-life of Thorium-232 = 14.0 billion years

3. How long will it take for the amount of Rubidium-87 (which has a half-life of 48.8 billion years) in a rock to decay from 80.0 milligrams to 10.0 milligrams?

$\frac{10 \text{ billion years}}{80 \text{ billion years}} = \frac{1}{8}$; Three half-lives = 146.4 billion years

Name ______________ Class ______________ Date ______________



# Section 24.1 The Atmosphere
**(pages 746–751)**

*This section describes Earth's atmosphere, its composition, and its different layers. It also explains air pressure and the effects of altitude on air pressure.*

## Reading Strategy (page 746)

**Relating Text and Diagrams** As you read, refer to Figure 5 and the text to complete the table on the layers of the atmosphere. For more information on this Reading Strategy, see the **Reading and Study Skills** in the **Skills and Reference Handbook** at the end of your textbook.

| Layers of the Atmosphere | | |
|---|---|---|
| **Layer** | **Altitude Range** | **Temperature Change** |
| Troposphere | 0–12 km | Temperature decreases as altitude increases. |
| Stratosphere | 12–50 km | Temperature remains nearly constant to 20 km, then increases with altitude. |
| Mesosphere | 50–80 km | Temperature decreases as altitude increases. |
| Thermosphere | above 80 km | Temperature increases rapidly with altitude. |

## Earth's Protective Layer (page 747)

1. Is the following sentence true or false? The layer of gases that surrounds Earth is called the atmosphere. true
2. How does the atmosphere make Earth's temperatures suitable for life? The atmosphere forms a protective layer between Earth and space.
3. Name two gases in the atmosphere that are essential for life.
   a. Carbon dioxide b. Oxygen

## Composition of the Atmosphere (page 747)

4. Is the following sentence true or false? The composition of the atmosphere changes every few kilometers as you move away from Earth. false
5. Earth's atmosphere is a mixture of nitrogen, oxygen, water vapor, and many other gases.
6. What two gases together make up about 99% of Earth's atmosphere? a. Nitrogen b. Oxygen
7. Is the following sentence true or false? Both water droplets and solid particles are suspended in the atmosphere. true

## Air Pressure (page 748)

8. What is air pressure? Air pressure is the force exerted by the weight of a column of air on a surface.
9. As altitude increases, air pressure and density decrease.

10. Circle the letter of the instrument used to measure air pressure.
   a. a thermometer
   (b.) a barometer
   c. a psychrometer
   d. Doppler radar

## Layers of the Atmosphere (pages 749–751)

11. Scientists divide the atmosphere into layers based on variations in temperature.

12. List the four layers of the atmosphere.
   a. Troposphere
   b. Stratosphere
   c. Mesosphere
   d. Thermosphere

13. Is the following sentence true or false? Weather is the average condition of the atmosphere in a particular place over a period of many years. false

14. What is the ozone layer? The ozone layer is a region of high ozone concentration in the stratosphere.

15. How is ozone formed? An oxygen atom (O) collides with a molecule of oxygen ($O_2$).

16. Is the following sentence true or false? Infrared radiation in sunlight is absorbed by ozone before it reaches Earth. false

17. The layer above the stratosphere is the mesosphere.

18. Is the following sentence true or false? The temperature of the outer thermosphere is quite high. true

*Match the layer of the atmosphere with a characteristic that would best describe it.*

| | Layer of the Atmosphere | Characteristic |
|---|---|---|
| d | 19. troposphere | a. Contains the ozone layer |
| a | 20. stratosphere | b. The outermost layer of the atmosphere |
| c | 21. mesosphere | c. The layer where most meteoroids burn up |
| b | 22. thermosphere | d. The layer where most weather occurs |

23. What is the ionosphere? The ionosphere is a region of charged particles, called ions, that overlaps the lower thermosphere.

24. When charged particles from the sun are attracted to Earth's magnetic poles, a(n) aurora may appear.

# Section 24.2 The Sun and the Seasons
**(pages 752–754)**

*This section describes the two major ways Earth moves. It also explains what causes the seasons.*

## Reading Strategy (page 752)

**Building Vocabulary** Copy the table on a separate sheet of paper. As you read, complete it by defining each vocabulary term from the section. For more information on this Reading Strategy, see the **Reading and Study Skills** in the **Skills and Reference Handbook** at the end of your textbook.

| Vocabulary Term | Definition |
|---|---|
| Rotation | The spinning of Earth on its axis |
| Revolution | The movement of one body in space around another |

1. What are the two major ways Earth moves?
   a. Rotation
   b. Revolution
2. The spinning of Earth on its axis, called rotation, causes day and night.
3. Is the following sentence true or false? It takes Earth one year to complete one rotation. false
4. The movement of one body in space around another is called revolution.
5. Earth completes a full revolution around the sun in one year, about 365 $\frac{1}{4}$ days.
6. The path Earth takes around the sun is called its orbit.

## Earth's Latitude Zones (pages 752–753)

7. What is latitude? Latitude measures distance in degrees north or south of the equator.
8. Circle the letter that identifies the latitude of the North Pole.
   a. 70° north
   b. 80° south
   (c.) 90° north
   d. 100° south

9. The part of Earth that receives the most direct sunlight is near the equator.

10. Is the following sentence true or false? Scientists use lines of latitude to mark out three different types of regions on Earth. true

*Match each type of region to its latitude.*

| | Region | Latitude |
|---|---|---|
| c | 11. temperate zone | a. Falls between latitudes of 23.5° south and 23.5° north |
| a | 12. tropic zone | b. From 66.5° north to the North Pole, and 66.5° south to the South Pole |
| b | 13. polar zone | c. From 23.5° north to 66.5° north, and 23.5° south to 66.5° south |

## The Seasons (pages 753–754)

14. In which type of region is most of the United States located? the temperate zone

15. Is the following sentence true or false? Earth's axis of rotation is tilted at an angle of about 25.3°. false

16. The north end of Earth's axis points to the North Star.

17. The seasons are caused by the tilt of Earth's axis as it moves around the sun.

18. Circle the letter of each sentence that is true about a solstice.
   a. A solstice occurs when the sun is directly above the North Pole.
   b. A solstice occurs when the sun is directly above the South Pole.
   (c.) A solstice occurs when the sun is directly above the latitude 23.5° north or 23.5° south.
   d. A solstice occurs when the sun is directly above the latitude 66.5° north or 66.5° south.

19. Is the following sentence true or false? When the winter solstice begins in the Northern Hemisphere, the Southern Hemisphere is tilted toward the sun. true

20. Is the following sentence true or false? Earth is closer to the sun when it is summer than when it is winter in the Northern Hemisphere. false

21. Circle the letter that identifies the season that begins with the vernal equinox.
   a. summer
   (b.) spring
   c. autumn
   d. winter

Name ______________________ Class ________________ Date ____________



# Section 24.3 Solar Energy and Winds
**(pages 755–759)**

*This section explains what happens to solar energy that reaches Earth's atmosphere and how it is transferred within the troposphere. It also describes the different winds on Earth and what causes them.*

## Reading Strategy (page 755)

**Comparing and Contrasting** After you read, complete the table to compare and contrast sea and land breezes. For more information on this Reading Strategy, see the **Reading and Study Skills** in the **Skills and Reference Handbook** at the end of your textbook.

| Sea and Land Breezes | | |
|---|---|---|
| | **Day or Night?** | **Direction of Air Movement** |
| Sea breeze | Day | Cool air moves toward land. |
| Land breeze | Night | Cool air moves toward water. |

## Energy in the Atmosphere (page 755)

1. What happens to the solar energy that reaches Earth's atmosphere?
   a. It is reflected back into space. b. The atmosphere absorbs it.
   c. Earth's surface absorbs it.

2. Is the following sentence true or false? The atmosphere is heated mainly by energy that is reradiated by Earth's surface. true

3. The process where certain gases in the atmosphere radiate absorbed energy back to Earth's surface, warming the lower atmosphere, is called the greenhouse effect.

4. Circle the letter of each way energy can be transferred within the troposphere.
   (a.) convection (b.) radiation
   c. precipitation (d.) conduction

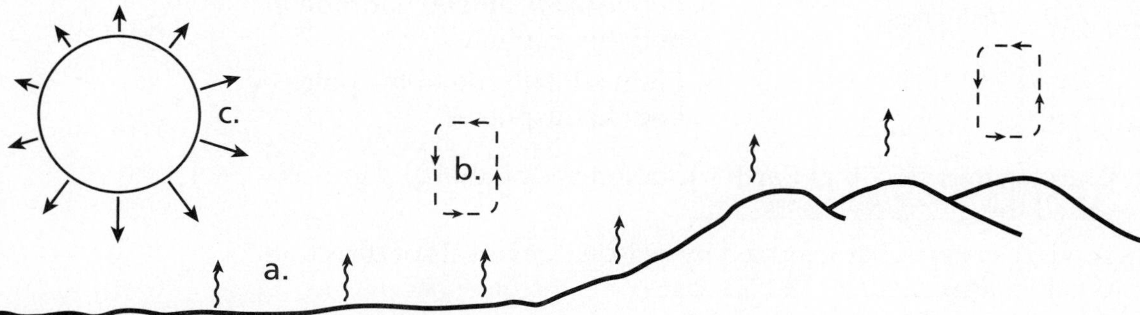


5. Name the type of energy transfer in the troposphere that each type of arrow on the diagram represents.
   a. Conduction/radiation b. Convection c. Radiation

6. Is the following sentence true or false? The air that directly contacts Earth's surface is heated by conduction. ____true____
7. Heat is circulated through the troposphere by ____convection____.

## Wind (page 757)

8. Is the following sentence true or false? Air flows from areas of high pressure to areas of low pressure. ____true____
9. What causes winds? ____Winds are caused by differences in air pressure.____
10. Is the following sentence true or false? The equal heating of Earth's surface causes differences in air pressure. ____false____
11. What happens to air as it warms, expands, and becomes less dense? ____It rises.____

## Local Winds (page 757)

12. Is the following sentence true or false? A local wind blows over a long distance. ____false____
13. Circle the letter of each example of a local wind.
    - (a.) a sea breeze
    - b. a trade wind
    - c. a jet stream
    - (d.) a land breeze
14. Would you expect to find a land breeze on the beach during the day or during the night? ____during the night____

## Global Winds (pages 758–759)

15. Is the following sentence true or false? Winds that blow over short distances from a specific direction are global winds. ____false____
16. Global winds move in a series of circulating air patterns called ____convection cells____.

*Match the global winds to their locations.*

| | Global Winds | Location |
|---|---|---|
| c | 17. polar easterlies | a. Just north and south of the equator |
| a | 18. tradewinds | b. Between 30° and 60° latitude in both hemispheres |
| b | 19. westerlies | c. From 60° latitude to the poles in both hemispheres |

20. The curving effect that Earth's rotation has on global winds is called the ____Coriolis effect____.
21. A wind system characterized by seasonal reversals of direction is called a(n) ____monsoon____.
22. Is the following sentence true or false? A jet-stream is a belt of high-speed wind in the upper troposphere. ____true____

Name ______________________ Class ______________ Date ____________



# Section 24.4 Water in the Atmosphere
**(pages 760–764)**

*This section discusses the water in the atmosphere. It explains the effect water has on processes in the atmosphere such as cloud formation and precipitation.*

## Reading Strategy (page 760)

**Sequencing** As you read, complete the flowchart to show how a cloud forms. For more information on this Reading Strategy, see the **Reading and Study Skills** in the **Skills and Reference Handbook** at the end of your textbook.

**Cloud Formation**

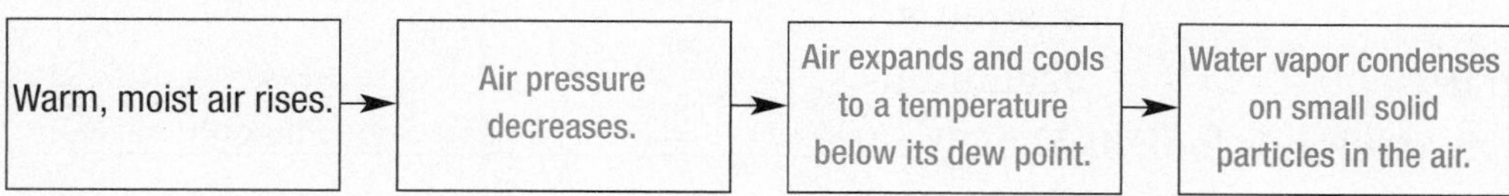


## Humidity (pages 760–761)

1. The amount of ___water vapor___ in the air is called humidity.
2. Is the following sentence true or false? The ratio of the amount of water vapor in the air to the amount of water vapor the air can hold at that temperature is relative humidity. ___true___
3. What is the dew point? ___The dew point is the temperature at which air becomes saturated.___
4. Name what water vapor may condense into.
   a. ___Dew___ b. ___Frost___
   c. ___Clouds___ d. ___Fog___
5. When water vapor in air changes directly from a gas to a solid, ___frost___ forms.

## Cloud Formation (page 761)

6. What is a cloud? ___A cloud is a dense, visible mass of tiny water droplets or ice crystals that are suspended in the atmosphere.___
7. Is the following sentence true or false? Clouds are formed when cool, dry air rises and water vapor condenses. ___false___
8. Clouds may form when moist air rises and the temperature cools below the ___dew point___.
9. Besides water vapor, what must be present for a cloud to form? ___Solid particles such as dust and salt must be in the air for a cloud to form.___

## Classifying Clouds (pages 762–763)

10. Scientists classify clouds based on their form and ___height___.

11. What are the three basic cloud forms?
    a. Stratus b. Cumulus c. Cirrus
12. A cloud that is near or touching the ground is called fog.
13. Is the following sentence true or false? Flat layers of clouds that cover much of the sky are stratus clouds. true
14. The letters *nimbo-* or *–nimbus* are added to a cloud's name to mean that the cloud produces precipitation.
15. Is the following sentence true or false? Altostratus clouds are low-level clouds similar to fog. false
16. Circle the letter of the cloud form that looks like puffy, white clouds with flat bottoms.
    a. fog
    b. stratus
    c. altostratus
    (d.) cumulus
17. What do cirrus clouds look like? Cirrus clouds are thin, white, wispy clouds that often have a feathery appearance.
18. Circle the letter of each type of cloud you often see on sunny days.
    a. cumulonimbus
    (b.) cumulus
    c. altostratus
    (d.) cirrus

*Match each cloud to its description.*

| Cloud | Description |
|---|---|
| b 19. cumulus | a. Thin, high-altitude clouds that generally produce no rain |
| a 20. cirrus | b. "Fair-weather clouds" that look like piles of cotton balls |
| d 21. altostratus | c. Clouds that produce heavy precipitation and are sometimes called thunderheads |
| c 22. cumulonimbus | d. Middle-level clouds that can produce light rain |

## Forms of Precipitation (page 764)

23. What are the five most common types of precipitation?
    a. Rain b. Snow
    c. Hail d. Sleet
    e. Freezing rain
24. Is the following sentence true or false? Snow is precipitation in the form of ice crystals. true
25. How does hail form? Small pellets of ice are tossed up and down by rising and falling air. They collide and combine with water droplets that then freeze and fall to the ground.
26. Rain that freezes as it falls is called sleet.

# Section 24.5 Weather Patterns
**(pages 765–771)**

*This section describes the weather patterns on Earth. It explains how air masses form and create fronts, low and high-pressure systems, and storms.*

## Reading Strategy (page 765)

**Outlining** Complete the outline with information from the section. Use the green headings as the main topics and the blue headings as subtopics. As you read, add supporting details to the subheadings. For more information on this Reading Strategy, see the **Reading and Study Skills** in the **Skills and Reference Handbook** at the end of your textbook.

| Weather Patterns |
|---|
| I. Air Masses |
| II. Fronts |
| A. Cold fronts occur when a cold air mass overtakes a warm air mass. |
| B. Warm fronts occur when a warm air mass overtakes a cold air mass. |
| C. Stationary fronts occur when two air masses collide and form a boundary but neither is moving. |
| D. Occluded fronts occur when a warm air mass is caught between two cooler air masses. |

## Air Masses (pages 765–766)

1. A large body of air that has fairly uniform physical properties such as temperature and moisture content at any given altitude is a(n) ___air mass___.

2. When do air masses form? Air masses form when a large body of air becomes fairly stationary over a region of Earth's surface or when air moves over a large uniform region like an ocean.

*Match the classifications of air masses to where they form.*

| | Classification of Air Mass | Where They Form |
|---|---|---|
| b | 3. maritime | a. Originates where it is very warm |
| a | 4. tropical | b. Forms over water transpiration |
| d | 5. polar | c. Forms over land |
| c | 6. continental | d. Originates where it is very cold |

## Fronts (pages 767–768)

7. When a continental polar air mass collides with a maritime tropical air mass, a(n) ___front___ forms.

8. Circle the letters of the weather conditions often associated with cold fronts.

   (a.) large amounts of precipitation  b. clear skies
   (c.) severe thunderstorms  (d.) strong winds

Name _______________ Class _______________ Date _______________



*Match each front to the way it forms.*

| | Front | How It Forms |
|---|---|---|
| c | 9. cold front | a. Occurs when a warm air mass is caught between two cooler air masses |
| b | 10. warm front | b. Occurs when a warm air mass overtakes a cold air mass |
| d | 11. stationary front | c. Occurs when a cold air mass overtakes a warm air mass |
| a | 12. occluded front | d. Occurs when two unlike air masses have formed a boundary and neither is moving |

## Low- and High-Pressure Systems (page 769)

13. A weather system around a center of low pressure is called a(n) cyclone.

14. Circle the letter of each weather condition associated with cyclones.
   (a.) precipitation  (b.) clouds
   (c.) stormy weather  d. clear skies

15. Is the following sentence true or false? An anticyclone is a weather system with a swirling center of low pressure. false

16. What kind of weather conditions are associated with an anticyclone?
   Clear skies, little precipitation, and generally calm conditions are associated with anticyclones.

## Storms (pages 770–771)

17. Is the following sentence true or false? A thunderstorm is a small weather system with thunder and lightning. true

18. Circle the letter of each characteristic of a thunderstorm.
   (a.) strong winds and heavy rain or hail
   b. only occurs on cool days
   (c.) forms when columns of air rise within a cumulonimbus cloud
   (d.) thunder and lightning

19. Is the following sentence true or false? A tornado is a small, intense windstorm in the shape of a rotating column that touches the ground. true

20. How does a tornado form? A tornado forms when a vertical cylinder of rotating air develops in a thunderstorm.

21. A hurricane is a large tropical cyclone with winds of at least 119 kilometers per hour.

Name ____________ Class ____________ Date ____________



# Section 24.6 Predicting the Weather
**(pages 774–777)**

*This section explains some of the technology meteorologists use to predict the weather. It also explains some of the symbols found on weather maps.*

## Reading Strategy (page 774)

**Identifying the Main Idea** As you read the text, write the main idea for each heading of this section in the table. For more information on this Reading Strategy, see the **Reading and Study Skills** in the **Skills and Reference Handbook** at the end of your textbook.

| Heading | Main Idea |
|---|---|
| Weather forecasting | Meteorologists use a variety of technologies to help forecast the weather. |
| Weather maps | Weather maps include a variety of symbols that help to illustrate the weather patterns across a certain region. |

## Weather Forecasting (pages 774–776)

1. What is meteorology? Meteorology is the study of Earth's atmosphere.
2. Is the following sentence true or false? Scientists who study weather are called weatherologists. false
3. What are four technologies that help meteorologists predict the weather?
   a. Doppler radar
   b. Automated weather stations
   c. Weather satellites
   d. High-speed computers
4. With Doppler radar, radio waves are bounced off particles of precipitation in moving storms.
5. Scientists can calculate a storm's speed by calculating how much the frequency of Doppler radar waves changes.
6. The types of weather data that can be collected by a typical weather station include temperature, precipitation, wind speed, and direction.
7. Meteorologists use high-speed computers to analyze data and create short- and long-term weather forecasts.
8. Meteorologists can accurately forecast the movement of large weather systems for a period of 3 to 7 days.
9. Why is it difficult for meteorologists to predict the weather beyond a week? There are too many variables regarding the movement of weather systems for meteorologists to forecast reliably.

## Weather Maps (pages 776–777)

10. What does a weather map show? A weather map shows weather patterns of different regions.

## Chapter 24 Weather and Climate

11. Circle the letter of each type of information that a typical weather map shows.
   a. temperatures
   b. mountain altitudes
   c. symbols for cloud cover
   d. areas of precipitation
12. Is the following sentence true or false? Weather maps often include symbols for fronts and areas of high and low pressure.
   true

*Look at the weather map and the key to answer questions 13–15.*

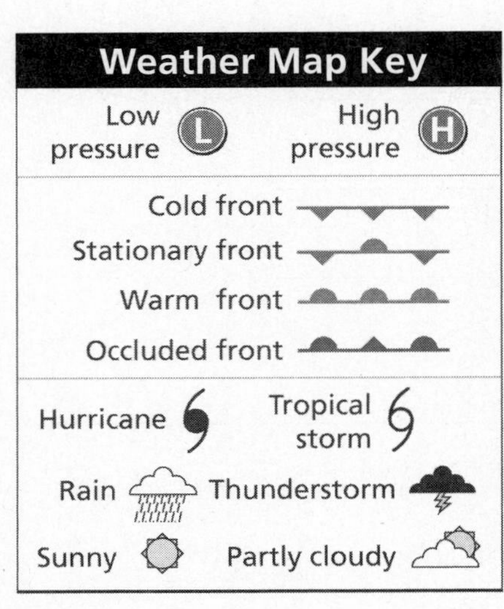


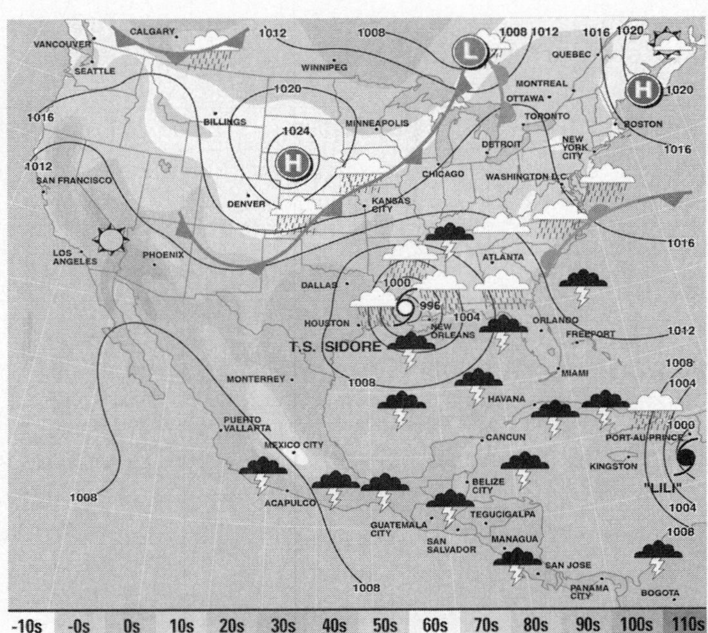


13. What type of front is shown near Calgary, Canada?
   cold front
14. What are the weather conditions in Los Angeles?
   sunny
15. What is the highest air pressure shown on the map?
   1024 mb
16. A line on a map that connects points of equal air temperatures is called a(n) isotherm.
17. How is a map with isotherms helpful to meteorologists? Meteorologists can quickly see temperature patterns on a map with isotherms.
18. Is the following sentence true or false? An isobar is a line that connects points of unequal air pressure. false
19. Circle the letter of each type of weather information that isobars help meteorologists to identify.
   a. areas of cloud cover
   b. centers of low-pressure systems
   c. locations of fronts
   d. centers of high-pressure systems

# Section 24.7 Predicting the Weather
**(pages 778–782)**

*This section describes climate and climate changes. It also describes factors that affect the patterns of temperature and precipitation of a region.*

## Reading Strategy (page 778)

**Building Vocabulary** As you read, complete the concept map with terms from this section. For more information on this Reading Strategy, see the **Reading and Study Skills** in the **Skills and Reference Handbook** at the end of your textbook.

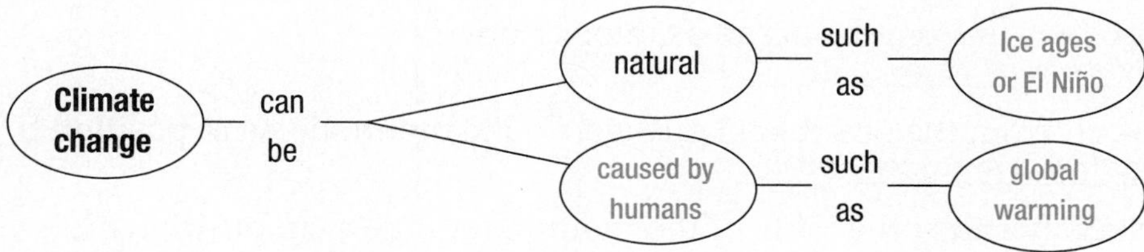


1. What is climate? Climate is the long-term weather conditions of a place or region.

## Classifying Climates (pages 778–779)

2. What are the six major climate groups?
   a. Tropical rainy  b. Temperate continental
   c. Dry  d. Temperate marine
   e. Polar  f. Highlands

3. Circle the letters of the two main factors that determine a region's climate.
   a. elevation  (b.) temperature
   (c.) precipitation  d. winds

## Factors Affecting Temperature (pages 779–780)

4. What are four factors that affect a region's temperature?
   a. Latitude  b. Distance from large bodies of water
   c. Ocean currents  d. Altitude

5. What factors influence the temperature of coastal regions? The temperature of coastal regions is influenced by large bodies of water and ocean currents.

6. Is the following sentence true or false? As altitude increases, temperature generally increases. false

## Factors Affecting Precipitation (page 780)

7. Circle the letter of each factor that can affect a region's precipitation.
   (a.) the existence of a mountain barrier  (b.) distribution of air pressure systems
   (c.) distribution of global winds  (d.) latitude

8. Precipitation is generally higher near the equator than the poles.

*Use the diagram below to answer the questions that follow.*

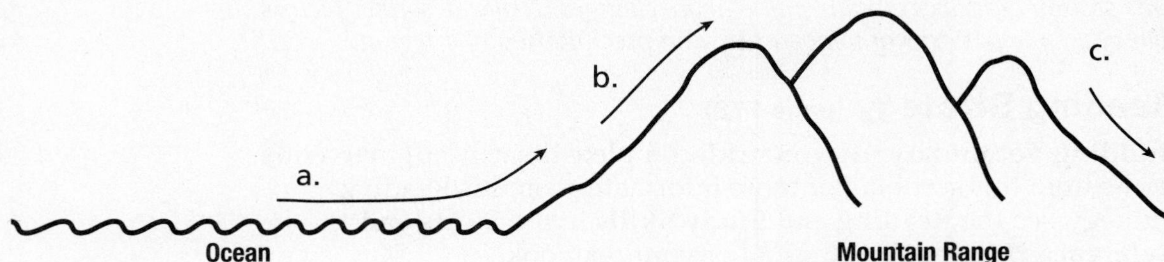


**9.** What type of air blows in from the ocean as in position a?
relatively warm, moist air

**10.** What happens as air from the ocean gets pushed up the mountain as in position b?
It cools and releases moisture as precipitation.

**11.** What type of air reaches the other side of the mountain range as in position c?
dry air

## Natural Climate Change (page 781)

**12.** Is the following sentence true or false? The climate of a region never changes. false

**13.** Circle the letters of two factors that may contribute to changes in climate.

(a.) human activities
b. animal activities
c. meteorologists
(d.) natural forces

**14.** Glaciers covered a portion of Earth's surface and temperatures were colder than usual during ice ages.

**15.** Is the following sentence true or false? El Niño is the periodic cooling of water in the central and eastern Atlantic Ocean.
false

## Global Warming (page 782)

**16.** The addition of carbon dioxide and certain other gases to the atmosphere may cause global warming.

**17.** The greenhouse effect occurs when certain gases absorb radiation from Earth's surface and then radiate energy back toward the surface.

**18.** The process called global warming refers to an increase in the worldwide temperature of the lower atmosphere.

**19.** Circle the letters that identify some possible strategies to limit the effects of global warming.

a. increasing use of fossil fuels
(b.) increasing use of solar and geothermal energy
(c.) increasing use of nuclear energy
(d.) increasing energy conservation efforts

# WordWise

*Complete the sentences by using one of the scrambled vocabulary terms from Chapter 24.*

| | | |
|---|---|---|
| mertpoheas | ria superers | prehopotres |
| trainoot | quieoxn | hoeusegren tefefc |
| ase zebere | rilocosi ceteff | wed tinpo |
| rai sams | dunterh | mosthrei |
| emailtc | | |

The lower-most layer of the atmosphere is called the ___troposphere___.

A description of the pattern of weather over many years in a place or region is its ___climate___.

A time when neither hemisphere is tilted toward the sun and lengths of daylight and sunlight are approximately equal is called a(n) ___equinox___.

A large body of air that has fairly uniform physical properties such as temperature and moisture content at any given altitude is a(n) ___air mass___.

The process by which gases in the atmosphere radiate absorbed energy back to Earth's surface, warming the atmosphere is known as the ___greenhouse effect___.

The layer of gases that surrounds Earth is called the ___atmosphere___.

The spinning of Earth on its axis is called its ___rotation___.

A local wind that blows from sea to land is a(n) ___sea breeze___.

The curving effect that Earth's rotation has on all free-moving objects is the ___Coriolis effect___.

A line on a map that connects points of equal air temperature is called a(n) ___isotherm___ .

The force exerted by the weight of a column of air on a surface is called ___air pressure___.

The temperature at which air becomes saturated is its ___dew point___.

The sound produced by rapidly expanding air along the path of a lightning discharge is called ___thunder___.

# Calculating Volume of Gases

**Math Skill: Percents and Decimals**

You may want to read more about this **Math Skill** in the **Skills and Reference Handbook** at the end of your textbook.

About 78% of the volume of dry air is composed of nitrogen. About how much nitrogen would there be in a 500 $m^3$ volume of dry air?

**1. Read and Understand**

*What information are you given in the problem?*

Dry air = 78% nitrogen

**2. Plan and Solve**

*What unknown are you trying to calculate?*

500 $m^3$ volume of dry air contains __?__ $m^3$ of nitrogen

*Convert the percent of nitrogen in dry air (78%) to a decimal.*

*Move the decimal point in 78% two places to the left and drop the percent sign.* = 0.78

*To find the amount of nitrogen in a 500 $m^3$ volume of dry air, multiply 500 by the decimal conversion of 78%.* $0.78 \times 500\ m^3 = 390\ m^3$

*About how much nitrogen will a 500 $m^3$ volume of dry air have?*

500 $m^3$ volume of dry air contains about 390 $m^3$ nitrogen

**3. Look Back and Check**

*To check your answer, find what percent of 500 $m^3$ your answer is. To do this, first divide your answer by 500.*

$$\frac{390\ m^3}{500\ m^3} = 0.78$$

*Then, convert the decimal to a percent by moving the decimal point two places to the right and placing a percent symbol after the number. If the percent is the same as the percentage of nitrogen found in dry air, your answer is correct.* 0.78 becomes 78%

## Math Practice

*On a separate sheet of paper, solve the following problems.*

1. Helium makes up 0.00052% of dry air. About how much helium would there be in a 10,000 $m^3$ volume of dry air?

   $0.00052\% = 0.0000052 = 5.2 \times 10^{-6}$; $10{,}000\ m^3 = 10^4\ m^3$

   $5.2 \times 10^{-6} \times 10^4\ m^3 = 5.2 \times 10^{-2}\ m^3 = 0.052\ m^3$

2. A 500 $m^3$ volume of dry air contains 0.185 $m^3$ of carbon dioxide. What percent of this sample of air is made up of carbon dioxide?

   $$\frac{0.185\ m^3}{500\ m^3} = \frac{1.85 \times 10^{-1}\ m^3}{5 \times 10^2\ m^3} = 0.37 \times 10^{-3} = 0.00037 = 0.037\%$$

3. Oxygen makes up 20.946% of dry air. Argon makes up 0.934% of dry air. About much more oxygen than argon would you find in a 1000-$m^3$ volume of dry air?

   $20.946\% = 0.20946$; $0.20946 \times 1000\ m^3 = 209.46\ m^3$ $.934\% = 0.00934$;

   $0.00934 \times 1000\ m^3 = 9.34\ m^3$; $209.46\ m^3 - 9.34\ m^3$ = about 200.12 $m^3$ more oxygen than argon

Name ______________________ Class ____________________ Date ____________



# Section 25.1 Exploring the Solar System
**(pages 790–794)**

*This section explores early models of our solar system. It describes the components of the solar system and scientific exploration of the solar system.*

## Reading Strategy (page 790)

**Comparing and Contrasting** After you read, compare the geocentric and heliocentric systems by completing the table below. For more information on this Reading Strategy, see the **Reading and Study Skills** in the **Skills and Reference Handbook** at the end of your textbook.

| | Solar System Models | | |
|---|---|---|---|
| | **Location of Earth** | **Location of Sun** | **Developer(s) of Theory** |
| **Geocentric System** | Center of universe | Revolves around Earth | Ancient Greeks, Ptolemy |
| **Heliocentric System** | Revolves around sun | Center of solar system | Aristarchus, Copernicus |

## Models of the Solar System (pages 790–791)

1. Is the following sentence true or false? In the Northern Hemisphere, the stars appear to circle around the North Star. ___true___

2. Name the five planets besides Earth that ancient observers could see with the unaided eye.
   a. ___Mercury___ b. ___Venus___
   c. ___Mars___ d. ___Jupiter___
   e. ___Saturn___

3. Many ancient Greeks thought ___Earth___ was the center of the universe.

4. Circle the letter of each sentence that is true about a geocentric model.
   (a.) Earth is stationary at the center.
   (b.) Objects in the sky move around Earth.
   c. The sun is the center of the solar system.
   d. The planets revolve around the sun.

5. Name the center of the solar system in a heliocentric model. ___the sun___

6. Is the following sentence true or false? The first heliocentric model was widely accepted by most ancient Greeks. ___false___

7. Is the following sentence true or false? The sun, moon, and stars appear to move because the Earth is rotating on its axis. true

## Planetary Orbits (page 792)

8. Planets move around the sun in orbits that are in the shape of a(n) ellipse.
9. The plane containing Earth's orbit is called the ecliptic plane.
10. Name the two factors that combine to keep the planets in orbit around the sun. Gravity and inertia combine to keep the planets in orbit around the sun.

## Components of the Solar System (pages 792–793)

11. Circle the letters that identify objects in our solar system.
    - (a.) moons of the planets
    - (b.) nine planets
    - (c.) the sun
    - d. the stars other than the sun
12. Name three planets that were identified after the invention of the telescope in the early 1600s.
    a. Uranus b. Neptune c. Pluto
13. Is the following sentence true or false? All of the planets have moons. false
14. Unlike the sun, planets and moons do not produce their own light.
15. Is the following sentence true or false? The sun's mass is smaller than the combined mass of the rest of the solar system. false

## Exploring the Solar System (pages 793–794)

16. Name three examples of types of modern technology that scientists use to explore the solar system.
    a. Complex telescopes b. Piloted spacecraft c. Space probes
17. Circle the letter that identifies the first person to walk on the moon.
    - a. Alan Shepard
    - b. Yuri Gagarin
    - c. Chuck Yeager
    - (d.) Neil Armstrong
18. An unpiloted vehicle that sends data back to Earth is called a(n) space probe.
19. Describe the space shuttle. The space shuttle is a reusable space vehicle that is launched like a rocket but lands like an airplane.
20. Is the following sentence true or false? The International Space Station is a permanent laboratory designed for research in space. true

Name ______________________ Class ______________ Date __________



# Section 25.2 The Earth-Moon System
**(pages 796–801)**

*This section describes Earth's moon, how it was formed, and its phases. It also explains solar and lunar eclipses and tides on Earth.*

## Reading Strategy (page 796)

**Building Vocabulary** As you read, complete the concept map with terms from this section. Make similar concept maps for eclipses and tides. For more information on this Reading Strategy, see the **Reading and Study Skills** in the **Skills and Reference Handbook** at the end of your textbook.

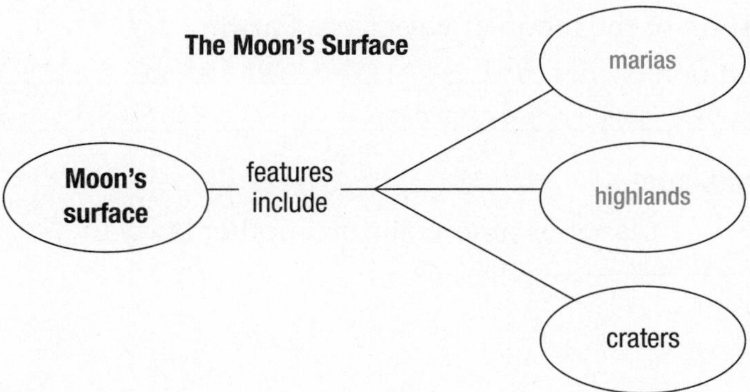


**1.** What is the force of gravity on the moon's surface compared to the force of gravity on Earth's surface? The force of gravity on the moon's surface is one sixth that of the force of gravity on Earth's surface.

## Earth's Moon (pages 796–797)

**2.** How does the moon's lack of an atmosphere affect its temperatures? The lack of atmosphere allows the moon's surface temperature to vary tremendously.

**3.** Evidence of ice on the moon has been found near the moon's North and South Poles.

## Surface Features (page 797)

**4.** Circle the letter of each major surface feature of the moon.

(a.) highlands (b.) maria
c. seas (d.) craters

*Match each lunar surface feature with its correct description.*

| | Description | Surface Feature |
|---|---|---|
| b | **5.** A round depression caused by a meteoroid | a. maria |
| a | **6.** Low, flat plains formed by ancient lava flows | b. crater |
| c | **7.** A rough, mountainous region | c. highland |

## Formation of the Moon (page 798)

8. Explain the leading hypothesis of how the moon formed. The moon formed after an enormous collision between the early Earth and a Mars-sized object.

## Phases of the Moon (pages 798–799)

9. Circle the letter of each sentence that is true about phases of the moon.
   a. The moon's phases change according to an irregular cycle.
   (b.) Phases are the different shapes of the moon visible from Earth.
   (c.) Phases are caused by changes in the relative positions of the moon, sun, and Earth as the moon revolves around Earth.
   d. The sunlit portion of the moon always faces Earth.

10. When does a full moon occur? A full moon occurs when the moon is on the opposite side of Earth from the sun, and the whole side of the moon facing Earth is lit by the sun.

## Eclipses (pages 799–800)

11. When the shadow of a planet or moon falls on another body in space, a(n) eclipse occurs.

**Solar Eclipse**

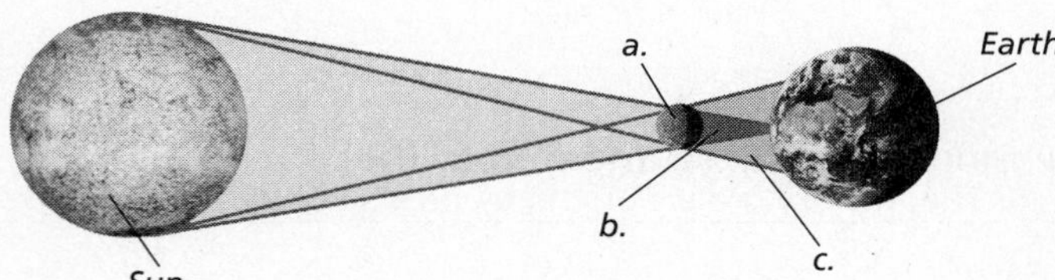


12. Look at the diagram showing a solar eclipse and label the parts.
    a. Moon b. Umbra c. Penumbra

13. Circle the letter of each sentence that is true about a lunar eclipse.
    (a.) A lunar eclipse occurs when Earth casts a shadow on the moon.
    b. A lunar eclipse occurs when the moon casts a shadow on a portion of Earth's surface.
    (c.) A lunar eclipse occurs during a full moon, when Earth is between the sun and moon.
    d. A lunar eclipse occurs during a new moon, when the moon is between the sun and Earth.

## Tides on Earth (page 801)

14. Describe the cause of tides. Tides are caused by differences in the moon's gravitational pull on Earth.

15. Is the following sentence true or false? A spring tide is produced when the change between daily high and low tides is the greatest.
    true

Name ______________________ Class ________________ Date __________



# Section 25.3 The Inner Solar System
**(pages 803–809)**

*This section describes the terrestrial planets found in the inner solar system.*

## Reading Strategy (page 803)

**Summarizing** Copy the table on a separate sheet of paper. Write all the headings for the section in the table. Write a brief summary of the text for each heading. For more information on this Reading Strategy, see the **Reading and Study Skills** in the **Skills and Reference Handbook** at the end of your textbook.

**The Terrestrial Planets**

Answers may include:

I. The Terrestrial Planets
- Four planets closest to the sun
- Small, dense, with rocky surfaces

II. Mercury
- a. Smallest terrestrial planet, closest planet to the sun, fastest moving planet, extreme temperatures

III. Venus
- b. Thick atmosphere, very hot surface, many volcanoes

## The Terrestrial Planets (pages 803–804)

**1.** Identify the four terrestrial planets.

a. Mercury b. Venus

c. Earth d. Mars

**2.** Circle the letter of each sentence that is true about the terrestrial planets.

(a.) They all are relatively small and dense.
(b.) They all have rocky surfaces.
c. They all have thick atmospheres.
(d.) They all have a crust, mantle, and iron core.

## Mercury (pages 804–805)

**3.** Circle the letter of each sentence that is true about Mercury.

(a.) It is the closest planet to the sun.
(b.) It is the smallest of the terrestrial planets.
(c.) It is geologically dead.
d. It is the slowest-moving planet.

**4.** Is the following sentence true or false? Mercury has a large number of craters, suggesting that the surface has been largely unchanged for billions of years. true

## Venus (page 805)

5. Circle the letter of each sentence that is true about Venus.
   (a.) It rotates in the direction opposite to which it revolves.
   (b.) It is the brightest object in Earth's night sky besides the moon.
   c. It rotates once every 24 hours.
   d. Its rotation rate is very fast.
6. Describe the effect that carbon dioxide in Venus's atmosphere has on its temperature. The carbon dioxide traps heat and raises the planet's temperature.

## Earth (pages 805–806)

7. Circle the letter of each sentence that is true about Earth.
   a. Its atmosphere is very thin and composed mostly of carbon dioxide.
   (b.) It supports millions of different species of living things.
   (c.) It has a suitable atmosphere and temperature for liquid water to exist.
   d. Its core has cooled down to the point where it is geologically dead.
8. Why does Earth's surface continue to change? Earth has retained its internal heat because it is large and has not had a chance to cool down much. Also, it still has moving tectonic plates.

## Mars (pages 807–808)

9. Circle the letter of each sentence that is true about Mars.
   (a.) The largest volcano in the solar system is on Mars.
   (b.) Iron-rich rocks on Mars's surface give it a reddish color.
   c. It has a thick atmosphere that keeps the planet warm.
   (d.) The surface of Mars is colder than Earth's surface.
10. Is the following sentence true or false? Mars shows evidence of once having liquid surface water. true

## Asteroids (page 809)

11. Small, rocky bodies in space are called asteroids.
12. Circle the letter of each sentence that is true about asteroids.
   (a.) Most small asteroids have irregular forms.
   b. The asteroid belt formed when a giant planet was shattered by a collision with a meteoroid.
   c. Most asteroids are found in the asteroid belt between Earth and Mars.
   (d.) Most asteroids are less than 1 kilometer in diameter.
13. What do scientists hypothesize about how the asteroids formed? The asteroids are remnants of the early solar system that never came together to form a planet.

# Section 25.4 The Outer Solar System
**(pages 810–815)**

*This section describes the planets in the outer solar system. It also describes comets and meteoroids and the edge of the solar system.*

## Reading Strategy (page 810)

**Summarizing** Copy the table on a separate sheet of paper. Fill in the table as you read to summarize the characteristics of the outer planets. For more information on this Reading Strategy, see the **Reading and Study Skills** in the **Skills and Reference Handbook** at the end of your textbook.

| The Outer Planets | |
|---|---|
| **Outer Planets** | **Characteristics** Answers may include the following: |
| Jupiter | Largest; most mass; most moons; Great Red Spot |
| Saturn | Second largest; largest and most visible rings; at least 30 moons |
| Uranus | Axis tilted more than 90°; immense storms |

## Gas Giants (page 811)

1. Circle the letter of each sentence that is true about Jupiter, Saturn, Uranus, and Neptune compared to the terrestrial planets.
   a. Their years are shorter than the terrestrial planets.
   (b.) They are colder than the terrestrial planets.
   (c.) They are further from the sun than the terrestrial planets.
   (d.) They are much larger than the terrestrial planets.
2. Why are the outer planets called the gas giants? They are made mostly of hydrogen and helium.
3. Describe the cores of the gas giants. The cores are small and dense.

## Jupiter (pages 811–812)

4. The Great Red Spot is a huge storm on Jupiter.
5. Circle the letter of each sentence that is true about Jupiter's moons.
   (a.) Callisto and Ganymede are Jupiter's largest moons.
   (b.) Scientists hypothesize that Europa could support life.
   (c.) Ganymede has a metal core and rocky mantle.
   d. Io is covered with ice.

## Saturn (pages 812–813)

6. Saturn has the largest and most visible ___rings___ in the solar system.

7. Is the following sentence true or false? Saturn has the largest atmosphere and the lowest average density of all the planets in the solar system. ___true___

## Uranus (page 813)

8. Is the following sentence true or false? Uranus gets its distinctive blue-green appearance from large amounts of methane in its atmosphere. ___true___

9. Uranus's ___axis of rotation___ is tilted more than 90°.

## Neptune (page 814)

10. Circle the letter of each sentence that is true about Neptune.
    - (a.) It has visible cloud patterns in its atmosphere.
    - b. It has only five known moons.
    - (c.) It has large storms in its atmosphere.
    - d. It has no rings.

11. The ___methane___ in Neptune's atmosphere causes its bluish color.

## Pluto (page 814)

12. Is the following sentence true or false? Pluto is both larger and denser than the other outer planets. ___false___

13. Describe Pluto's probable composition. ___Pluto may be a mixture of ice and rock.___

## Comets and Meteoroids (page 815)

14. A(n) ___comet___ is made of ice and rock that partially vaporizes when it passes near the sun.

15. Chunks of rock, usually less than a few hundred meters in size, that travel through the solar system are called ___meteoroids___.

16. The radioactive dating of ancient meteoroids has allowed scientists to establish that the age of the solar system is ___4.6 billion years___.

## The Edge of the Solar System (page 815)

17. The ___Kuiper Belt___ contains tens of thousands of objects made of ice, dust, and rock that orbit the sun beyond Pluto.

18. The thick sphere of comets encircling the solar system out to a distance of about 50,000 AU is called the ___Oort cloud___.

# Section 25.5 The Origin of the Solar System

**(pages 818–820)**

*This section explains a theory of how the solar system originated. It also describes how this theory explains the composition and size of the planets.*

## Reading Strategy (page 818)

**Identifying Main Ideas** As you read, write the main idea for each topic. For more information on this Reading Strategy, see the **Reading and Study Skills** in the **Skills and Reference Handbook** at the end of your textbook.

| Theories on the Origin of the Solar System | |
|---|---|
| **Topic** | **Main Idea** |
| The Nebular Theory | The solar system formed from a large rotating cloud of dust and gas. |
| Formation of the protoplanetary disk | As the solar nebula rotated, it began to flatten out and form a protoplanetary disk. |
| Planetesimals and protoplanets | Dust grains within the protoplanetary combined and grew larger. Eventually, these combined to form planetesimals and later protoplanets. |
| Composition and size of the planets | The temperatures in the early solar system were very high near the sun and much lower in the outer system. These temperatures affected which materials condensed to form planets. |

## The Nebular Theory (pages 818–819)

1. The generally accepted explanation for the formation of the solar system is called the nebular theory.
2. Circle the letter of each sentence that is true about the nebular theory.
   (a.) The solar nebula formed from the remnants of previous stars.
   (b.) The explosion of a nearby star likely caused the solar nebula to start to contract.
   c. As the solar nebula contracted, it began to spin more slowly.
   (d.) The solar system formed from a rotating cloud of dust and gas.
3. Describe a solar nebula. A solar nebula is a large, thin cloud of dust and gas.
4. A large, spherical cloud of dust and gas in space is called a(n) protoplanetary disk.
5. Is the following sentence true or false? Most planets and moons are revolving now in the direction that the protoplanetary disk was spinning. true

6. Circle the letter of each sentence that is true about the formation of the protoplanetary disk.
   (a.) The disk was densest in the center and thinner toward the edges.
   (b.) At the center of the disk, nuclear reactions fused hydrogen and helium and the sun was formed.
   c. The temperature at the center of the disk was extremely low.
   d. Nearly all of the mass of the solar nebula became concentrated near the outer edge of the disk.

7. Asteroid-like bodies that combined to form planets were called planetesimals.

8. The process by which planetesimals grew is called accretion.

9. Put the following events about the formation of planetesimals and protoplanets in correct order. Number the events 1–5 in the order that they occurred.

1 Balls of gas and dust collided and grew larger.
3 Planetesimals became large enough to exert gravity on nearby objects.
2 Planetesimals grew by accretion.
5 Protoplanets joined to form the current planets in a series of collisions.
4 Planetesimals grew into protoplanets.

## Composition and Size of the Planets (page 820)

10. At low pressures, such as those found in space, cooling materials can change from a gas directly into a solid.

11. Ice-forming materials vaporize at temperatures between 500 K and 1200 K.

12. Why are the terrestrial planets relatively small and rocky? They are relatively small and rocky because the inner solar system was too hot when they formed for ice-forming compounds to solidify.

13. Circle the letter of each sentence that is true about the formation of the gas giants.
   a. The gravity of the gas giants decreased as they grew larger.
   (b.) Ice-forming material could condense in the outer solar system.
   (c.) The planets grew large and were able to capture hydrogen and helium from nearby space.
   d. Less material was available for the gas giants to form than was available for the terrestrial planets.

14. Is the following sentence true or false? Scientists have found planets in orbit around distant stars that provide support for the nebular theory. true

Name ______________________ Class ________________ Date __________



# WordWise

*Test your knowledge of vocabulary words from Chapter 25 by completing this crossword puzzle.*

**Clues across:**

3. A model where Earth is stationary while objects in the sky move around it
4. A small natural body in space that revolves around a planet
6. Asteroid-like bodies that eventually combined to form planets
9. The regular rise and fall of ocean waters
10. A chunk of rock that moves through the solar system

**Clues down:**

1. The event that occurs when the shadow of one body in space falls on another
2. Dusty pieces of ice and rock that partially vaporize when they pass near the sun
5. Small, rocky bodies that travel through the solar system
7. Low, flat plains on the moon
8. A disk made of many small particles of rock and ice in orbit around a planet

1 ECLIPSES
2 COMETS
3 GEOCENTRIC
4 MOON
5 ASTEROIDS
6 PLANETESIMALS
7 MARIA
8 RING
9 TIDES
10 METEOROID

# Calculating Distances Between Objects in Space

**Math Skill: Conversion Factors**

You may want to read more about this **Math Skill** in the **Skills and Reference Handbook** at the end of your textbook.

Jupiter is, on average, 5.2 astronomical units (AU) from the sun. About how many kilometers is Jupiter from the sun?

**1. Read and Understand**

*What information are you given?*

Jupiter's distance = 5.2 AU from the sun

**2. Plan and Solve**

*What are you asked to find?*

Jupiter's distance = ? kilometers from the sun

*How many kilometers are in one AU?*

149,598,000 kilometers

*Write a conversion factor that can be used to change AU to kilometers.*

$$\frac{149{,}598{,}000 \text{ km}}{1 \text{ AU}}$$

*Multiply the distance from the sun to Jupiter in AU by the conversion factor.*

$$5.2 \text{ AU} \times \frac{149{,}598{,}000 \text{ km}}{1 \text{ AU}} = 780 \text{ million km}$$

Jupiter's distance = 780 million km from the sun

**3. Look Back and Check**

*Is your answer reasonable?*

To check your answer, convert the distance between the sun and Jupiter in kilometers back to AU.

$$\frac{780{,}000{,}000 \text{ km}}{149{,}598{,}000 \text{ km/AU}} = 5.2 \text{ AU}$$

## Math Practice

*On a separate sheet of paper, solve the following problems.*

1. Pluto is an average distance of 39.5 AU from the sun. How many kilometers from the sun is Pluto?

$$39.5 \text{ AU} \times \frac{149{,}598{,}000 \text{ km}}{1 \text{ AU}} = 5{,}910{,}000{,}000 \text{ km} = 5.91 \times 10^9 \text{ km}$$

2. Mercury is $58.3 \times 10^6$ km from the sun on average. How many AU is Mercury from the sun?

$$(58.3 \times 10^6 \text{ km}) \times \frac{1 \text{ AU}}{1.4958 \times 10^8 \text{ km}} = 0.392 \text{ AU}$$

3. Mars is 1.52 AU from the sun on average. Saturn is 9.54 AU. About how far apart, in kilometers, are Mars and Saturn when they are closest to each other?

$9.54 \text{ AU} - 1.52 \text{ AU} = 8.02 \text{ AU}; 8.02 \text{ AU} \times 1.4958 \times 10^8 \text{ km/AU} = 1.20 \times 10^9 \text{ km}$

Name ______________ Class ______________ Date ______________



# Section 26.1 The Sun

**(pages 828–833)**

*This section describes how the sun produces energy. It also describes the sun's interior and atmosphere.*

## Reading Strategy (page 828)

**Build Vocabulary** Copy the table on a separate sheet of paper and add more lines as needed. As you read, write a definition of each vocabulary term in your own words. For more information on this Reading Strategy, see the **Reading and Study Skills** in the **Skills and Reference Handbook** at the end of your textbook.

| The Sun | |
|---|---|
| **Vocabulary Term** | **Definition** |
| Core | The central region of the sun where fusion occurs |
| Radiation zone | A region of highly compressed gas where energy is transferred mainly by radiation |
| Convection zone | The outer layer of the sun's interior, where energy is transferred mainly by convection |

## Energy from the Sun (pages 828–829)

**1.** The sun gives off a large amount of energy in the form of electromagnetic radiation.

**2.** Circle the letter of each sentence that is true about nuclear fusion in the sun.

(a.) Less massive nuclei combine into more massive nuclei.

b. The end product of fusion is hydrogen.

c. Fusion is a type of chemical reaction.

(d.) Hydrogen nuclei fuse into helium nuclei.

## Forces in Balance (page 829)

**3.** For the sun to be stable, inward and outward forces within it must be in equilibrium or balance.

**4.** Is the following sentence true or false? The sun remains stable because the inward pull of gravity balances the outward push of thermal pressure from nuclear fission. false

## The Sun's Interior (pages 830–831)

**5.** Circle the letter of each layer of the sun's interior.

(a.) the radiation zone

b. the photosphere

(c.) the convection zone

(d.) the core

Name ______________________ Class ______________ Date __________



6. Circle the letter of each way that energy moves through the sun.
   a. gravity
   (b.) convection
   (c.) radiation
   d. nuclear fusion

7. List the layers of the sun's interior shown on the diagram.

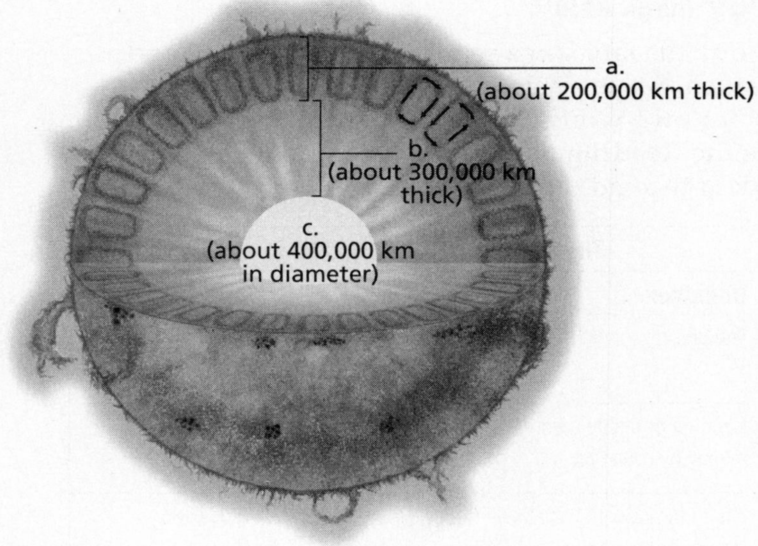


a. Convection zone

b. Radiation zone

c. Core

## The Sun's Atmosphere (page 831)

8. Circle the letter of each layer of the sun's atmosphere.
   (a.) photosphere
   (b.) chromosphere
   (c.) corona
   d. core

9. When can the corona be seen? The corona is usually seen only during a total solar eclipse.

## Features of the Sun's Atmosphere (pages 832–833)

*Match each description to a feature of the sun's atmosphere.*

| | Description | Feature of Sun's Atmosphere |
|---|---|---|
| b | 10. Spectacular features of the sun's atmosphere that occur near sunspots | a. solar flares |
| c | 11. Areas of gas in the atmosphere that are cooler than surrounding areas | b. prominences |
| a | 12. Sudden releases of energy that produce X-rays and hurl charged particles into space | c. sunspots |

Name ______________________ Class ______________________ Date ______________



# Section 26.2 Stars

**(pages 834–839)**

*This section discusses how scientists classify stars. It also describes other important properties of stars.*

## Reading Strategy (page 834)

**Using Prior Knowledge** Add what you already know about stars to the concept map. After you read, complete your concept map, adding more ovals as needed. For more information on this Reading Strategy, see the **Reading and Study Skills** in the **Skills and Reference Handbook** at the end of your textbook.

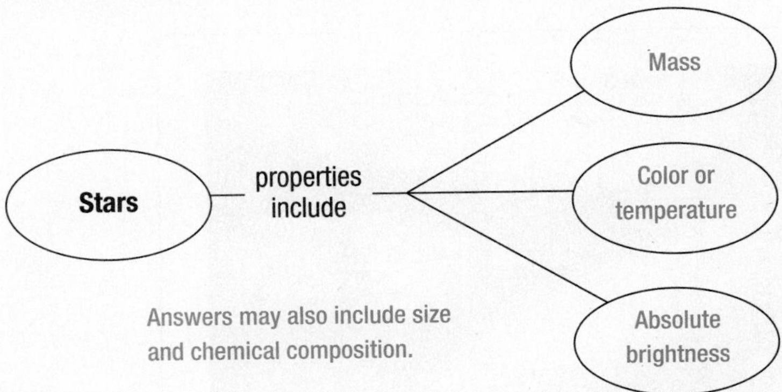


## Distances to the Stars (pages 834–836)

1. Circle the letter of each sentence that is true about a light-year.
   a. It is a typical unit of measure for distances on Earth.
   (b.) It is a distance of about 9.5 trillion kilometers.
   (c.) It is the distance that light travels in a vacuum in a year.
   d. It is a unit of time.

2. Is the following sentence true or false? Parallax is the apparent change in position of an object with respect to a distant background. ___true___

3. Astronomers measure the parallax of a nearby star to determine its ___distance___.

## Properties of Stars (pages 836–837)

4. Circle the letter of each property that astronomers use to classify stars.
   (a.) brightness
   b. distance
   (c.) color
   (d.) size

5. Is the following sentence true or false? The brightness of a star as it appears from Earth is called its absolute brightness. ___false___

6. A star's ___absorption lines___ can be used to identify different elements in the star.

Name ______________________ Class ________________ Date ____________



**7.** Describe the chemical makeup of most stars. Hydrogen and helium combine to make up 96 to 99.9 percent of the mass of most stars.

## The Hertzprung-Russell Diagram (pages 838–839)

**8.** Circle the letter of each way that Hertzprung-Russell (H-R) diagrams might be used.

(a.) to study sizes of stars

b. to study distant planets

(c.) to determine a star's absolute brightness

(d.) to determine a star's surface temperature or color

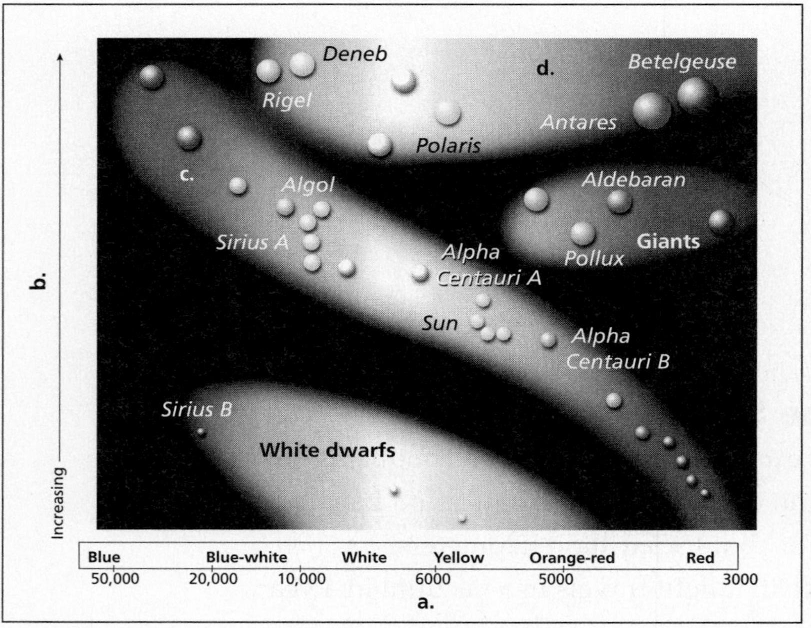


**9.** Provide labels for each of the letters shown on the H-R diagram above.

a. Surface temperature or color  b. Absolute brightness

c. Main sequence  d. Supergiants

**10.** Circle the letter of each sentence that is true about supergiants.

(a.) They are found at the upper right of the H-R diagram.

(b.) They are much brighter than main sequence stars of the same temperature.

(c.) They are 100 to 1000 times the diameter of the sun.

d. They are smaller and fainter than giants.

**11.** How does the brightness of white dwarfs compare to the brightness of main sequence stars? White dwarfs are dimmer than main sequence stars of the same temperature.

# Section 26.3 Life Cycles of Stars
**(pages 840–844)**

*This section explains how stars form, their adult stages, and how they die.*

## Reading Strategy (page 840)

**Sequencing** Copy the flowchart on a separate sheet of paper. As you read, extend and complete it to show how a low-mass star evolves. For more information on this Reading Strategy, see the **Reading and Study Skills** in the **Skills and Reference Handbook** at the end of your textbook.

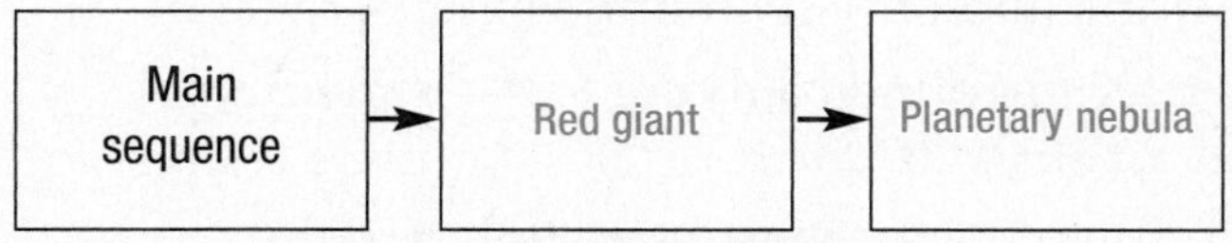


Extended answers include white dwarf and black dwarf

## How Stars Form (pages 840–841)

1. A large cloud of dust and gas spread out over a large volume of space is called a(n) nebula.
2. Circle the letter of each sentence that is true about a protostar.
   a. Nuclear fusion is taking place within it.
   (b.) It has enough mass to form a star.
   (c.) Its internal pressure and temperature continue to rise as it contracts.
   (d.) It is a contracting cloud of dust and gas.
3. Describe how a star is formed. A star is formed when a contracting cloud of gas and dust becomes so dense and hot that nuclear fusion begins.

## Adult Stars (page 841)

4. A star's mass determines the star's place on the main sequence and how long it will stay there.
5. Circle the letter of each true sentence about adult main-sequence stars.
   (a.) High-mass stars become the bluest and brightest main-sequence stars.
   b. Low-mass stars are usually short-lived.
   (c.) Yellow stars like the sun are in the middle of the main sequence.
   d. Red stars are the hottest and brightest of all visible stars.

## The Death of a Star (pages 842–844)

6. The core of a star starts to shrink when the core begins to run out of hydrogen (or fuel).

Name ______________ Class ______________ Date ______________



7. Name three possible end stages of a star.

a. White dwarf or black dwarf b. Neutron star c. Black hole

8. Is the following sentence true or false? The final stages of a star's life depend on its mass. true

9. Circle the letter of each sentence that is true about the death of low-mass and medium-mass stars.

a. The dying stars are called planetary nebulas.

(b.) They remain in the giant stage until their supplies of helium and hydrogen are gone and there are no other elements to fuse.

(c.) The energy coming from the stars' interiors decreases and the stars eventually collapse.

d. The cores of the stars shrink and only their atmospheres remain.

10. The glowing cloud of gas that surrounds a dying low- or medium-mass star is called a(n) planetary nebula.

11. List the stages in the evolution of a low-mass star shown in the diagram below.

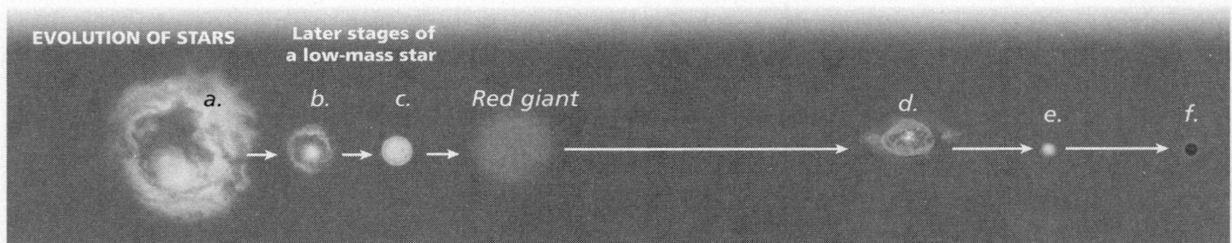


a. Nebula b. Protostar

c. Main sequence star d. Planetary nebula

e. White dwarf f. Black dwarf

12. Is the following sentence true or false? A high-mass star dies quickly because it consumes fuel rapidly. true

13. An explosion so brilliant that a dying high-mass star becomes more brilliant than an entire galaxy is called a(n) supernova.

*Match each final stage of a high-mass star to its correct description.*

| | Description | Final Stage of a High-Mass Star |
|---|---|---|
| b | 14. Surface gravity is so great that nothing can escape from it | a. pulsar |
| a | 15. A spinning neutron star that gives off strong pulses of radio waves | b. black hole |
| a or c | 16. The remnant of a high-mass star that has exploded as a supernova, which begins to spin more and more rapidly as it contracts | c. neutron star |

Name ______________________ Class ______________ Date __________



# Section 26.4 Groups of Stars
## (pages 846–849)

*This section describes star systems, star clusters, and galaxies.*

## Reading Strategy (page 846)

**Comparing and Contrasting** After you read, compare types of star clusters by completing the table. For more information on this Reading Strategy, see the **Reading and Study Skills** in the **Skills and Reference Handbook** at the end of your textbook.

| Types of Star Clusters | | |
|---|---|---|
| **Cluster Type** | **Appearance** | **Age and Type of Stars** |
| Open cluster | Disorganized, loose appearance | Bright supergiants and other young stars, also gas and dust clouds |
| Associations | Larger and more spread out than an open cluster | Bright, young stars |
| Globular cluster | Spherical, densely packed | Older stars, generally no bright blue stars |

1. A group of stars that seems to form a pattern as seen from Earth is called a(n) constellation.

2. Is the following sentence true or false? Constellations are important to astronomy because they help to form a map of the sky. true

## Star Systems (pages 846–847)

3. A group of two or more stars that are held together by gravity is called a(n) star system.

4. Is the following sentence true or false? Astronomers have concluded that more than half of all stars are members of groups of two or more stars. true

5. A star system with two stars is called a(n) binary star.

## Star Clusters (page 847)

*Match each basic kind of star cluster to its description.*

| | Description | Star Cluster |
|---|---|---|
| b | 6. A loose grouping of no more than a few thousand stars that are well spread out | a. globular cluster |
| c | 7. Loose groupings of bright, young stars | b. open cluster |
| a | 8. A large group of older stars | c. associations |

**9.** Is the following sentence true or false? Astronomers estimate that the oldest globular clusters are at least 20 billion years old.
______false______

## Galaxies (pages 848–849)

**10.** A huge group of individual stars, star systems, star clusters, dust, and gas bound together by gravity is called a(n) ______galaxy______.

**11.** Our galaxy is called the ______Milky Way______.

**12.** Galaxies that have a bulge of stars at the center with arms extending outward like a pinwheel are called ______spiral galaxies______.

**13.** Is the following sentence true or false? The arms of spiral galaxies contain very little gas and dust. ______false______

**14.** A spiral galaxy that has a bar through the center with the arms extending outward from the bar on either side is called a(n) ______barred-spiral galaxy______.

**15.** Circle the letter of each sentence that is true about elliptical galaxies.

(a.) They are spherical or oval shaped.
b. They typically have lots of dust and gas.
(c.) They come in a wide range of sizes.
(d.) They usually contain only old stars.

**16.** A(n) ______irregular______ galaxy has a disorganized appearance and is typically smaller than other types of galaxies.

*Match each type of galaxy to its description.*

| Description | Galaxy |
|---|---|
| __b__ **17.** Spherical or oval, no spiral arms, and usually contains only old stars | a. barred-spiral galaxy |
| __c__ **18.** Bulge of stars at the center with arms extending outward like a pinwheel | b. elliptical galaxy |
| __d__ **19.** Composed of many young stars, comes in many shapes, and has a disorganized appearance | c. spiral galaxy |
| __a__ **20.** Has a bar through the center with arms extending outward from the bar on either side | d. irregular galaxy |

**21.** Is the following sentence true or false? The Milky Way appears as a band from Earth because we are looking at it edgewise.
______true______

**22.** The enormously bright centers of distant galaxies are called ______quasars______.

# Section 26.5 The Expanding Universe
**(pages 852–855)**

*This section describes Hubble's Law. It also explains the big bang theory.*

## Reading Strategy (page 852)

**Previewing** Before reading, examine Figure 26 and write at least two questions to help you understand the information in it. As you read, write answers to your questions. For more information on this Reading Strategy, see the **Reading and Study Skills** in the **Skills and Reference Handbook** at the end of your textbook.

| The Evolution of the Universe |
|---|
| **Questions on the Evolution of the Universe** |
| Students' questions may include: What was the big bang? |
| What happened afterwards? |
| What evidence supports the big bang theory? |

## Hubble's Law (pages 852–853)

1. Is the following sentence true or false? The apparent change in frequency and wavelength of a wave as it moves towards or away from an observer is known as the Doppler effect. true

2. How can astronomers use the Doppler effect? The Doppler effect can be used to determine how fast stars or galaxies are approaching or moving away from Earth.

3. Circle the letter of each sentence that is true about spectrums of stars or galaxies.
   a. As a star or galaxy circles the Earth, the lines in its spectrum shift toward the middle of the spectrum.
   (b.) As a star moves toward Earth, the lines in its spectrum are shifted toward shorter wavelengths.
   (c.) As a star or galaxy moves away from Earth, the lines in its spectrum are shifted toward longer wavelengths.
   (d.) The greater the observed shift in spectrum, the greater the speed the star or galaxy is moving.

4. The shift in the light of a galaxy toward the red wavelengths is called a(n) red shift.

5. Describe Hubble's Law. Hubble's Law says that the speed at which a galaxy is moving away is proportional to its distance from us.

6. Is the following sentence true or false? The most distant galaxies that can be seen from Earth are moving away at more than 90% of the speed of light. true

7. Describe what the observed red shift in the spectra of galaxies shows.
It shows that the universe is expanding.

## The Big Bang Theory (page 854)

8. Astronomers theorize that the universe came into being in an event called the big bang.
9. Circle the letter of each sentence that is true according to the big bang theory.
   (a.) The matter and energy in the universe was once concentrated in a very hot region smaller than a sentence period.
   (b.) The universe began billions of years ago with an enormous explosion.
   (c.) The universe came into existence in an instant.
   d. The matter and energy in the universe has taken billions of years to form.
10. After the big bang, it is theorized that the universe expanded quickly and cooled down.
11. How large was the universe when the sun and solar system formed?
It was about two thirds of its present size.
12. Circle the letter of each sentence that gives evidence that supports the big bang theory.
   (a.) The existence of cosmic microwave background radiation.
   (b.) The red shift in the spectra of distant galaxies.
   c. The fact that the sun is about 20 billion years old.
   d. The pulling of atoms together into gas clouds by gravity.
13. Recent measurements of the microwave background radiation have led astronomers to estimate that the universe is 13.7 billion years old.

## Continued Expansion (page 855)

14. Matter that does not give off radiation is known as dark matter.
15. Circle the letter of each sentence that is true about dark matter.
   (a.) Astronomers currently don't know what it is or how it is distributed.
   (b.) It cannot be seen directly.
   c. It can be measured using the Doppler effect.
   (d.) It can be detected by observing how its gravity affects visible matter.
16. Why is it significant that the galaxies contain as much as ten times more dark matter than visible matter? Without this amount of dark matter, there would not be enough gravitational force to keep galaxies from flying apart.

Name ______________________ Class ________________ Date ____________



# WordWise

*Answer the questions by writing the correct vocabulary terms from the chapter in the blanks. Use the circled letter in each word to find the hidden word.*

| Clues | Vocabulary Terms |
| --- | --- |
| What is the central region of the sun? | (c) o r e |
| What is the surface layer of the sun? | p (h) o t o s p h e r e |
| What is a dramatic eruption on the sun that produces X-rays and hurls charged particles into space at nearly the speed of light? | s o l a (r) f l a r e |
| What is a contracting cloud of gas and dust with enough mass to form a star? | p r (o) t o s t a r |
| What is the diagonal band of stars on the H-R diagram? | (m) a i n s e q u e n c e |
| What is the dense remnant of a high-mass star that has exploded as a supernova? | n e u t r (o) n s t a r |
| What are the very bright stars at the upper right of the H-R diagram? | (s) u p e r g i a n t s |
| What is the apparent change in position of an object with respect to a distant background? | (p) a r a l l a x |
| What is an object whose surface gravity is so great that nothing, not even light, can escape from it? | b l a c k (h) o l e |
| What is the distance that light travels in a vacuum in a year? | l i g h t - y (e) a r |
| What is a large glowing ball of gas in space? | s t a (r) |
| What is a large cloud of gas and dust spread out over a large volume of space? | n (e) b u l a |

**Hidden Word:** c h r o m o s p h e r e

**Definition:** The middle layer of the sun's atmosphere, normally visible only when the brighter photosphere is blocked.

Name ______________________ Class ________________ Date ____________



# Calculating Distances to Stars

A star is $3.6 \times 10^{19}$ kilometers from Earth. How many light-years is this?

**Math Skill: Exponents**

You may want to read more about this **Math Skill** in the **Skills and Reference Handbook** at the end of your textbook.

**1. Read and Understand**

*How many kilometers from Earth is the star?*

Star = $3.6 \times 10^{19}$ kilometers from Earth

*What are you asked to find?*

Star = ? light-years from Earth

**2. Plan and Solve**

*Write the number of kilometers in a light-year using scientific notation.*

$9.5 \times 10^{12}$ kilometers

*To find the number of light-years the star is from Earth, divide its distance by the number of kilometers in a light-year. Begin by dividing 3.6 by 9.5. Round your answer to the nearest hundredth.*

0.38

*To divide numbers with exponents, subtract the exponents. What will the exponent of the answer be?*

7

*To write your answer in scientific notation, a number other than zero must be in the ones place. Move the decimal one place to the right and subtract one from the exponent. How many light-years is the star from Earth?*

$3.8 \times 10^{6}$ light-years

**3. Look Back and Check**

*Is your answer reasonable?*

To check your answer, multiply the number of light-years away the star is by the number of kilometers in a light-year. Remember to add the exponents when you multiply. Your answer should be the distance from Earth to the star in kilometers.

$3.6 \times 10^{19}$ kilometers

## Math Practice

*On a separate sheet of paper, solve the following problems.*

1. A star is $8.6 \times 10^{14}$ kilometers from Earth. How many light-years away is the star? Round your answer to the nearest tenth.
   Dividing 8.6 by 9.5 and rounding = 0.91. The exponent is 2.
   Scientific notation = $9.1 \times 10$ = 91 light-years
2. The star Proximi Centauri is about 4.3 light-years from Earth. How many kilometers from Earth is it?
   $4.1 \times 10^{13}$ kilometers
3. A star is $6.8 \times 10^{8}$ light-years from Earth. How many kilometers from Earth is the star? $6.5 \times 10^{21}$ kilometers